THE PSYCHOLOGY AND TEACHING
OF ARITHMETIC

THE PSYCHOLOGY
AND TEACHING OF
ARITHMETIC

by

HARRY GROVE WHEAT

Professor of Education
West Virginia University

D. C. HEATH AND COMPANY

BOSTON   NEW YORK   CHICAGO   LONDON
ATLANTA   SAN FRANCISCO   DALLAS

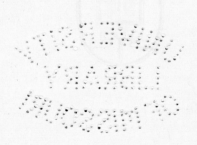

PREFACE

There appears to exist among teachers of arithmetic in the schools and among writers upon the teaching of arithmetic the belief that number is to be found in the world of things and of experiences and of practical affairs, and that all one needs to do to lead children to the discovery of number is to bring them into contact with objects and experiences and situations. The belief expresses itself in the prevailing methods of introducing the procedures of arithmetic to children. Thus, to introduce the activity of counting, children are surrounded with objects which must be attractive enough to gain attention; to introduce the process of addition, children are immersed in the activity of scoring a game or keeping a store which requires addition for its complete performance; and to introduce the idea of percentage, children are shown the outward workings of the business practices which make use of percentage. The belief suggests that arithmetic is part of the material world in which children live, and that it may be extracted by them in proportion to their contacts with the material world.

One of the major purposes of this book is to combat such belief. Although number may be applied to everything in the world, it exists nowhere in the world. The world does not of itself possess number; the world has been invaded by trained minds which have been equipped with number. Objects in the world do not make themselves countable; the child counts the objects which surround him only when he has learned to count. Playing store does not project addition to be beheld and studied; the child keeps accounts only when he has learned to add. Business practices do not of themselves portray percentage; the idea of percentage is brought to business practices to make them meaningful. The com-

iii

plex world does not impress the number system upon the
individual; the individual brings the system, as and when he
learns it, to the complex world and uses the system as a means
of bringing order out of complexity. The savage lived in the
world a long long time before he invented counting and was
able to use counting as a means of giving some system and
order to his world of material things; and many children
move through the public schools without gaining an understanding of arithmetic because they have been overwhelmed
with their sensations of material things and material processes.

It is important for the teacher from time to time to take
stock of his beliefs relative to the subject he teaches, to
correct and enlarge his views, and to distinguish between
what his subject appears to be and what it actually is. This
book has been written in order to describe the peculiarities
and characteristics of arithmetic, and to distinguish between
its appearances and its actualities, with the conviction that
once a teacher understands the essential features of the subject he will have some intelligence about holding them up to
the attention of his pupils. How the primitive mind groped
after more exact number ideas, how earlier peoples adopted
more and more systematic devices for developing and expressing number relationships, to what they finally learned
through long centuries of haphazard experimentation to give
their attention in order to bring to perfection the number
system in use today, the intimate relationships between the
various parts of the system, and to what the learner of today
must give his attention in order to become acquainted with
the system are, accordingly, major topics for discussion.
Reference to much of the recent writings about arithmetic as
a composite of unrelated skills and about corrective and
remedial instruction in arithmetic is conspicuously absent
from the present discussions. What the pupil should learn
rather than what the pupil should avoid is the theme. The
discussions of this book are intended to describe the number

system, and to suggest means of making children intelligent about the number system.

Grateful acknowledgment is due the authors and publishers of various books and periodicals from which quotations have been taken. The author thanks especially Silver Burdett Company for permission to paraphrase at appropriate points certain paragraphs from his chapter on "The Psychology of Arithmetic" in his book *The Psychology of the Elementary School*. Other obligations are indicated in the footnotes.

H. G. W.

Morgantown
West Virginia

CONTENTS

THE PSYCHOLOGY AND TEACHING
OF ARITHMETIC

CHAPTER I

THE BEGINNING OF NUMBER

ARGUMENT

1. Early ideas of number were closely related to experience with groups. Their degree of exactness was determined by the nature of the experience.

2. Attention to groups as a whole led only to crude ideas of their sizes and to crude distinctions between sizes.

3. Such crude ideas of number stimulated further interest and newer methods of inquiry. The motives were perhaps as much logical as they were practical.

4. More careful study of groups involved the giving of attention to the individual objects that composed them. Such methods as the following were used by primitive peoples:

   (a) Naming the objects of a group.
   (b) Matching the objects one-to-one with those in another chance group.
   (c) Matching the objects one-to-one with those in a model group.
   (d) Matching the objects with tallies of various kinds, including fingers.

5. All such methods of study failed to lead to exact ideas of groups, though they did lead to increased familiarity with them as quantities.

6. The names of model groups did not supply counting words. Such names referred to groups as wholes, not to objects that were countable; they were attached to concrete sets of things and were thus not detachable into abstract number names.

7. The foregoing all points to the fact that exact ideas of number do not grow out of mere experience, however abundant such experience may be.

1

The arithmetic that we teach children in our schools today is a number system that has been perfected by the race over a long period of time from very crude beginnings. In order to understand thoroughly our present number system, it is desirable to have a reasonable acquaintance with the beginnings of numerical thinking among primitive peoples and with some of the main steps that were taken by the race in its passage from these early crude beginnings to our present, highly complex science of mathematics.

The actual origin of the concept of number is of course something that we do not know; it is lost in the obscurities that surround our ancestors of long ago. There is abundant evidence, however, that this earliest concept of number was closely related to experience — in other words, that it was essentially concrete, not abstract. We find in the records of early peoples some indications as to the nature of these early number concepts, and we also find in the languages and customs of primitive tribes of the present day, like the tribes living in some parts of South America, and the South Sea Islands, Africa, and Australia, other indications of these early concepts. From such evidences we can piece together the story of number — how it began and how it grew — and at the same time we can clarify our notions of the number system that the human race has finally developed and that modern society now calls upon children in the school to learn.

I. ATTENTION TO GROUPS

Primitive man lived in a world of things and memories of these things. He competed for his very existence with other men and with the animals about him. He obviously had to be alert to what was going on about him—at least sufficiently alert to cope with whatever threatened his existence. The evidence shows, however, that from a quantitative (arithmetical) point of view his ideas about nature and his general surroundings were of a very crude sort. If he was watching an animal, his attention was given to it as an individual thing, as one item of experience. If he was watching more than one animal, he observed them either singly or as a single group; if the animals were not assembled together but were moving about as individuals, he watched them as individuals; but if they were assembled together and moved about in a pack, he watched the movements of this pack as a single individual thing.

Very early he developed ideas about the size of the pack, or group, that he could express by simple words that were equivalent roughly to our 'many,' and 'not many,' and for very large groups to 'many, many.' His idea of size was often expressed by a gesture instead of by words; for instance, the notion of a large group was expressed by extending the arms to indicate the amount of space occupied by the group. We see young children make similar gestures for 'whole lot' or 'great big' so-and-so.

We have just said that primitive man thought of an assemblage of individuals as a single thing, a single group; of course, he was not oblivious of the fact that this single group was made up of individual members, whether he gave thought to it or not. This idea of composition of a group is illustrated in such English terms as *herd, pack, flock, bunch, swarm*, and *lot*. We have in English also words referring specifically to a group of two objects: *couple, team, twin, brace*, and *pair*. But even in these small groups the thought was of the group as a unit; 'pair of shoes,' for instance, is a phrase that refers essentially to one thing rather than to two separate, discrete things.

Such terms as have just been mentioned will serve to show how primitive man had ideas about the group that embodied very little about the individuals as such that composed the group. This limitation of the primitive man in his conception of groups is something that is very difficult for us to appreciate, because we are accustomed to deal with groups in a way that gives us exact ideas. We may partly appreciate the vagueness of the ideas about groups that primitive man had if we resort to this simple experiment. Look at these three groups of dots without trying to count them all. You can distinguish a small group, a large group, and a middle-sized group. But just how small, and just how large are these groups? You will have only a rough notion of the size of each group and of their relative sizes unless you stop to count them; mere sensory impression, mere looking, does not reveal the exact sizes; that is, the precise number of dots in each case. If you are thus helpless in your attempt to estimate at all precisely the sizes of these groups,

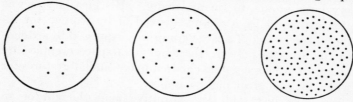

how helpless must have been primitive man who could not count, who had no names for numbers, and who thus was limited to sensory impression to guide him in thinking about the groups that came within the range of his attention, even though they were groups of as few as seven, five, or even three or two individual objects.

II. Groping for the Number Idea

While the primitive man was engaged in the arduous business of seeking his food or guarding his safety, he had no time for reflection; but while he rested in the retreat of his cave, he could pass in review the experiences of the day, could see again in imagination the things he had seen individually and in groups, and could then try to think of one group as compared with another one. He might then want to exchange experiences with his fellows. We may imagine him telling about his experience with this group of animals and that one, and referring to their relative sizes, let us say, in some terms that could be roughly equivalent to our 'many' and 'many, many.' We may imagine one of his fellows differing with him and insisting that the two groups were 'many, many' and 'many,' respectively. It may be that an argument developed that would certainly have led to mental confusion, if not to physical violence, on the part of both of these primitive men. Here may well have been a motive for trying to make a closer, more exact inspection of a group the next time it was met.

Once more, when men in their social relations had come to the point where they could coöperate with one another and where they had accumulated items of property — arrow heads, spears, skins, beads — they needed some sort of accounting to keep track of these possessions.

Thus, through one motive or another, whether logical or practical, early men must at some time have come to the point where they felt the need for a quantitative exactness that they did not possess and that they could perhaps only vaguely feel to be possible — in short, to the point of groping for the idea of number. Certainly in the course of human development from the most primitive conditions, man would come to employ one means after another to give him a more precise idea of the sizes of the groups of objects that he had to deal with. Whatever means were thus developed and employed were passed on to the generation that succeeded, until in the course of some centuries of blind trial, man stumbled upon the beginnings of a way of thinking that has developed into the present method of dealing with numbers that we term 'arithmetic.'

III. Attention to Individual Objects — Naming

One of the very simple developments that helped man to think more exactly about the individuals in the group was the use of names. Each thing that came into a man's possession came as an isolated item and thus had given to it the attention that was due it as an individual thing. That sort of attention was sufficient for him to keep the thing in mind so long as there were not many of these things — so long as his possessions were few. Each of these things was given a name, the same as each member of a family is given a name. The name made each object a distinct individual item and kept it in its proper place in his thinking. For example, the early herdsman thought of his sheep as individuals; the appearance and the peculiarities of each sheep made it an individual sheep. He gave each one a name, and this name served to fix in his mind this individual animal. He remembered the names of his sheep, and in this way he could keep track of his flock. A primitive shepherd could not say that he owned "nine" sheep, but he knew that he owned "Whitey" and "Brownie" and "Wagtail" and the others that he could name. Thus there is a special significance attached to the biblical allusion to the good shepherd who knew his sheep by name. If he did not know his sheep by name — that is, as individuals — he had but a vague idea of the number in his flock, because he had no other way of knowing the individuals of his flock with any degree of exactness.

Nevertheless, this use of names to keep track of property units was a clumsy device, a cumbersome means of keeping an account. Naming was not numbering. The names of sheep had no permanence, and they had no fixed order of sequence. Consequently, the primitive man had to turn eventually to other and better devices to clarify his ideas of groups.

IV. Matching, or One-to-One Correspondence

Primitive man came early into possession of another device that led to more serviceable, if not more exact, ideas of groups than he otherwise would have gained. This was the device of *matching* the objects of one group with the objects of another group. If both groups were exhausted simultaneously, equality became evident; if one was exhausted before the other, inequality became evident. In illustration, imagine a primitive chieftain matching a group of warriors with a pile of spears. If there turned out to be a spear for every warrior and no spears left over, this one-to-one correspondence between the warriors and the spears showed the equality of the two groups. If the spears turned out to be too few or too many, the inequality between warriors and spears was readily observed.

This matching naturally led to such ideas of comparison as we express by the words 'more,' 'less,' and 'as many as,' and led finally to a feeling of familiarity with the sizes of groups of a higher degree than had been experienced before.

V. MATCHING WITH MODEL GROUPS

The device of matching the objects of one group with the objects of another may have come into use first by accident, but later, as we shall see, it was very often used with deliberate intent. The extent of the practice among primitive tribes is indicated in the following excerpt from Gow's interesting historical sketch:

Two is in Thibet *paksha* 'wing,' in Hottentot *t'Koam* 'hand'; and so also among the Javanese, Samoyeds, Sioux, and other peoples. So again with the Abipones; 'four' is *geyenknate*, 'ostrich-toes'; 'five' is *neenhalek*, 'a hide spotted with five colors'; with the *Marquesans* 'four' is *pona*, 'a bunch of four fruits,' etc.[1]

The quotation from Gow indicates the progress that was being made by primitive man in obtaining more exact, and more usable ideas of the groups that came under his observation. It calls attention to the fact that nature provided certain model groups, or collections, of objects — ears of a man, wings of a bird, leaves of a clover, toes of an ostrich, fingers of a hand, and so on — that were common enough to become familiar to all. So, when the primitive man at this

[1] James Gow. *A Short History of Greek Mathematics* (The Cambridge University Press, 1884), pp. 6–7.

stage of development of his ideas of number wanted to reckon
a group of things that concerned him, in order either to keep
it in memory or to express it with understanding and with
no equivocation to his fellows, he matched the objects one
by one, not with the objects in any group that happened to
be at hand but with those in an appropriate *model group*.
The method of studying the group that concerned him was
a method of comparison. Accordingly, his method of thinking about the group, once it had been told off, was also one
of comparison. When he thought about his group, or talked
about it, he had in mind such comparisons as the following:
"I caught as many fish as the ostrich has toes," "I have as
many skins as the clover has leaves." As similar model
groups were used again and again in comparisons, they became more and more familiar and understandable, or as we
might say, they became *standard groups*. Any chance group
that had been compared with a model group became also a
familiar and understood one. By means of such comparisons
the primitive man developed his ideas of groups toward
clarity and exactness.

VI. Tallying

In order to think about and comprehend groups larger
than the model groups just mentioned, early peoples continued to employ the method of matching, but with certain
modifications. Instead of using many model groups as the
basis for the matching operations, they employed what we
may call *ready-made groups*, using the objects of these ready-
made groups as 'tallies,' or 'counters,' for the objects in the
larger groups they wanted to study. The device employed
is known as the device of *tallying*.

Our own ancestors must have used the device of tallying
a good deal. Our words 'tally' and 'calculate' are derived
from the Latin *talea*, 'cutting,' and *calculus*, 'pebble,' and
take us back to the time when a record of a group was made
by cutting a notch in a stick for each object or by laying

aside a pebble to represent each object. In our own day the Apache Indians of Arizona keep records of their ponies by carrying a bag of pebbles that correspond in number with the number of the ponies. Should an Indian lose or mislay his bag of pebbles, he becomes very much confused.

To get an idea of how early peoples employed the device of tallying, let us imagine a primitive herdsman taking a record of his flock of sheep by matching them with pebbles. He would have his sheep pass before him one by one and for each animal he would lay aside a pebble. He thus accumulated a pile of pebbles that he recognized as corresponding in number to his flock. The pebbles and the sheep were unlike in all concrete characteristics, but each pebble represented a unit and each sheep represented a unit. There was a 'one-to-one correspondence' between them. The pebbles thus came to stand in the herder's thinking for his sheep. He used the pebbles first to take a record of his sheep; he later could use the particular pile of pebbles to recheck upon their number — to see if any sheep were missing or if there had been any additions to the flock. The pile of pebbles was a more easily handled, apparently more comprehensible, and, thus, more definite group than the flock of sheep.

Whenever primitive man made use of tallies — notches cut in sticks, pebbles, commemorative knots in string, etc. — to take account of his possession, he built up for a particular purpose a model group or collection. The equality between this model group and the group he was trying to account for became evident to him by the one-to-one matching. He reserved his model group for any later one-to-one matching that would seem necessary in order to discover whether the equality had been disturbed.

VII. The Limited Value of Tallying

Tallying, then, was a systematic method of studying a group in order to arrive at an idea of the group. It was not, however, an entirely satisfactory method of study.

Although in the process each object was attended to one by one, and recorded by a tally, and although at the end one had a group of tallies that was in a certain way the same as the group being reckoned, still the idea obtained was not complete. The explanation is that tallying was merely a means of substituting one group in consciousness for another. One could think back and forth from one group to the other, recognizing the while that one was the same (in size) as the other. But *how many*, after all, was the tallied group? This remained a question still unanswered. The primitive man could feel them, lift them, look at them, but whatever idea of number he had was an idea based upon mere experience, which remained an idea more closely associated with sensing then with knowing.

Though the tallies of primitive man may have inspired in him some confidence in being able to record and to check his possessions, nevertheless his group of tallies, once they had been accumulated, still remained vague and indefinite, though less vague and less indefinite perhaps than the possessions he was trying to record. The point is that, when he had acquired his collection of tallies, he was unable to think or to name their number. In other words, he could not, like modern man, count his tallies, and so they remained a group that had no special meaning or advantage except what came from ease of handling.

VIII. THE LIMITED VALUE OF MODEL GROUPS

It may very well seem to us that primitive peoples should have had little difficulty in learning to count their tallies, since they had ready for such use the names of their familiar model groups. The words like 'wing,' 'clover-leaf,' 'ostrich-toes,' 'hand,' which they used as comparative words in referring to groups of two objects, three objects, four objects, and five objects, respectively, appear to lead easily and naturally to actual counting. We can readily use these names as counting words, thus: *nose, wing, clover-leaf, ostrich-*

toes, hand, in place of the usual counting words *one, two, three, four, five.* It may thus be easily inferred that the savage mind must have found no difficulty in making the transition from the names of model groups to counting words.

The ease with which the inference arises should place it and any other similar inference under suspicion. Whenever one is tempted to ascribe to primitive man an ability possessed by civilized man, he should be reminded of the great gulf that exists between the untrained mind and the trained mind. He should consider how different is the situation of using a set of names in the familiar process of counting from that of taking a set of familiar names and *inventing* the process of counting. In the one case, the familiar process remains the same; in the other, a wholly new, a previously unknown, process must be created.

The savage lived, as we know, in a world of concrete, material things, and all his thoughts were directed toward the concrete rather than toward the abstract. The name 'wing,' which we can readily use, if and when we like, as a substitute for the word 'two,' stood in the savage mind once and always for the actual wing possessed by a bird. When he used the word as reference to a model group for comparison, his concept was that of the actual wings of a bird, not of the abstract idea *two.* Tallies were things to be seen and handled. A collection of pebbles was a collection of pebbles. Wings were wings. It was a long step from words which referred to model collections to words that stand for the abstract ideas of number. So great, indeed, was the step that the savage usually forsook the names of his model collections and — at least, in the beginning — developed other words that corresponded more closely with the mental processes he pursued in going from the concept of concrete things to the concept of abstract numbers. The fact that early peoples seldom used what would appear to us as ready-made counting-words in developing the process of counting is pointed out by Gow:

In Aryan languages there is a difference in kind between the first three or four numerals and the last six or seven. The former are adjectives and are so inflected; the latter are nouns neuter in form and uninflected; interjections, as it were, thrust into the sentence in brackets, like the dates in a history book. This difference in kind seems to point to a difference in etymology and also in antiquity. The higher numerals, being nouns, are names of things which are not readily connected with, and subject to, the same relations as the other things mentioned in the same sentence. Secondly, the general abruptness of the transition from low inflected numerals to higher uninflected forms points to some sudden stride in the art of counting. All the facts are readily explained if we conceive that among the Aryans, as among other races, the counting of low numerals was learned before the use of the fingers suggested itself, and that so soon as the fingers were seen to be the natural *abacus*, a great advance in arithmetic was immediately made. The higher unit-numerals would then be the names of the gestures made in finger-counting, or, as among the Algonquins, etc., the actual names of the fingers in the order in which they were exhibited in counting.[2]

The paragraph from Gow may be summarized by saying that the use of model groups did not lead to the development of number ideas as employed in counting, but that, after counting began, the names of such model groups came to be useful as the names of number ideas that had been developed by processes somewhat different from those employed in matching objects. To put it in another way, it may be said that sensory experiences did not lead to number ideas, but were useful in illustrating the number ideas *after they had been developed through other means.*

IX. FINGER-TALLYING

Records of primitive peoples indicate that the process of counting was usually related to the use of the fingers as

[2] Gow, *op. cit.*, pp. 9–10.

model groups for matching 'one-to-one.' The hand is the natural abacus. Children and sometimes adults count 'on their fingers.' So did primitive peoples, *after* they had learned to count. Primitive peoples, however, had fingers, and often used them, as natural and accessible *tallies* before they had number ideas that they could employ in counting. We need to guard against the suggestion that counting grew out of the use of fingers as natural tallies, and that finger-tallying and finger-counting are one and the same thing. Thus, modern man, when he uses marks for tallying, may say as he makes each mark, "check," "check," "check," and so on until the checking is complete. But he does not know the number of his checks until he counts them. *Tallying and counting are different processes.*

The primitive man, in reckoning a group of objects by matching with his fingers, may have said, or thought, as he tallied each object by turning down or raising a finger, "finger," "finger," "finger," and so on. When the tallying was completed, he had brought together for inspection and consideration a group of fingers, but like the modern man with his check marks, he did not know their number until he had counted. Before he had learned to count, his finger-tallies were uncounted and unnumbered tallies. Finger-tallying became finger-counting only after the savage had learned to count. Finger-tallying, like the matching with such model groups as are represented by the words 'wing,' 'clover-leaf,' and the like, did not bring itself into relation with counting; rather, counting, after it had been invented by means other than perceptual experiences, brought itself into relation with finger-tallying.

X. The Limitation of Experience

It should go without saying that experience with a group is necessary in order that one may have knowledge of it. On the other hand, as our discussion has indicated, mere experience is insufficient to give one any more than a vague, undefined knowledge of the group. Even when one views and handles each member of the group, tallies each one by one, and finally compares the group with the group of tallies he has accumulated, he still is left with uncertainty. More than sensory experience is needed to clarify and make definite the idea of the group.

The foregoing observations need to be kept in mind, because the notion is prevalent that, wrapped up in the group, is the quality or characteristic that, when brought within the range of one's experience, gives the idea of number. Thus it has been stated that the child acquires the number idea 'five,' for example, by seeing five apples, five boys, five chairs, five pencils, and five of enough other things. Within a group of five objects, we are told is the 'quality of fiveness.' Let the quality once be observed, or let it be experienced frequently enough so that this 'quality of fiveness' is abstracted a little here and a little there from enough groups of five, and the various modicums of 'fiveness' become generalized by the child mind into his idea of 'five.'[3] It will be well, whenever one encounters such statements, for one to remind himself that primitive man did not begin to develop and to employ the idea 'five' with other ideas in counting until he had taken at least a step beyond his direct perceptual experiences. Man lived in the world, surrounded by objects that appeared singly and in groups of two, three, four, and so on, for a long time before he began to make a beginning in what we now consider the very primitive process of counting.

Let the child have the number names, and associate them with the appropriate groups, 'two' with a group of two objects, 'three' with a group of three objects, and so on — we are advised — and he will eventually derive the appropriate ideas. Here, again, we must remember the limitations of mere experience, even when it is accompanied by appro-

[3] E. L. Thorndike. *The Psychology of Arithmetic* (The Macmillan Company, New York, 1922), pp. 170–172.

priate names. We should recall that primitive man had his model groups and their appropriate names a long, long time before he developed exact number ideas through counting. His model groups, as we have seen, gave him neither the abstract ideas of number nor the names for such ideas — at least, not before he had developed ideas by methods not in use in the beginning.

Our discussions to this point ought not to be taken as indicating that primitive man's reliance upon his perceptual experiences did not prepare him for the succeeding activities that led to exact ideas of number. As we shall see, he continued to use in his later and more fruitful study of groups the essential features of the methods we have been viewing. What we should gain, however, from our study of the gropings of primitive man after more and more exact ideas of the groups that came within his observation is the conclusion that, so long as he depended merely upon what he could see and hear, he never arrived at anything more than feelings of familiarity. We should be impressed with the limitations of mere experience. We should note that primitive man had to go beyond, or back of, experience before he succeeded in even starting the development of the ideas of number that we know and use with such confidence today. We should gather that primitive man was in need of a device for dealing with his experience.

CHAPTER II

THE BEGINNING OF COUNTING

ARGUMENT

1. The distinctions between counting and other primitive methods of studying groups are brought out in studies of early peoples, such as Conant's. Chief among these distinctions are the following:

    (a) The first counting words were adjectives; that is, 'distinguishing' words.

    (b) The first counting words were related to each other in orderly sequence.

2. A counting word serves the double purpose of fixing attention upon an object in a group both as a single individual item and also as belonging with all the objects that precede it in the counting; that is, it supplies both the *ordinal* and the *cardinal* sense.

3. Until such double-purpose words were invented, or their use discovered, the names of model groups could not become counting words. Such names supplied only *cardinal* number, not the system inherent in *ordinal* number.

4. A word that might become a number name is useless for the purpose without the accompanying *idea* that such use is possible.

5. Counting was extended and new number names were adopted as new number ideas were developed.

6. New number ideas were developed by various methods of combining number ideas already acquired. Old number names were often compounded to form new number names.

7. Such combination and compounding generally followed a *system* that had often been hit upon accidentally.

8. The accident of the fingers served to fix the number base that was used most frequently for combination and compounding.

9. Though separate number names facilitated the de-

velopment of new number ideas through combination and compounding, they had a limited value that was determined by the limited span of attention.

10. The accidental selection of ten as a number base does not remove the use of separate number names very far, if at all, from the advantages of direct perceptual experience.

The preceding chapter has called attention to certain methods of studying groups that were employed by primitive peoples and to the nature of the number ideas resulting from the use of such methods. It has indicated that, though these methods of study give the appearance of completeness, they nevertheless resulted in ideas that were incomplete. The number ideas of primitive man were neither clear nor dependable; they could not be used with clarity or assurance; they were felt rather than known; they left something to be desired.

I. Earlier Methods Summarized

Primitive man, as we have seen, named the items of his property; he tallied the items by a 'one-to-one correspondence' with his fingers; he compared them 'one-to-one' with various kinds of tallies; and he thought of their number in comparison with the number of objects in certain familiar model groups. He thus gave attention to each individual item in the given group, and he gave attention to the group as a whole, composed as it was of all its individual items. Insofar as the giving of attention to a group is concerned, that is about all any one can do. There is no other feature or quality pertaining to the group to which one can give attention. Why, then, did not primitive man quickly gain such exact number ideas as those with which we are familiar, especially since he might readily have turned the names of his model groups into number names? The only answer that can be given is that some essential was lacking in his methods of study.

II. How Counting Began

We may, perhaps, gain some notion of the essential that was lacking if we turn to a description of the activities of counting as they first began to develop:

By the slow, and often painful, process incident to the extention and development of any mental conception in a mind wholly unused to abstractions, the savage gropes his way onward in his counting from 1, or more probably from 2, to the various higher numbers required to form his scale. The perception of unity offers no difficulty to his mind, though he is conscious at first of the object itself rather than of any idea of number associated with it. The concept of duality, also, is grasped with perfect readiness. This concept is, in its simplest form, presented to the mind as soon as the individual distinguishes himself from another person, though the idea is still essentially concrete. Perhaps the first glimmering of any real number thought in connection with 2 comes when the savage contrasts one single object with another — or, in other words, when he first recognizes the *pair*. At first the individuals composing the pair are simply 'this one,' and 'that one,' or 'this and that'; and his number system now halts for a time at the stage when he can, rudely enough it may be, count 1, 2, many. There are certain cases where the forms of 1 and 2 are so similar that one may readily imagine that these numbers really were 'this' and 'that' in the savage's original conception of them; and the same likeness also occurs in the words for 3 and 4, which may readily enough have been a second 'this' and a second 'that.' In the Lushu tongue the words for 1 and 2 are *tizi* and *tazi*, respectively. In Koriak we find *ngroka*, 3, and *ngraka*, 4; in Kolyma, *niyokh*, 3, and *niyakh*, 4; and in Kamtschatkan, *tsuk*, 3, and *tsaak*, 4. Sometimes, as in the case of the Australian races, the entire extent of the count is carried through by means of pairs. But the natural theory one would form is that 2 is the halting place for a very long time; that up to this point the fingers may or may not have been used — probably not; and that when the next start is made, and 3, 4, 5, and so on are counted, the fingers first come into requisition. If the grammatical structure of the earlier languages of the world's history is examined, the student is struck with the prevalence of the dual number in them — something which tends to disappear as language undergoes extended development. The dual number points unequivocally to the time when 1 and 2 were *the* numbers at mankind's disposal; to the time when his three numeral concepts, 1, 2, many, each demanded distinct expression. With increasing knowledge the necessity for this differentiation would pass away, and but two numbers, singular and plural, would remain. Incidentally it is to be noticed that the Indo-European words for 3 — *three, trois, drei, tres, tri,* etc., have the same root as the Latin *trans,* beyond, and give us a hint of the time when our Aryan ancestors counted in the manner I have just described.

The first real difficulty which the savage experiences in counting, the difficulty which comes when he attempts to pass beyond 2, and to count 3, 4, and 5, is of course but slight; and these numbers are commonly used and readily understood by almost all tribes, no matter how deeply sunk in barbarism we find them. But the instances that have already been cited must not be forgotten. The Chiquitos do not, in their primitive state, properly count at all; the Andamans, the Veddas, and many of the Australian tribes have no numerals higher than 2; others of the Australians and many of the South Americans stop with 3 or 4; and tribes which make 5 their limit are still more numerous. Hence it is safe to assert that even this insignificant number is not always reached with perfect ease. Beyond 5 primitive man often proceeds with the greatest difficulty.[1]

III. CHARACTERISTICS OF COUNTING

From Conant's description of the beginnings of counting we can discern certain essential features of the activity.

1. The First Counting Words Were Distinguishing Words

The first that strikes the attention is that the first counting words were used as adjectives to qualify, or point out,

[1] From L. L. Conant. *The Number Concept,* pp. 74–76. By permission of The Macmillan Company, publishers, New York, 1896.

the objects to which they referred. By the use of such words, the primitive man gave his attention to the objects in a group in a new and different way. Note how his first words for one and two were such as to give the sense of 'this' and 'that.' These were *distinguishing* words. They made the objects, to which they thus referred, stand out each as distinct from the other. They separated the objects so named quite as much as our words, 'this one' and 'another one,' or 'first' and 'next,' or 'first' and 'second.' Even though the words were able to carry counting only as far as two — or, by the use of somewhat similar words for 'another this' and 'another that,' as far as four — they moved the ability to give attention to the objects of a group a step in advance of what it could ever have been by the use of tallies. To be sure, one could say "finger," "finger," when he tallied on his fingers, and each finger could be used to designate an object tallied, but the words, 'finger,' 'finger,' carried no sequence. The words 'this' and 'that' were *sequential;* 'that' must follow 'this' in ordered sequence; 'another this' must follow 'that,' and so on. 'This' always came first; 'that' came next. There was no mistaking the order of succession, once it had been established; whereas, when fingers or pebbles were used as tallies, it made no difference in what order the tallies were used. The tallies were for all practical purposes all alike. There was no order, and no established sequence among them.

2. Counting Words Established a Sequence

The second feature of early counting that strikes the attention is closely the ally of the first mentioned; yet it is distinct from the first. The second feature is that, since the counting words established a sequence, each succeeding word took into account and depended upon all that preceded. Each counting word thus had a place in the series that was both determined and fixed by the preceding words and that helped to determine and to fix the place of the fol-

lowing words. Such a feature of the counting words served
not merely as a means by which each object counted was
distinguished as an individual item of attention, but also as
a means establishing in consciousness the extent of the
group that was being counted. Because of the ordered succession of the counting words, *each word served a double purpose.* It both called attention to the individual item in the
group to which it particularly applied and also called attention to this item in connection with all the items that had
preceded. The first feature gave number its *ordinal* sense,
and the second gave number its *cardinal* sense; and because
both features were determined by the ordered sequence in
which the counting words came, each word was used at one
and the same time in the double sense. Ordinal and cardinal
numbers were thus for the first time united in thought.

IV. THE COUNTING SYSTEM

The essence of counting is its system. It provides, just as
tallying and matching with model groups provide, attention
both to the objects of a group one by one and to the group
as a whole. It does more. *It provides a system.* Though the
activities of tallying and matching undoubtedly prepared
the primitive mind for the somewhat similar activities performed in connection with counting, to insist that they grew
into counting would constitute a perversion of the true
meaning of counting. In order to create the process of
counting, the savage mind had to have at its disposal something more than a motley array of model groups, however
extensive the array may have been. It had to create an
order and a system in its procedure of attending to objects
and to groups. This order and system, which grew as counting grew, constituted the beginnings of mathematics. *Without system, there was no mathematical thinking; with the system,
mathematics started to develop.*

We can now begin to see what the earlier methods of
studying groups lacked. We can discover the reason why

the primitive mind did not immediately proceed to the process of counting as soon as it had learned to resort to the use of words for model groups, such as 'wing,' 'clover-leaf,' 'ostrich-toes,' 'hand.'

Counting is a complex procedure. One must have the number names in serial order ready for use. One must discriminate the objects being counted; that is, one must attend to each object singly, one at a time. One must apply the number names to the discriminated objects. And one must think the whole number of objects counted together as a group. Thus, in counting: one, two, three, four, we apply the name 'three' to the third object both as a means of setting it off from all the others and as a means of grouping it with those that have preceded it in the counting. At one and the same time 'three' means *third* object and *three* objects. When one counts his fingers, stopping with the thumb, he calls the thumb *five*. In this sense 'five' means *fifth;* it is an ordinal numeral. At the same time 'five' as applied to the thumb means that the thumb, combined with the rest of the fingers, is actually *five;* it is then a cardinal numeral. Thus, at one and the same time the counting word applies both to the single object and to the group.

In developing a concept of number in a collection by a one-to-one comparison with a model group, such as the fingers on his hand, for example, the savage used his word 'hand' in the cardinal sense only. He matched the objects being checked off with his fingers. Each finger checked an object. In the process he needed no separate names in a series to check the objects. He used a name — 'hand,' let us say — when the matching was complete. The name was used to designate the group as a whole. In the same way, he could check off four objects by matching with the toes of an ostrich, the picture of which he carried in his mind. To check one group, he used his hand; to check another, he used the toes of an ostrich. Since he used such model collections at separate times to tally first this group, then that one, it would conceivably be a long time before it occurred to him to match the toes of an ostrich with the fingers of his hand and thus to discover that the one preceded the other in number. As our quoted paragraphs from Gow and Conant indicate, he conceived his number ideas by means other than such comparison of his model collections. Thus, because they were used for separate purposes on separate occasions, the model collections, like 'wing' and 'clover-leaf,' were never arranged in thought in an ordered series until the creation of counting supplied the system that permitted that sort of use.

Moreover, even if the names of his model collections had ever been conceived in an ordered series — 'nose,' 'wing,' 'clover-leaf,' 'ostrich-toes,' 'hand' — primitive man could not have used them as counting words, for the reason that the name of a model group lends itself as a means of designating number in the *cardinal* sense only. The objects of the model group check one by one with the group being tallied. Each object of the model group serves as a means of discriminating each object of the group with which it is matched. The name of the model group refers to the whole group being tallied. Being a noun, the name of the model group does not suggest itself as a designating word — an adjective — to describe an object. So, even if the savage had compared his model groups to the point of arranging them in a series, he would still have had words that referred to groups and not to objects. He had to create a series of counting words that served a double purpose. His matching gave him *cardinal* number, and that did not lead him backward to *ordinal* number. His creation of counting, beginning as it did with adjective words in ordered sequence to designate objects one by one, gave him *ordinal* number, and that could lead him to *cardinal* number. *Cardinal* number did not supply *ordinal* number; *ordinal* number suggested *cardinal* number.

V. Ideas before Words

After primitive man began to count, he did in many instances use for his number names words that originally referred to concrete objects. Thus, many tribes used the word 'hand' for five, 'man' (all the fingers) for ten, and 'whole man' (fingers and toes) for twenty. The significance of such words, when they were used as counting words, was determined by the process of counting that had previously been created. It can hardly be said that such words, including 'wing,' 'clover-leaf,' etc., led to counting or assisted the primitive man in learning to count. There is a wide difference between our own ability to convert such words into counting words and the ability of the savage *before he had created the idea of counting.* We ourselves have the key that makes the conversion easy. The savage did not come into possession of the key until he had created the idea of using words in a series to designate objects one by one. When he had conceived the idea, he could take over and use as counting words any such names as suited his purpose.

We may summarize our whole discussion to this point in the statement that it takes an idea to make a word significant. Without the idea, the word is neither useful nor suggestive; with the idea, the word becomes serviceable and meaningful.

VI. Number Names as Counters

The development and use of number names as counters further illustrate the development of number ideas as well as certain of their unique characteristics. Let us return to a paragraph from Conant's discussion of the number concept for an illustration of the early use of number names.

In certain parts of the world, notably among the native races of South America, Australia, and many of the islands of Polynesia and Melanesia, a surprising paucity of numeral words has been observed. The Encabellada of the Rio Napa

have but two distinct numerals; *tey*, 1, and *cayapa*, 2. The
Chaco languages of the Guaycuru stock are also notably poor
in this respect. In the Mbocobi dialect of this language, the
only native numerals are: *yña tvak*, 1 and *yñoaca*, 2. The
Puris count *omi*, 1; *curiri*, 2; *prica*, many; and the Boto-
cudos, *mokenam*, 1; *uruhu*, many. The Fuegans, supposed
to have been able at one time to count to 10, have but three
numerals — *kaoueli*, 1; *compaïpi*, 2; *maten*, 3. The Campas
of Peru possess only three separate words for the expression
of number — *patrio*, 1; *pitteni*, 2; *mahuani*, 3. Above 3 they
proceed by combinations, as 1 and 3 for 4, 1 and 1 and 3 for 5.
Counting above 10 is, however, entirely inconceivable to
them, and any number beyond that limit they indicate by
tohaine, many.[2]

The paragraph just quoted illustrates the development of
new number ideas — for example, *one and three* — through
the combination in thought of ideas already developed and
made serviceable by their individual and separate names.
In the course of experience new names were invented for the
ideas that were first expressed as *one and three*, and *one and
one and three*. These new names, which came to stand for
the ideas already developed in the course of experience, made
possible further combination of familiar ideas into new ideas.
Let us illustrate, using our own number names.

We shall imagine a primitive man who is able to count,
one, two, many, returning from the hunt and describing as
best he can his experiences. He speaks of having seen *two*
animals here and *two* animals there, or he perhaps further
unites them in thought by speaking of *two and two* animals,
and he tells of how *two and one* escaped. Thus in the course
of his experience he has been induced to combine the ideas
he already possessed, and these very combinations extend
his ability to count. He now can count, *one, two, two and
one, two and two, many*. Later, he may develop, through
combination, the idea *two and one and two*. Beyond this

[2] Conant, *op. cit.*, p. 22.

point he cannot go because of the difficulty of holding the combinations in mind without verbal aids.

In the course of time new names are invented for the new ideas — *three, four,* and *five,* let us say. The new names for the familiar ideas extend the possibilities of number thinking. Now the primitive man can count, *one, two, three, four, five,* and by means of combinations made possible through the new names, *five and one, five and two, five and three, five and four, five and five, many.*

And so through the centuries, as primitive man developed new number ideas through a combination of his old ideas, he developed new names and new combinations of names to stand for his ideas. He developed his ideas in the course of experience, making use of what meager number names he already possessed. The names he possessed helped him to clarify his ideas and to free his thinking for the development of new ideas. Through comparison and grouping of objects, new ideas were developed; through the use of language to express the ideas, the methods of grouping were facilitated. We can distinguish a double development, a number language and number ideas developing concurrently.

We have seen how the use of pebbles as counters assisted early people in thinking by making possible easier and readier grouping. We can see how the use of number names as counters facilitated grouping by helping to make it a matter of thought without constant reference to the objects to be grouped and without the use of objects as counters, which are not so easy to handle and to move about as names.

VII. Counting and the Number Base

Counting was created by primitive man through his efforts to get a clearer and fuller idea of the group. It lent itself to the study of groups and was used for that purpose. By means of counting, attention was given systematically to each object of the group both by itself and also in connection with all the objects previously counted, so that at the conclusion of the counting there were united in thought the idea of the group and the idea of the individuals that composed it.

As counting came into use as a means of giving systematic attention, first to this group, then to that, the ideas of the groups counted came to be more and more familiar, more and more definite, and hence more and more understandable and usable. Let groups be counted — that is, studied through counting — over and over, and the ideas will come to be used with more and more certainty and assurance, though the ability to count is extended only to four or five. When the ideas to four or five come to be familiar they lend themselves to all sorts of applications, and sooner or later suggest the possibility of all sorts of combinations. The importance of feelings of familiarity and assurance may not be discounted, though they apply to number ideas no farther up the scale than four or five. So engrossed would one become with those ideas which grew out of his earlier efforts at counting that he would be inclined to give more attention to combinations of the ideas than to the effort to extend his separate number names farther up the scale.

It may thus be seen that counting served a double purpose. First of all, it made possible a systematic study of a few small groups which resulted in definite and exact number ideas. Secondly, with the development of these number ideas, the process of counting, limited as it was to the groups to which the ideas belonged, so fixed attention upon these ideas that they were employed over and over in the later study of larger groups.

The extent to which counting was carried in the beginning determined, at least for a period, the number idea which was used as a base for the study of larger groups. The foregoing quoted paragraph from Conant indicates how certain tribes dealt with a group of four by thinking of it as *three and one* and how they dealt with a group of five by thinking of it

as *three and one and one*, or as *three* and *two*.   The compre-
hensive studies of Conant indicate such number bases as
two, four, five, ten, and *twenty*.[3]

The most prominent of the number bases are *five* and *ten*,
which are to be explained by the five fingers on a hand and
the total of ten fingers.   The fingers served to set the limits
of straightforward counting without resort to combination
both in the counting systems of primitive peoples and in the
counting system in common use today.   One learned to
count by the use of separate names to the extent of a certain group — two, three, four, five, ten, or twenty, as the
case may be — and then, holding the group in mind through
repetitions of the name, proceeded with his counting as he
began.

The following account of the number system of the Zuñi
Indians is illustrative.   Their number words began:

1.	*topinte*	taken to start with.
2.	*kwilli*	put down together with.
3.	*hai*	the equally divided finger.
4.	*awite*	all the fingers all but done with.
5.	*opte*	the notched off.

Compounding now begins:

6.	*topalikya*	another brought down to add to the done with.
7.	*kwillilikya*	two brought to and held up with the rest.
8.	*hailikye*	three brought to and held up with the rest.
9.	*tenalikya*	all but all held up with the rest.
10.	*astemthila*	all the fingers.[4]

VIII. The Development of Number Names

Foregoing paragraphs have indicated the value of separate and distinct number names in clarifying the thinking

---

[3] Conant, *op. cit.*, Chaps. V–VII.
[4] F. H. Cushing.   "Manual Concepts."   *American Anthropologist, V:*
1892, p. 289.
C. H. Judd.   *Psychology of Social Institutions* (The Macmillan
Company, New York, 1926), p. 84.

of primitive people about related number ideas. The separate name helps to set the idea off as a distinct entity and provides for its serviceable use, both separately and in combination with other ideas. The act of compounding the name for a larger group out of the names of smaller ones that compose it no doubt led in many instances to the development and use of a new number name for the larger group.

The illustration of compounding taken from the counting system of the Zuñi Indians suggests how new names may have resulted from the original activities of combination and compounding. Whenever a name for an object, or group of objects — *astemthila*, 'all the fingers' — or the name of an act of grouping — *hailikye*, 'three brought to and held up with the rest' — was borrowed for number usage and adopted as a number name, there arose the necessity of distinguishing between the sound of the word when it referred to the object or activity and the sound when it was used as a number name. In the course of experience the distinction would often become so marked that no observable connection would remain between the two sounds of what was originally the same word. The number name, in order to be a real and serviceable number name, had finally to lose all connection with the concrete object or activity for which it first stood. As the number concept was developed, the number name came to refer to it, and to it only. With the number idea the number name was developed. Without the idea, there was no number name.

One can distinguish in the development of counting the tendency to develop a separate name for the idea of each new group as it came slowly and gradually into consciousness as a distinct idea. All sorts of combinations of groups were resorted to in distinguishing the larger groups and all sorts of compounding of names were used. The counting of the Zuñi Indians gives one set of illustrations. Others are given in the following account:

One other method of combination, that of subtraction, remains to be considered. Every student of Latin will recall at once the *duodeviginti*, 2 from 20, and *undeviginti*, 1 from 20, which in that language are the regular forms of expression for 18 and 19. At first they seem decidedly odd; but familiarity soon accustoms one to them, and they cease entirely to attract any special attention. This principle of subtraction, which, in the formation of numeral words, is quite foreign to the genius of English, is still of such common occurrence in other languages that the Latin examples just given cease to be solitary instances.

The origin of numerals of this class is to be found in the idea of reference, not necessarily to the last, but to the nearest, halting-point in the scale. Many tribes seem to regard 9 as 'almost 10,' and to give it a name which conveys this thought. In the Mississaga, one of the numerous Algonquin languages, we have, for example, the word *cangaswi*, "incomplete 10," for 9. . . . The same formation occurs in Malay, resulting in the numerals *delapan*, 10–2, and *sambilan* 10–1. In Green Island, one of the New Ireland group, these become simply *andra-lua*, "less 2," and *andra-si*, "less 1." In the Admiralty Islands this formation is carried back one step further, and not only gives us *shua-luea*, "less 2," and *shu-ri*, "less 1," but also makes 7 appear as *sua-tolu*, "less 3." Surprising as this numeral is, it is more than matched by the Ainu scale, which carries subtraction back still another step, and calls 6, 10–4. The four numerals from 6 to 9 in this scale are respectively, *iwa*, 10–4, *arawa*, 10–3, *tupe-san*, 10–2, and *sinepesan*, 10–1. Numerous examples of this kind of formation will be found in later chapters of this work; but they will usually be found to occur in one or both of the numerals, 8 and 9. Occasionally they appear among the higher numbers; as in the Maya languages, where, for example, 99 years is "one single year lacking from five score years," and in the Arikara dialects, where 98 and 99 are "5 men minus" and "5 men 1 not." The Welsh, Danish, and other languages less easily accessible than these to the general student, also furnish interesting examples of a similar character.

More rarely yet are instances met with of languages which

make use of subtraction almost as freely as addition, in the composition of numerals. Within the past few years such an instance has been noticed in the case of the Bellacoola language of British Columbia. In their numeral scale 15, "one foot," is followed by 16, "one man less 4"; 17, "one man less 3"; 18, "one man less 2"; 19, "one man less 1"; and 20, "one man." Twenty-five is "one man and one hand"; 26, "one man and two hands less 4"; 36, "two men less 4"; and so on. This method of formation prevails throughout the entire numeral scale.[5]

IX. The Limited Value of Separate Names

Though the lack of a system of grouping and of compounding names served to facilitate the development of separate and distinct number names that could very readily lose their earlier relationships, it failed to provide corresponding progress in the development of clear and distinct number ideas. The failure is to be explained by the fact that the span of attention is limited. The mind encounters difficulty in keeping a multitude of names in orderly array, and in distinguishing large groups and in apprehending their exact relations in thought. Thus it comes about that, when a separate name fixes attention upon a large group as a separate item of experience, it may serve to hide, instead of bringing out, the relations between this group and smaller groups.

A word is useful and valuable only when the meaning that it is intended to carry is clear and unmistakable. When the meaning is involved, uncertain, or hazy, the word not only is difficult to use but also misdirects and impedes thinking. Thus, to be useful, a number name that is separate and distinct must stand for an idea of a group that can be readily apprehended or for an idea that can be conceived without a great deal of preliminary thinking. Separate names for the ideas to ten can be described as possessing this quality.

[5] Conant, *op. cit.*, pp. 44–46.

Primitive man, as we have seen, learned to distinguish groups up to three and four by means of direct perceptual discrimination. In a group of four, for example, it is possible to distinguish at once each individual member of the group and the group as a whole. Civilized man, despite his elaborate number training, cannot go much beyond a group of four. With all of our experience we cannot immediately apprehend a group larger than six or seven. However, we are able by a single act of grouping to recognize a group of nine or ten. We can do it by noticing at once five here and four there beside the five, for example. Groups of twelve, fifteen, and sixteen require a double or a triple act of grouping. We learn, to be sure, to think of sixteen as eight and eight, or as ten and six, but this does not make 'sixteen' highly serviceable as a separate and distinct idea, for the reason that sixteen is learned through the combination of ideas that are themselves the products of combination. A number idea, to be serviceable as a distinct idea, must relate closely enough to direct experience to stand in thought as a distinct idea. The ideas, 'one' to 'four' or 'five,' are distinct because they may be related to readily comprehensible groups. The ideas, 'five' to 'nine' or 'ten,' are also learned and used as distinct ideas because they may be learned as applying to groups that are readily comprehensible by an act of grouping that is only one step removed from direct experience. Ideas beyond those of nine and ten may not be considered useful as distinct ideas because their conception and development involve mental processes of grouping too many steps removed from direct experience. As we shall see, they are learned as ideas related to more easily developed ideas, and they are so used in our number system.

CHAPTER III

COUNTING DEVICES

Argument

1. The use of objects as counters was both an aid in counting and a means of recording the result of the process. It helped to extend the process beyond the limit of the number base.

2. The use of objects facilitated the division of a large group into smaller groups each corresponding in size to the number base.

3. As number names were serviceable in counting objects of whatever sort, so they became useful in counting groups.

4. Since objects as counters and number names as counters were used together, the use of a number name to designate a group suggested the use of an object to designate a group. Objects thus became counters of groups as well as counters of the individual items of any given group.

5. When the same kind of counters was used for the double purpose, it was necessary to distinguish between the counters that stood for individual items and those that stood for groups.

6. The position in which the counters were placed was hit upon as the means of keeping them distinguishable. Position as a sign of value, that is, as a sign of the size of a group, is a counting device of ancient origin.

7. The abacus was an invention to keep clear and distinguishable the positions of counters that were used for different purposes.

8. The abacus made possible an easy reckoning with the sizes of groups as well as with their number. Size was represented by position and number by the counters.

9. The abacus set off positions whose values increased regularly in the decimal scale.

10. The abacus took care of the sizes of groups so well that the computer could devote most of his attention to the manipulation of his counters.

11. Interest in the manipulation of counters led to modifications of the abacus that departed from the decimal scale. Later discussions will indicate the results of such neglect of the original significance of position.

12. The suggestion is made that the interest in number manipulation today frequently serves to distract from the significance of position as a means of representing the idea of size.

I. Objects as Counters

Fingers were the first counting device. Used as tallies before counting began, they were ready for use in finger-counting as counting was created. Finger-counting served a double purpose. In the first place, it helped to inspire a feeling of confidence in the one whose counting activities were just beginning. The use of the fingers in the set order that had been hit upon accidentally or copied from another helped to keep the counting words in order. Since counting words were often derived from the names of fingers or of certain uses of the fingers, the association persisted. Primitive man sought the fullest possible reactions of meaning from his counting activities. He relied upon all the help the use of his fingers seemed to give him as he groped his way toward a better and better use of his number names.

Moreover, when the counting of a group had been completed, the fingers that had been told off in the process of counting stood as a record of the group. Matching, as in tallying, continued, and so the group of fingers was recognized as the equal of the group of counted objects. One could hold up so many fingers to indicate the size of the group. These he or another could count to confirm or to get in mind the idea of the group indicated.

As fingers were useful both as an *aid during the process* of counting and as a *record* when the process had been completed, so were other objects, such as pebbles, sticks, marks in the sand, etc. A pile of pebbles, accumulated during the process of counting a group, continued to stand for the group and to aid the memory in retaining the idea of the group. When the number of the group had been forgotten, or if it had become confused, one could always return to the pile of pebbles and count them.

II. NUMBERS OF HIGHER ORDER

The use of objects in counting at its beginning level seemed quickly to suggest their use as a means of raising counting to a higher level. Through their use the number base that at first was merely the stopping point of the counting activity became the point of departure for new adventures in counting. To illustrate, let us imagine a primitive chieftain who has *twenty-five* warriors to count, but who has number names only to *five*. Using the names, he can count to *five*, proceed with *five* and *one*, and so on. We can imagine his confusion when he gets as far as *two fives* and *one* if we will reflect that his ideas of groups even as far as five are not altogether perfect and that he probably labors a good deal keeping his ideas and names straight even to that point. Let us watch him, however, as he uses objects to assist his counting. As the warriors pass by to be counted, he lays aside an object for each until he has counted to five, and accumulated a group of five; he proceeds as before, counting to five, and accumulates another group of five; finally, the counting is completed, and he can count his five groups. By means of the objects, the counting was enabled to progress far beyond the point that would have been possible if nothing but the names, *one* to *five*, had been used.

When the chieftain counts his *groups* of fives, he takes a step in advance; he raises his counting activity to a new level; he begins to deal with numbers of higher order. As he counts the groups — *one*, *two*, etc. — he is counting neither warriors nor objects that stand for warriors. *One* no longer means merely *one*, whether warrior or object. *One* now means *one five*. In the final counting, groups are treated just the same as objects — dealt with, spoken of, counted, each as a unit, though it is perfectly clear that each group is unlike the units of which it is composed.

When the savage had begun his counting, he developed and used it as a process having general applicability. He could count men, trees, spears, animals — anything. Thus, when he learned to set aside a group as an understood and manageable unit, he could just as easily count groups. From earliest times large and unwieldy groups have been divided into small and comprehensible groups. Sheep were divided into herds, armies into bands or companies, skins into bundles, and so on. When the division had been made, each herd, or band, or bundle, was treated as a unit and was counted just as readily as the unit items that composed it. When the division was made through preliminary counting into groups of the same size, the groups took on an added meaning and the counting of the groups, a deeper significance. Thus, five groups of five meant a great deal more than five groups of different sizes. Moreover, when five or ten had been used over and over as the basis of divisions and groupings, a group of this particular size became better understood than a group of any other size. Such a group became with usage a *standard* of counting, grouping, dividing, measuring, comparing.

III. Objects as Counters of Groups

If we were to represent graphically the grouping of objects as the primitive chieftain used them in counting twenty-five warriors, as illustrated in the foregoing topic, we would picture *five fives* thus:

Or, as objects used as counters later came to be grouped, we would have the grouping pictured thus:

$$\cancel{||||} \quad \cancel{||||} \quad \cancel{||||} \quad \cancel{||||} \quad \cancel{||||}$$

that is, the fifth stick, or mark, in a given group was placed across the rest to indicate the completion of the group and to make it easily distinguishable from any smaller and uncompleted group.

As early man learned to attend to groups in the same way as he had attended to individuals, and to apply to given groups the same number names as he had applied to individuals, he gradually came to the point where he found it just as easy to represent a group with an object as it was to represent an individual with an object. Objects came gradually into use as counters for groups as well as counters for individuals. If the same names can be used in counting groups as in counting individual units, why could not the same objects be used as counters for both?

The procedure may be illustrated by the use that is often made of the fingers in counting. One often uses the fingers of one hand, the left, for example, to count the individuals until a group of five is counted, and at that point turns down a finger of the right hand to stand for the group of five. He then proceeds as before, and with each group of five counted off on the fingers of the left hand, he turns down a finger of the right hand. Suppose, when the counting is completed, four fingers on each hand are turned down. One does not think of the two sets of fingers as having equal values. The group counted is not *four* and *four*, but *four fives* and *four*. Each finger turned down is like every other finger, to be sure; but the *places* where the fingers are located make a difference.

Let us picture the ancient chieftain again, using objects to count his warriors, supposing this time that he has *twenty-four* to count. He counts to *five*, laying down an object for each warrior. When *five* have been counted, he lays aside an object to stand for the group, and so on until the counting is completed. At the end, he has accumulated objects in groups thus:

////   ////

He now counts his counters: *four* and *four;* but in the one case, each object stands for a warrior, and in the other, each object stands for a group. Instead of having counted only *four* and *four*, the chieftain has counted *four fives* and *four*.

Conant [1] reports a curious method of counting soldiers that was observed by travellers in Madagascar more than a century ago. The soldiers were made to file through a narrow passage, and one pebble was dropped for each. When a pile of ten pebbles had accumulated, a pebble was set aside to stand for the ten and the counting was continued. When ten pebbles had accumulated in the second pile, a pebble was set aside in a third location to stand for the ten tens or the hundred, and so on until the entire army had been counted.

IV. POSITION AS A SIGN OF VALUE

It was of paramount importance, when objects were used both as counters of individual units and as counters of groups, to distinguish between the objects that were used for the different purposes. Suppose, after laying aside so many pebbles to stand for the groups of ten and so many to stand for the remaining individual soldiers, the enumerator of the army in Madagascar had forgotten which pebbles stood for groups and which stood for soldiers. His confusion would have been without limit. Instead of aiding him to arrive at a definite idea of the number, his counters would have led either to a very erroneous and undependable idea or into hopeless confusion. It was necessary, when

[1] L. L. Conant. *The Number Concept* (The Macmillan Company, New York, 1896), pp. 8–9.

objects were used as counters for the different designations, to keep the objects separate and distinguishable.

What schemes might be used to keep distinguishable the objects used as counters in this way? One might use objects of different colors: red for *units*, white for *fives* or *tens*, as the case may be, and blue for *five fives* or *ten tens*. Or one might use objects of different sizes: small objects for units, objects of an intermediate size for the groups of *fives* or *tens*, and so on. Either scheme will serve the purpose, but either scheme requires the enumerator, after selecting the objects he will use as counters, to give attention to the preparation of the objects so they will be distinguishable. He would have to keep the distinguishing features of the counters ever in mind; and this would make difficult, if not prevent, the treating of all the counters according to a common method. Moreover, the colors might fade, or the sizes of objects intended for one use might not be uniformly larger than those intended for another use. Neither color nor size seems appropriate as a scheme for making and keeping counters certainly distinguishable.

The use of the fingers of the two hands as counters of both units and groups suggests the scheme that is both easy to manage and thoroughly reliable. The fingers of the two hands are separately located. They cannot become mixed or confused. Their positions are provided by nature and are kept clear without preliminary planning or subsequent thinking. Once one decides to use one set of fingers as counters of units and the other set as counters of groups, his mind is relieved of all need for distinguishing between the two sets of counters. The counters are all alike and may be treated alike, because position keeps their values clear.

Whether the use of the fingers suggested the idea of making use of position to keep distinguishable the counters that were used for different purposes, or the idea was hit upon by accident, there is no means of knowing. The important fact is that position did come to be used as a device for

indicating value. When the enumerator of the soldiers in
Madagascar had used his pebbles as counters to ten, he put
aside *in another position* a pebble that stood as a counter of
a group of ten. It was *one* pebble just like every other pebble but, because of the position in which it was placed, it
stood not for a unit but for a group. The enumerator kept
the positions of his counters clear, and the positions in turn
helped him to keep his counting manageable and his thinking
clear.

V. The Abacus

The enumerator of the soldiers in Madagascar, and others
like him, had during the process of enumeration not only to
use their counters, but also to decide upon and to keep in
memory the places where they would put the counters of
different values. In the beginning there was no method or
scheme for the places chosen and used. The places were
determined upon and used according to the dictates of individual and momentary caprice. Counters for the soldiers
could, for example, be placed at one's right hand; counters
for groups of tens at one's left hand; and counters for tens
of tens, or hundreds, immediately in front. Any placing of
the counters would serve the purpose. All that was necessary was to keep the positions chosen for units, tens, and
hundreds constantly in mind, and not confuse one chosen
position with another.

Chance selection of positions for the placing of counters
gave way to an ordered scheme. This was effected through
the development and use of a mechanical contrivance known
as the abacus.

The abacus was originally (1) a dust covered board upon
which figures could be marked with a stylus and erased with
the finger when necessary, whence the name 'abacus,' from
the Greek *abax*, dust. It later was developed into (2) a
table marked with lines upon or between which loose counters were placed; and (3) a table or frame on which the

counters were kept in position, or fastened, by means of grooves, wires or rods. Many forms of the abacus have been developed. They all may be classified, however, according to the three general types.[2]

A form of the abacus used by the Romans is shown in the accompanying illustration. The columns were outlined on a wax tablet. As many columns as one desired could be outlined. A counter in 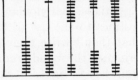 the first column represented one unit; a counter in the second column represented one ten; and so on; and a counter in any column represented ten counters in the next column to the right. The number 1737 is represented in the illustration.

The simplest form of the line abacus may be represented as shown below. Each line gave a place value to the counters placed upon it. Each line had a value ten times the value of the line below it. The number 1737 is represented in the illustration.

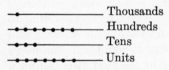

The Russian abacus is perhaps the simplest form of the frame abacus. This form employs beads in strings of tens. The string of beads at the right represents units, the next tens, and so on. The beads are set to show 1737.

Each form of the abacus employed the same principle in representing number; namely, the principle of position. In the figures shown the importance of position is clear. Each counter is like every other counter, but each column or row

[2] D. E. Smith. *History of Mathematics*, II (Ginn and Company, Boston, 1925), Chap. III.

L. C. Karpinski. *The History of Arithmetic* (Rand, McNally and Company, Chicago, 1925), pp. 25–28.

of counters is unlike every other column or row. A unit counter in unit's column or row stands for a unit, but a unit counter in ten's column or row stands for a group of ten units. In each illustration seven counters are shown in hundred's position and seven counters in unit's position. What each set of seven shows is determined quite as much by position as by the number of counters used.

1. Counting on the Abacus

Because the abacus kept position clear, it was a useful device in counting. The enumerator of soldiers, or of items

of property in Ancient Egypt, Babylonia, Greece, or Rome would lay down a counter in unit's column for each soldier, or item, until he came to nine. Now when he counted the tenth one, he would remove the counters in unit's column and place a counter in ten's column, and so on. When he had counted to the point where he had nine counters in each of ten's and unit's columns, he would place the next counter in hundred's column and remove the counters in the first two columns.

2. Operations on the Abacus

The abacus was used as a means of computation by early Egyptians, Babylonians, Greeks, and Romans. Herodotus testifies to the use of the abacus by the Egyptians, saying that they "write their characters and reckon with pebbles, bringing the hand from right to left, while the Greeks go from left to right."[3] Smith mentions evidences of the early use of the abacus by the Ancient Maya civilization in Yucatan.[4] The abacus was used as a computing device in Medieval Europe, and it continues in use today in China, Russia, and Persia. The Chinese laundryman in America may frequently be observed to carry on his computations with an abacus in the form of beads on a wire frame.

---

[3] Smith, *op. cit.*, p. 160.   [4] *Ibid.*, p. 45.

Addition was a straightforward process corresponding to methods used in counting. It is illustrated by Smith as follows:

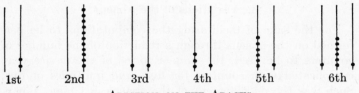

1st 2nd 3rd 4th 5th 6th

ADDITION ON THE ABACUS

An early computer, wishing to add 22 and 139, might have proceeded as follows: Place 2 pebbles on the unit's line, as shown in the First Step. Then place 9 more, as shown in the Second Step. Then take away 10 of these pebbles and add one pebble to the ten's line, as shown in the Third Step. Then add 2 pebbles to the ten's line because of the 20 in 22, as shown in the Fourth Step. Then add 3 more because of the 30 in 139, as shown in the Fifth Step. Finally draw a line for hundreds, and on this place one pebble because of the 100 in 139. The answer is 161.[5]

Subtraction was a 'take away' process, the opposite of addition.

Multiplication was a process of partial additions by doubling, and division was a most difficult operation, sometimes performed by continued subtractions, and sometimes by completing the division to a multiple of ten. To multiply 132 by 5, additions were performed as follows:

$$\begin{array}{ccc} 132 & 264 & 528 \\ \underline{132} & \underline{264} & \underline{132} \end{array}$$

To divide 660 by 132, subtractions could be made thus:

$$\begin{array}{ccccc} 660 & 528 & 396 & 264 & 132 \\ \underline{132} & \underline{132} & \underline{132} & \underline{132} & \underline{132} \end{array}$$

Counting the times 132 has been subtracted, one finds the answer 5. These operations were performed on the abacus

[5] Smith, *op. cit.*, p. 159.

without the use of the Arabic numerals. We have used them here merely to indicate the kinds of processes that were performed.

3. Variations of the Abacus

For the sake of facilitating the computations to be performed on the abacus through a reduction of the number of counters to be used, the simpler forms of the device were complicated with counters for fives and multiples of five. Such was the development of the abacus in China, Japan, and Medieval Europe. The principle of position remained

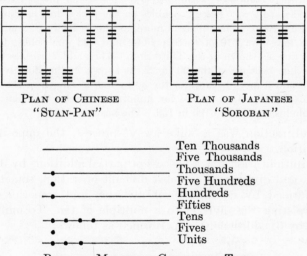

PLAN OF CHINESE   PLAN OF JAPANESE
  "SUAN-PAN"   "SOROBAN"

Ten Thousands
Five Thousands
Thousands
Five Hundreds
Hundreds
Fifties
Tens
Fives
Units

PLAN OF MEDIEVAL COMPUTING TABLE

unchanged in the Chinese and Japanese abaci, but was complicated somewhat in the line abacus of Western Europe by the use of intermediate positions for fives and multiples of five. The developments are illustrated above. In each of these three illustrations the number 1648 is represented.

The illustration of the line abacus shows the form that was used in Western Europe for several hundred years. To represent a number one would "lay" the sum; to add and subtract he would "lay and seize." Thus the pupil was told in the arithmetic of the day (Albert's Arithmetic, 1534):

> Write right, lay right, seize right, speak right,
> And you will always get the answer right.

Addition and subtraction, as suggested by the arithmetics of the day, may be represented as follows: [6]

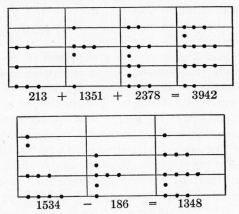

213 + 1351 + 2378 = 3942

1534 — 186 = 1348

VI. Size and Number as Exemplified in the Abacus

Counters were first used as a means of enumerating and representing the number of individual units; they finally came to be used as an aid in enumerating and representing the number of groups with which one had to deal. When groups were made, dealt with, and thought of, it was necessary to devise some means of distinguishing the groups from the units and from each other. Since a unit counter is always a unit counter, counters were useful only in dealing with numbers. A unit counter could stand for a unit individual or a unit group. The position in which a counter may be placed was hit upon as a means of showing the size

[6] Smith, *op. cit.*, pp. 181–185.

of the group to be represented. Position came to be resorted
to in order to distinguish groups from units and from each
other. *Size* was represented by position and *number* by the
counters.

Thus, in gaining an idea of a large group of objects, the
total group was broken down into smaller related groups;
rather, the individual units of the large group were built
into a number of smaller related groups. To get in mind
and to keep in mind the values of the smaller groups in their
relations to each other and to the large group being dealt
with, the number of the smaller groups had to be accounted
for and the size of the smaller groups had to be definitely
and accurately represented. Ideas of *number* and ideas of
size thus developed as complementary ideas. They both
had to be dealt with at once. The number of groups was
important; the size of the groups was equally important.

The abacus was a useful device in representing sizes by
position; it represented related sizes by a systematic scheme
of positions for the counters that were used to show numbers;
it kept sizes clear by keeping position clear; moreover, it
relieved the mind from thinking continually about the sizes
of groups. The abacus may be described in another way.
The abacus was developed out of man's efforts to deal with
groups in a systematic way, and its use improved and made
more fruitful man's efforts to handle groups systematically.
So well was it contrived for a systematic arrangement of the
groups with which man had to deal that it finally took over
the necessity of giving continuous attention to the sizes of
the groups and left the enumerator and computer comparatively free to give their attention to the manipulation of the
counters. As the computer became more skilled in the manipulation of his counters, he gave less thought to the groups
with which he was dealing and to their ordered relations.
We have seen how the later development of the line abacus
was in the direction of a more facile use of the counters
through a reduction of the number of counters employed

and away from the former and original relations of the groups each to the other. We shall be reminded in a later chapter of the difficulty into which the computer was led through the employment of fives and multiples of five in the line abacus when the necessity arose of improving his methods of computation at the time when the Hindu-Arabic numerals were introduced in Western Europe.

Moreover, the neglect of the sizes and relations of his groups by the medieval computer, which was made possible through the relief from the necessity of thinking about them which the abacus provided, may give some hint to the reason for the almost total neglect of the ideas of size and position by teachers and textbooks today. We shall have occasion in later chapters to refer to the engrossment of our modern methods of teaching arithmetic in number manipulation to the neglect of the idea of size and the significance of position. The psychology of the medieval computer may be of some assistance in explaining the psychology employed by the arithmetic teacher and arithmetic textbook writers of our own day.

CHAPTER IV

ANCIENT NUMERALS

1. The first numeral was a set of counters that was left to stand as a record.

2. Constant use of a set of counters to stand for a group served to attract attention to the form in which the counters had been placed.

3. Reproducing the numeral became finally the act of copying a single form rather than one of representing all the individual details. Thus, a single numeral came to substitute for a set of counters in representing a group.

4. The use of numerals tended to pattern after the use of counters, and thus to become an aid in the development of number thinking.

5. In spite of the apparent mutual assistance of names, counters, and numerals, the arithmetic of today has experienced an extraordinarily retarded development.

6. The retardation was due to the inflexibility of numerals, to their fixity of form, and to their relative permanence when written as a record. A numeral system that was once useful in aiding number thinking could not change itself so as to keep pace with improved methods of number thinking.

7. The Roman system of numerals serves as an illustration:

    (a) Of irregularity in the use of a number base,

    (b) Of irregularity in representing large groups in relation to small related groups,

    (c) Of incompleteness as an aid in thinking,

    (d) Of the manner in which a numeral system may confuse, instead of keep clear and related, the ideas of size and number; in short,

    (e) Of a numeral system that did not employ the ideas of number relations that had been developed by other means.

I. The Origin of Numerals

Following his creation of the art of counting, and coincident with his use of objects as an aid in counting, primitive man acquired the motive to record with some degree of permanence the number ideas that he had gained and used under various circumstances. Whether the motive in the beginning was practical or logical, we have no means of discovering. The fact that numerals were developed, however, evidences man's interest in the recording of number ideas.

The first numerals were not numerals at all as we know and use them today. They were in reality nothing more than relatively permanent impressions of such counters as man had used from earlier days. They met the needs of the time by serving as a record and in that way they served the original purpose of numerals.

Primitive man, as we have seen, learned to resort to the use of all sorts of convenient objects as counters — sticks, stones, marks in the sand, marks in clay, and the like. Let him use marks in clay or scratches on a stone, let us say, in counting a group of objects, thus: ////. If such marks are not erased, they remain as a record. They take on the characteristics of permanency. They do not move themselves about, and are not scattered in disarray by chance disturbance. Such marks as counters //// remain as a notation, a written record, of the number idea arrived at in counting. They thus possess, whether by accident or design, the character of a numeral. Moreover, because they possess a certain permanence, they impress their form upon the mind. After using and then observing such a set of counters as a record for a number idea, one would be inclined to use the same kind of counters in the same way again to serve a similar purpose.

The fact that early numerals were simply counters used for the purpose of recording is evidenced by the following illustrations:

The Babylonian numerals 1 to 9 were formed somewhat as follows:

$$\begin{matrix} & & & \text{vvv} & \text{vvv} & \text{vvv} & \text{vvv} & \text{vvv} & \text{vvv} \\ \text{v} & \text{vv} & \text{vvv} & \text{v} & \text{vv} & \text{vvv} & \text{vvv} & \text{vvv} & \text{vvv} \\ & & & & & & \text{v} & \text{vv} & \text{vvv} \end{matrix}$$

Chinese rod numerals from 1 to 5 are:

I	II	III	IIII	IIIII

Roman numerals from 1 to 4 are:

I   II   III   IIII [1]

II. The Attractiveness of Form

The arrangement of counters for the purpose of recording an idea of number gradually took upon itself a characteristic form. This form gradually impressed itself upon the mind, and came finally to stand out in clearer perspective than the individual counters that composed it. As a particular form of arrangement was used and observed again and again, it came to provide the means by which the idea it represented was recognized. One was able finally to recognize the numeral by its form, without having to count the objects that produced it. For example, the Babylonian numeral for nine
vvv
vvv has a characteristic form which is impressive. After a
vvv
short acquaintance with this numeral, one would be able to recognize it by its characteristic form.

The Greeks were especially interested in the various configurations that could be taken by the objects they used originally as counters. They went to such lengths in their interest in form and arrangement as to classify certain numbers as *triangular*, *square*, *pentagonal*, and so forth. For example, triangular numbers are those that can be built up

[1] D. E. Smith. *History of Mathematics* II (Ginn and Company, Boston, 1925), pp. 37, 40–41.

as sums of the sequence 1, 2, 3, 4, 5, etc. Such sums are 1, 3, 6, 10, 15, etc., and can thus be represented:

Square numbers are those that can be built up as sums of the sequence 1, 3, 5, 7, 9, etc. Such sums are 1, 4, 9, 16, 25, etc., and can thus be represented:

Pentagonal numbers are those that can be built up as sums of the sequence, 1, 4, 7, 10, 13, etc.

Probably our word 'figures' as referring to numbers, and hence 'figuring,' can be traced to this Greek interest communicated to Latin Europe by Boethius and for a thousand years taught as a part of arithmetic in the church school of Europe.[2]

III. The Development of Numeral Forms

Because attention was attracted to the form of any given arrangement of counters that had been preserved as a record, the efforts of the one who was interested in producing a record came to be directed more and more toward either a perpetuation or a development of the form and less and less toward a faithful representation of the counters originally used to produce the form. Our present numerals 2 and 3 are merely cursive forms of the original = and ≡. The Roman numeral X is said to have originated from an arrange-

---

[2] L. C. Karpinski. *The History of Arithmetic* (Rand, McNally and Company, Chicago, 1925), p. 19.

ment of ten counters.[3]   One may go further on the same
theory and hazard the guess that the Roman V was suggested by the following arrangement of five counters, *LHT*, or
by the angle made by the thumb and fingers of the open
hand.

By whatever theories the origin of numeral forms may be
explained, however, the fact remains that the forms developed more and more as conventionalized signs with less and
less obvious relationship either to counters or to the number
ideas they represented.   The counters in a given arrangement produced a single form, and the singularity of the
form, rather than the plurality of the counters, became the
object of attention.   The single form came to represent a
single given group.   Finally, it made little difference what
character or sign was used to represent a group, so long as
there were general agreement and understanding about the
relation between the group and its sign.   The laying of the
rod numerals of the Chinese horizontally instead of verti-
cally changed the values they represented from units to tens.
Similarly, the counter and the numeral used by the Babylonians for 'one' became, when written horizontally, the
numeral for the group of ten.   For example, ∨ represented
one; < represented ten.   Thus the numeral lost its relation
with counters and came to represent such number idea as
the social group chose to have it represent.   The complete
severance of the original relationship between numerals and
counters is illustrated in the use of the letters of the alpha-
bet as numerals.   The Greeks used their first nine letters
for units, the next nine for tens, and, adding three other
characters making another nine, they used these for hundreds.   The use of letters in the Roman system of notation
is familiar.

The conventionality of the later numeral forms is to be
seen in the difference between the method by which they
were treated and the use of counters or of numerals that

[3] Smith, *op. cit.*, pp. 5, 67–68.

were closely related to counters. Let one, for example, put two groups of counters together, || and |||, for example, or two numerals that are closely related to counters, vv and vvv, for example, and the result in each case is clearly evident. Let him, however, put two strictly numeral signs together — L and X, let us say, or 2 and 3 — and the result is known only to the initiated.

IV. Use of Numerals Suggested By Use of Counters

At the outset the use of numerals patterned after the use of counters. This is as one would expect. The development of numerals followed the development of counters, and, as we have seen, the numerals were in their beginnings very much the same as counters. Since the two were barely distinguishable in appearance, and, without doubt, not distinguishable in the thinking of the early peoples who were using them, the use of the one would be suggested by the use of the other. Moreover, since the use of numerals followed the early development of number names and the language of counting, their use would conceivably be patterned after the ideas suggested by and couched in the oral language.

The earliest use of the oral language of number and of counters was in building up the idea and the representation of a given group by a one-by-one process of addition. Addition was the prevailing method of proceeding in thought from one group to another. In the course of progress, additions were made, as we have seen, first one by one to a number base and next in a similar manner from the base as a point of reference. Moreover, the ideas that were close to the base, smaller as well as larger, came to be thought of in terms of their relations to the base. As a consequence, the subtractive principle was also employed in the use of numerals.

Let us illustrate. The Babylonian numerals for two and three, vv and vvv, when put together, give the numeral for five $\overset{vv}{vv}$. The numerals for ten and one <, and v, give their numeral for eleven < v. On the other hand, nineteen was represented as twenty less one, << v > v, the symbol, v >, meaning 'less.' Further illustration of the use of the additive and subtractive principles is to be found in the more familiar Roman numerals that will presently be described.

V. The Service of Numerals

From the beginning, the written language of number has presented the possibility of rendering a double service. In the first place, the written numeral stands as a record of the results of thinking. After one has counted, or otherwise arrived at an idea of number, he may set down the appropriate numeral to record his result. As such, the numeral serves as a reminder. Because it thus frees the mind for further thinking, it is capable of performing its second and closely related service. As a record of one step in the process of thinking, it not only frees the mind so that it can go on to the next step, but it also serves as a means for breaking up into a series of easy steps what otherwise would be a difficult performance. Like the language of any science, the language of number is both a means of expression and an instrument of thinking.

The service of numerals may be described in another way. The creation of counting and the invention of counting devices preceded the writing of numerals, and determined at the outset how the numerals were to be used. The invention of numerals in turn contributed to the oral language of number and to the employment of counting devices by permitting the computer to set down a partial result of his thinking and to proceed with an untrammeled mind to the next step. Each instrument — number names, counters, and numerals — played its part in the thinking process, such as it was in the beginning, and each participated in mutual and reciprocal advantages. Number thinking had already progressed a long distance from its earliest beginning when the primitive mind first conceived of the written sign as a record of the size of a group. As numerals were developed and as their uses patterned after and paralleled the uses of the number devices that preceded them in development, they set the minds of early people free to extend their ideas of number and to push back a little further the veil hiding the unknown. The science of arithmetic, though in its infancy, had as its handmaids the three great instruments that have been responsible for its development — number names, counting devices, and numerals. With these three working in coöperation there would appear to have been nothing to prevent a normally rapid development of the science. We shall next see that the development really was not rapid.

VI. The Retarded Development of Arithmetic

Though reckoning is an ancient art, arithmetic is a modern science. The Egyptians had a most clumsy arithmetic. In order to add fractions, they were obliged to raise these fractions to the denominator sixty. The Greeks and the Romans knew little arithmetic. Though great in the fields of geometry and measurement, they could do little more than add and subtract, and these only with considerable effort. Not until comparatively recent times were the arts of multiplication and division attempted, or even conceived. Dantzig tells the story [4] of a German merchant of the fifteenth century who, desiring to give his son an advanced commercial education, appealed to a university professor for advice as to where he should send his son for training. The reply was that if the mathematical curriculum of the young man was to be confined to addition and subtraction, he could obtain such instruction in a German university; but, if instruction was desired in the difficult arts of multiplication and division, he would have to go to the universities in Italy for such advanced training.

[4] Tobias Dantzig. *Number, The Language of Science* (The Macmillan Company, New York, 1930), p. 26.

The calculations now performed by children in the third and fourth grades required only a short time ago the services of a specialist. Until recent times calculation was a hidden mystery to the common man; it was a laborious and somewhat uncertain procedure to the expert.

One who reflects upon the history of reckoning up to the invention of the principle of position is struck by the paucity of achievement. This long period of five thousand years saw the fall and rise of many a civilization, each leaving behind it a heritage of literature, art, philosophy and religion. But what was the net achievement in the field of reckoning, the earliest art practiced by man? An inflexible numeration so crude as to make progress well-nigh impossible, and a calculating device so limited in scope that even elementary calculations called for the services of an expert. And what is more, man used these devices for thousands of years without making a single worth-while improvement in the instrument, without contributing a single important idea to the system!

This criticism may sound severe; after all it is not fair to judge the achievements of a remote age by the standards of our own time of accelerated progress and feverish activity. Yet, even when compared with the slow growth of ideas during the Dark Ages, the history of reckoning presents a peculiar picture of desolate stagnation.[5]

The foregoing observations bring us face to face with a problem. In view of the fact that the use of numerals developed in coördination with the use of number names and the use of counters, making possible from their inception a higher level of thinking than could have been undertaken without them, and giving increased impetus to the development of number ideas, how can the long-continued and almost unbelievable stagnation in number thinking be accounted for? The advantages of a record as a substitute for memory and as an aid in thinking are evident. At the outset the use of numerals aided thinking. What accounts for the long halting of the progress once started?

[5] Dantzig, *op. cit.*, p. 29.

The problem may be put in another way. We look around us and observe some children in our schools, at least, progressing easily and rapidly from counting to the arrangement of groups in addition, subtraction, multiplication, and division, and going on to more involved and more abstract processes. To us it appears that they move from the lower stages of counting to the higher levels of the combinations in a series of easy steps. They appear to be prepared by the steps previously taken for each succeeding step. Their earlier steps are in the field of the counting and arrangement of objects as counters, and appear to us very like the early steps the race took in counting and in the manipulation of counters. We reflect that the children learn to count, later to add and subtract, later to multiply and divide. We may pause to wonder why the race halted so long after it began to count and could perform a few additions and subtractions. We remember, to be sure, that racial progress must be slow, and that the child has the experience of the race at his back and may be guided around the mistakes the race has made. But even such reflections give no explanation of the long-interrupted progress in number thinking. We can understand slow racial progress, however slow it may have been; but it is difficult for us, when we note the rapid strides made by some children, to understand no progress at all for such long periods of racial experience.

VII. The Inflexibility of Numerals

We have the answer to our questions in the fact that when numerals begin to be used after a given fashion they take upon themselves a fixity of order and arrangement that becomes, with continued use, harder and harder to disturb. A name may be uttered and then it is gone; a set of counters may be set down in a given order, and their arrangement is easily changed; but when a record is made it assumes, if it does not possess, the quality of permanence. Let a set of numerals be put together in a given order, and the order

fixes itself in the mind of everyone who turns to it for information. The given order tends to become not merely an
individual habit of recording information, but also a social
habit. The order extends its influence to the generations
succeeding the one that first determined it. Though suggested at first by the use of counters, the use of numerals
grew apart from the more progressive methods of computation. Systems of reckoning and systems of notation thus
became unrelated at many points.

The fact that the development of numerals could not, and
did not, keep pace with the development of counters may
be explained by analyzing the development of counting
devices into a series of stages and noticing the stages that
appropriately characterize and represent the growth of numerical devices. The preceding chapter has indicated the
following stages of development:

First, there was the stage in which the one-to-one correspondence between the counters used and the objects
counted was strictly preserved. For each object there was
set aside a corresponding counter. Likewise, the first numerals consisted of parts which preserved the one-to-one correspondence. Three, for example, was represented as ᴠᴠᴠ, or
≡, or |||.

Second, as we have seen, a counter was used to represent
a group. So, finally, was a numeral. The numeral for a
group differed in appearance from the numeral for an object,
whereas no such difference existed between counters used for
different purposes. In other words, the value of the numeral
was apparent, whereas the value of the counter was not
shown by the counter itself, but had to be either remembered
or kept in mind by some artificial means. At this stage of
development the numeral was a superior device. Perhaps
the superiority was recognized; perhaps not. At any rate,
the race appeared to be satisfied with the progress already
accomplished, for it continued to use numerals in the form
just described more than a score of centuries, whereas at an

early date it sought after and discovered a use of counters that was more advantageous by far than the one we have designated as belonging in the second stage of development.

The foregoing chapter has described the advance that was made in the third stage of development of counters, which came about through the discovery and elaboration of the idea that value could be represented by position. We have considered the remarkable advance in methods of reckoning due to the invention and perfection of the abacus, and we have been aware that in the numerals anciently developed and used there had been no corresponding and parallel advance. So superior had a single numeral become as a quick representation of a group that it was apparently inconceivable to the mind of the ancients to use the numeral in any other way.

Thus, we have the answer to our questions. Ancient numerals not merely freed the mind for further thought and a consequent further development of number ideas; they also operated to confine thought within the grooves set by their peculiar forms and uses. Having assumed the task of recording the results of thinking, their forms tended to congeal and thereby to clog the machinery of thinking.

VIII. ROMAN NUMERALS AS ILLUSTRATION

The best known of the early systems of numerals is the Roman system. This system has come down to us from early times and continues to be used to provide a little variety in our modern methods of numbering. Although the present forms of the Roman numerals are somewhat unlike the earlier forms, the essential character of the system remains the same. We are thus permitted to resort to a fairly familiar numeral system, which still retains a few uses in modern life, to serve as an illustration of the uses and limitations of ancient numerals. By studying the present forms of the Roman numerals we can get some idea of how cumbersome, involved, and inadequate the early systems of number notation were as aids to thinking.

1. The Irregularity of Roman Numerals

The Roman system may be characterized as systematic only in its irregularity. It drags the user's attention back and forth from one number base to another. The base of ten is expressed by the system and emphasized throughout, but the base of five is likewise used and is given almost as much emphasis. The ideas of ten, ten tens, ten hundreds, are fundamental in the system — X, C, M — but these ideas are consistently supplemented (and consequently interrupted) by the employment of the ideas of five, five tens, five hundreds — V, L, D. The system appears to seek a double advantage from the uses of two number bases instead of one. In some degree an advantage is secured, as we have seen in the use of lines and spaces to denote values in the medieval line abacus. On the other hand, the shifting of attention back and forth between the base of ten and the base of five prevents the mind from taking the fullest possible advantage of either. A little effort is saved in the writing of the numerals, just as a little effort was saved in the "laying and seizing" of counters with the line abacus, but the advantage gained is entirely with the externals. The attention does not have a chance to center upon one central idea, either of ten or of five, as a standard value around which all others may be grouped and by which all others may be judged.

Furthermore, irregularity characterized the method of representing larger groups as combinations of smaller groups. Although the method is predominantly addition, subtraction is used frequently enough to provide constant interruption. For example, thirty is recorded as ten and ten and ten, but sixty is recorded as ten added to fifty, while forty is recorded as ten subtracted from fifty: XXX, LX, XL. While there is apparent regularity in the additions and subtractions as one moves up the scale, there is no regularity in the amounts of the additions and subtractions (if one excepts the repetitions of the additions and subtractions that are made in the lower limits of the scale). Below tens, the additions and subtractions are in units of ones; from ten to one hundred, tens, fives, and ones are added or subtracted; beyond one hundred, the larger units are combined by adding or subtracting.

2. Roman Numerals Form an Incomplete System

Every written language is a system of conventionalized signs that are meaningful only to the initiated, but every written language reveals a certain systematic machinery of form and construction that, once learned, is most helpful in the revelation of ideas. The words of a sentence, for example, must be known before one can get meanings from them; the arrangement of the words in the sentence is likewise a carrier of meaning. When the language presents a series of constructions and forms in any consistent way, one may learn and be helped by these constructions and forms. When, however, there are many exceptions to, and variations from, these constructions and forms, the reader may be confused instead of being helped by them.

The Roman system of notation employs both symbols and what we may call 'constructions' to represent meanings. Reference has been made to the constructions by means of additions and subtractions. But when one has learned to rely upon these for the representation of smaller groups, he is obliged, temporarily at least, to abandon them when he comes to a representation of larger groups. This obstacle may best be explained by illustration.

The sign L for fifty shows no relationship of this idea with any that precede. After one has reached in his thinking the idea fifty by whatever method of combination he may have employed, he may record his result by the sign L. He may not record by the sign L how he arrived at the result, and he may not return to the

sign L for any help in establishing a relation with any number
idea that he may have used to build it up. The sign L does not
make use of a method of construction, and it does not suggest a
mode of thinking. Though L may stand for the idea of forty and
ten or of five tens, it does not suggest these, or any other, relations.

The sign L is, moreover, an incomplete record of the idea fifty.
It stands for fifty, to be sure; but it stands for fifty, as we have
just indicated, as a pure conventionality. Now, if the idea fifty
were an idea that one could hold in mind, or make use of, or even
conceive, as a separate and distinct idea, the sign L might be
considered as a sufficient record. The idea four may be held in
mind and used as separate and distinct from three. One can,
for example, recognize at a glance four objects in a given group,
or three in a group; but it is impossible to recognize fifty objects
in a group without doing a good many things to the objects in
order to arrive at the idea of fifty, and one cannot distinguish
forty-nine objects in one group from fifty in another. The idea
fifty is by no means separate and distinct. It has to stand in
thought as a composite of such number ideas as are separate and
distinct. So when L is made to stand for fifty, a partial record
only is written. L may record the result, but it does not record
the meaning of the result. The sign L frees the mind only partially.
The mind is compelled to retain the method by which the idea
was reached.

What has been said of the sign L for fifty may be said
with equal emphasis of the signs C, D, and M for one hundred, five hundred, and one thousand, respectively. They
all suggest for distinctive use number ideas that the mind
does not conceive and is powerless to use as distinct ideas.
In order to use the ideas for which these symbols stand, the
mind must free itself from the encumbrance of the suggestion of unrelation that the Roman system constantly imposes. The Roman system, in short, is an inadequate
system of recording number ideas; while it pretends to
record each idea, it fails to record the vital relationships
that in reality constitute the idea.

3. Roman Numerals Confuse Size and Number

Thinking is impeded in yet another way by the Roman system. There is no requirement and but little suggestion in this system that the mind conceive and employ number ideas of other than the lower order. Each symbol suggests its appropriate idea of so many individual units. The idea of groups, except that of the group of all the individual units being dealt with in a given case, is not suggested. To illustrate, V stands for five units, X for ten units, L for fifty units, C for one hundred units, and so on. XX for twenty shows ten and ten, not two tens, even though the mind may recognize the two symbols together as showing two tens. Moreover, what little tendency the mind may have so to recognize the symbols used in the illustration is broken down when the symbol for forty, XL, is turned to. XL by no means suggests four tens.

Again, the system confuses the ideas of size and number by offering no means of distinguishing them. Thus, X may be considered as representing either a single group or ten units together. Either way of holding to the idea is satisfied by the use of the sign. XX may be considered as representing two tens, as has been indicated; but there is nothing about the symbols, XX, to call attention especially to the fact that there are two tens; that is, no sign for the two of two tens is written. Because there is no sign for two, no suggestion is made in the writing of X and X that the tens may be treated in combinations in the same way that units are treated. One gets in the Roman system of numerals no suggestion of an ordered and systematic treatment of, or method of thinking about, groups of various sizes. One may reckon, or one may give his attention to size of groups and number of groups; but he must carry on all such activity apart from the system. Only when he has completed his reckoning or his thinking and wishes to record his final results, does he find a use for the Roman numerals.

CHAPTER V

THE HINDU–ARABIC NUMERALS

ARGUMENT

1. The Hindu-Arabic numerals are nine in number. The system possesses no numerals to represent groups larger than nine.

2. The numerals serve to represent numbers. The sizes of groups were early represented by written words.

3. Gerbert, and perhaps others, experimented with the method of representing size by writing the numerals in appropriate positions on the abacus.

4. The idea of the use of a numeral in one column that would keep the numeral in the column to the left in proper place somehow gradually developed. With this idea there developed the idea of a sign for the empty column as a means of holding position.

5. The zero as a place holder completed the Hindu-Arabic system of numerals. Gerbert's idea of using numerals in different positions to show both number and size could now be employed without the use of the abacus.

6. The zero is the most significant and characteristic sign in the Hindu-Arabic system.

7. The zero gives the appearance of being a numeral, and its use appears to be the same as that of the numerals. This appearance, coupled with the neglect of the significance of position in the abacus, explains the slow substitution of the Hindu-Arabic system for the cumbersome Roman system in Western Europe.

8. Treating zero as a numeral in elementary arithmetic today is responsible for much of the confusion of children with its proper use.

9. In elementary arithmetic the zero is not a numeral, but a place holder and should be treated as such.

10. Treating zero as a place holder makes unnecessary and meaningless the attempt to teach the so-called 'zero combinations.'

11. In later mathematics the zero does take on the characteristics and use of a numeral, but beginners in arithmetic are confused when later uses are mixed with earlier ones.

12. The simplicity of the Hindu-Arabic system accounts for its superiority. The system uses the numerals to represent numbers and their positions to represent size.

I. The Development of Number Ideas

Foregoing chapters have traced the development of ideas of number up to the introduction of the Hindu-Arabic numerals in Western Europe in the twelfth century; indeed, up to their general adoption as means of notation and calculation about four centuries ago. We have seen how number ideas grew through the systematic observation and study of groups, and how the methods of observation and study slowly but gradually developed; how counting and the use of number names fixed attention upon the group and all of its parts, and served to hold the idea of the group in mind; and how a group of convenient size came to be centered upon as a point of reference for the building up and study of larger groups and as a standard by which the sizes of larger groups could be measured and interpreted. We have had some introduction to the use of counting devices and have observed how early peoples finally came to use the device of representing a group by a counter, just as they represented an individual object by a counter; how they came to adopt a convenient means of distinguishing between these counters when used for different representations; and how they finally adopted the convenience of using relative positions to distinguish between the relative values of the counters. We have learned how names were used, not only to stand for various groups, but also to state the relations to the number base that was used; and how written signs were used to record the various number ideas. We have observed, moreover, how the development of numerals began parallel to the development of counting devices; and how the development of the former fell far behind the development of the latter. We have been brought to face the need for a method of number notation that would use the valuable ideas developed in connection with the abacus as a counting device, in order that the mind of the calculator could be set free for new developments. We are aware that the Hindu-Arabic numerals have met the need. Let us consider the development and the characteristics of these numerals in order to learn the part they play as a device for calculation and number thinking.

II. The Numerals Themselves

Aside from the forms of the first three, the origin of the forms of the Hindu-Arabic numerals is lost in the obscurities of oriental history. The forms of 1, 2, and 3 can be recognized as derived from the cursive forms of the corresponding counters $|$, $=$, and $\equiv$.

In the beginning, the use of the Hindu-Arabic numerals was no different from the use of other numerals. In one sense of the word a numeral is a numeral, and one is no better than another. The numerals, 5, V, and $^{VVV}_{VV}$, represent the idea five equally well. If there is any advantage, the cuneiform numeral has it, since it shows five as three and two. However, there is little advantage in the respect indicated, because one can always carry in his mind the relation between five and its addends.

In seeking for a difference, we may repeat here the characteristic of the Hindu-Arabic numerals; namely, that they make use of the principle of position. This description by itself is, however, a superficial one, inasmuch as other numeral systems have employed the principle of position as a means of representing values. The Roman numerals, for example, are set down in a certain order, which is attained by their relative positions. The symbols, IX, for example, do not express the same idea as they do when written in reverse order, XI. In the writing of larger numbers, a given order is always followed, thus: MDCLXV, never VXCLMD. The order, or positions, in which numerals were written was not unknown before the advent of the Hindu-Arabic numerals. Consequently, any superficial statement that they make use of the principle of position cannot be accepted as an adequate characterization of their unique merit.

The Hindu-Arabic numerals are nine in number and are used to represent the ideas one to nine. In this respect they differ from the Roman numerals, which have only three numerals in different arrangements to represent the first nine numbers; what is more to the point, however, they are in this respect no different from the more ancient Chaldean numerals that also differ in form for each of the first nine ideas to be represented.

A really fundamental difference appears, however, when we reflect that the Hindu-Arabic numerals are nine in number, and only nine, and that no special symbol is employed for the idea 'ten' and those ideas larger than ten. All other numeral systems have a separate symbol for the larger numbers; for example, using the Roman system as illustration, the symbols X, L, C, D, and M. Other systems had numerals for ten and beyond; the Hindu-Arabic system had no numeral for ten, or fifty, or one hundred, and so on. Herein we discover a peculiarity of the Hindu-Arabic system. Having no numeral for the idea of ten, the system had to make use of some method other than the use of numerals to represent ten.

When one can set down his idea of ten, or of one hundred, by a separate sign, he need give no special attention to any special significance of the idea. If ten and one hundred can be represented by symbols, just as five and nine can be represented by symbols, one is not required to attach any special importance to the larger groups. They mean no more, necessarily, than the smaller groups, except that one recognizes them as larger. But if the embryo arithmetician has no symbol that he can use to represent ten, or one hundred, he must give some special attention to these ideas. He must represent them in a different way. The difference in their representation helps to fix attention upon the special significance they possess. Wrapped up in the symbol X, for example, is the idea of *size*, but the idea has no special representation. Let the idea of the *size* of ten be expressed in a special manner, and the user will more likely give attention to the idea of *size*.

III. SIZE AND NUMBER

The Hindus in their oral language carried the expression of the decimal idea to great lengths. Working from the relation that ten bears to one, they proceeded by powers of ten up the scale to the ideas of hundred, thousand, and so on, and from these to the naming of the ideas by which the sands on the seashore, the raindrops of ten thousand years, and the "motes of the sun" could be numbered. They gave a special name to each power of ten, not only to the ones we name, such as tens, hundreds, and thousands, but also to the ones we express by compounding, such as ten thousand, hundred million, and so on. In their manner of expression they proceeded, as do we, from the higher powers in succession to the lower.

The method of number notation used by the Hindus followed their method of thinking and naming. Having a set of numerals to nine, they could proceed to write their ideas of ten and of the powers of ten. They proceeded from left to right in the writing of powers of ten from the higher powers in succession to the lower. Thus, the principle of position was maintained to the extent that order of arrangement provided for relative positions. In the early writing of their numerals to express ten and the higher powers of ten, the Hindus gave distinct expression both to the size of the groups to be represented and to the number of the groups. They could either spell or abbreviate the names that indicated the sizes of the groups, and use the nine numerals to indicate the numbers of groups.[1] Thus in writing the number which we express as 2155, they could write it, using their early numeral forms which correspond, as 2 *sahasra*, 1 *sata*, 5 *dasan*, 5; or as 2 *sa*, 1 *s*, 5 *d*, 5; or, if we abbreviate our own words for the sake of illustration, as 5th, 1h, 5t, 5. In writing the number that we express as 7020, they could write 7 *sahasra*, 2 *dasan* (or, in our words, 7th, 2t).

IV. THE PRINCIPLE OF POSITION

The Hindu-Arabic numerals were used a long time before the use of position as an expression of value was appropriated. For a long time the intellectual leaders were content to make use of the numerals in one form or another to express the ideas of quantity that they developed by other means and continued to employ their counting devices for the computations they had to carry on. One reason was that the thinking about number as powers of ten was carried on by the intellectual class but computations as a practical business procedure by the merchant class. Another, and perhaps the chief, reason was that the methods of computation in use were very highly developed and seemed to meet all their practical needs, while almost any scheme of notation was suitable to make a record of the results secured.

The Hindus had prepared themselves, however, as we have just seen, for the adoption of the use of position as a means of expressing values by their special development of the idea of size of groups. Now all they needed was to relate in their thinking the idea of size (expressed in numeration) with the idea of position (used in the placing of count-

[1] D. E. Smith and L. C. Karpinski. *The Hindu-Arabic Numerals* (Ginn and Company, Boston, 1911), pp. 40–41.
L. C. Karpinski. *The History of Arithmetic* (Rand McNally and Company, Chicago, 1925), pp. 39–40.

ers on the abacus), and they would be on the verge of an important discovery.

No doubt the use of the abacus suggested the relation. Numerals were used on the abacus before the advent of the Hindu-Arabic numerals in their present form and by persons who were unacquainted with the idea of place values of the numerals. The Romans at times used counters marked with their numerals for one to nine.[2] About the year 1000, Gerbert adopted the plan of numbering the counters for use on the abacus. His idea seems to have related more closely to the possible improvement of the abacus than to the possible improvement of his system of numerals. If, for example, he could put one counter marked "7" on a line instead of putting seven counters upon it, he would gain time in the placing of counters. The gain, however, was more apparent than real, because the computer had to meet the difficulty of picking out the right counter each time.[3] Because of the difficulty, Gerbert's abacus was not generally adopted.

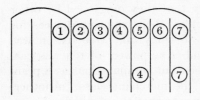

Gerbert's abacus was devised somewhat as follows: The counters shown in the cut represent on the top row the number 1,234,567; those on the lower row, the number 10,407.

It would appear but a single step to the writing of numerals in various positions to represent values. Indeed, it appears that numerals were once so written on the so-called 'dust abacus.'[4] In their proper positions, which were kept clear by the columns of the abacus, numerals were written in the dust of the counting board. The method was not generally adopted, and the method seems not to have trans-

---

[2] Karpinski, *op. cit.*, p. 26.

[3] D. E. Smith. *History of Mathematics*, II (Ginn and Company, Boston, 1925), pp. 180–181.   [4] Smith, *Ibid.*, p. 73.

ferred to the method of notation in use at the time. Though the method contained the germ of the idea that the system of numerals in use needed, it did not carry over to notation because it was employed as a possible improvement of the abacus as a counting device; when it was not generally adopted as part of the counting device, it dropped out of use and out of the minds of those who first employed it. This is one way of stating the case. Another method of statement is that the idea of position could not be employed in the numeral system so long as numerals were considered simply as accessories to the counting board in use, and not as a counting device possessing special merits in its own right.

V. The Empty Column

The reason why the expression of value by the use of the positions of numerals was so long delayed is that the nine numerals of the Hindus did not lend themselves to positional use. To be sure, they could be used on the dust abacus or on an abacus like Gerbert's, but when they were so used, it was the abacus and not the numerals themselves that kept position clear. The abacus possessed an advantage that the numerals could not have. The abacus was a mechanical contrivance that kept positions clear. The nine numerals did not possess the convenience of this contrivance.

Let us set the counters on the abacus to show three thousand two:

If now we substitute the numerals for the counters we can show the number thus:

```
| 3 |   |   | 2 |
|   |   |   |   |
```

In each case the machinery of the abacus keeps position clear. Let us express the number without the abacus, and we have 3 2, which may be three hundred two; three thousand two, or thirty-two.   When the columns of the abacus are filled, we have no such difficulty. We may express the number one thousand two hundred thirty-four in either of the following ways:

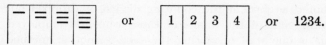

In the expression, 1234, each numeral not only represents a number, but maintains its own position and helps to keep the rest in position.   Owing, however, to the fact that one or another of the columns of the abacus is frequently empty of counters, one cannot use the nine numerals by themselves to keep each other in position.   The empty column delayed the adoption of the principle of position.

1. The Sign of the Empty Column

If, in the expression of the number three thousand two, something can be placed between the symbols, 3 and 2, that will keep them in their proper positions, all will be well. Suppose we first have them in the contrivance that establishes their positions: 3   2 Let us now remove the contrivance from all points except where it is needed and we have 3 ⌐ ⌐ 2, or as we now write it, 3002.   Why did it require centuries for the discovery of this scheme? Why did it take so long to invent a symbol for the empty column, especially after symbols for occupied columns came to be used?   The need for such a symbol is so obvious to us, and the connection between its use and the need for it seems so perfectly clear that we wonder how it is possible for any people who dealt in place values on the abacus to be so obtuse as not to make an almost immediate transition in their thinking from the empty column to a symbol that would represent it.   The use of the zero is simplicity itself. If we wish to write three thousand two, we write 3 in thousand's place, fill the blanks in hundred's and ten's places, and write 2 in unit's place.

If we will consider the mental attitude of earlier peoples toward the use of numerals, we may discover the answer to our questions. We may discover, too, a suggestion for an explanation of the difficulties and confusions that attend the learning of the zero in our schools today.

The numerals originated as representations of groups, or number ideas. They always served that purpose. There was no other reason for their existence. Anything so written, or that was given a similar use, was, accordingly, considered as serving a similar purpose. For the representation of a given group, a numeral was used. No group at all needed no representation. Besides, since the numerals represented groups, they in no wise were related to the absence of a group. The absence of a group was represented well enough by the absence of a numeral.

So when numerals came to be used in place of the counters in the columns of the abacus and as representations of these counters, there arose no suggestion of the need of a sign for the absence of counters, for the empty column. Where counters appeared, a sign was used; therefore, for no counters, no sign appeared to be appropriate. *There was no object in writing something to stand for nothing, when the nothing was evident.* Moreover, as has been pointed out, the abacus kept positions clear, and so there was no need of a sign for the empty column of the abacus so long as the abacus was used to keep either counters or numerals in place. The need for a sign for the empty column was very slow in suggesting itself, because there were so many evidences of no need at all to anyone who may have given thought to the matter.

If, under certain circumstances, necessity is the mother of invention, such circumstances did not exist in connection with the invention of the zero. For all the purposes of ancient and medieval calculation, the abacus was sufficiently satisfactory.   Arithmetic as a science had experienced very little development, and no demands for a better numeration issued from it.   Ideas of exactness such as are in constant use today did not exist; in fact, they could not exist until they had been developed through the use of a better system of numeration than the one in use.   The necessity for a more perfect system was absent, or, if not absent, was certainly not felt.   Since the abacus served the purposes and needs of the calculators of the time, it is conceivable that every new use of the numerals that suggested itself was interpreted in terms of the abacus.   As we have noted again and again, the abacus as a device for keeping position clear was entirely satisfactory and needed no additional aids.

2. The Importance of the Zero

However lacking may have been the practical need of a sign for the empty column at the time of its invention, someone did conceive the idea of such a sign and with the idea there developed the logical need for the sign.   The sign completed the Hindu-Arabic system of numerals and made possible the use which we make of them today.   Their use gradually superseded the use of counting devices, and thus paved the way for the progress of numeration from a mere means of expression to a means of thinking.   With the numerals serving the double purpose, the calculator could use the numerals as an aid in thinking; and, as his thinking progressed, he could have at all points in his calculations a record of the steps he had taken.   Serving thus the double purpose of thinking and recording, the numerals freed the mind at every step from the necessity of remembering the results of what had preceded, and at the same time they set the stage for progress to the next step.

In their discussion of the Hindu-Arabic numerals, Smith and Karpinski devote a chapter to the origin and history of the zero.   They say:

[because of] the importance of such a sign, the fact that it is a prerequisite to a place-value system, and the further fact that without it the Hindu-Arabic numerals would never have dominated the computation system of the western world.[5]

They state further:

. . . If there was any invention for which the Hindus, by all their philosophy and religion, were well fitted, it was the invention of a symbol for zero. This making of nothingness the crux of a tremendous achievement was a step in complete harmony with the genius of the Hindu.[6]

The following quotations from Dantzig's chapter discussing "The Empty Column" and from Judd's chapter on "The Psychology of Number" are pertinent:

. . . the achievement of the unknown Hindu who some time in the first centuries of our era discovered the *principle of position* assumes the proportions of a world event. Not only did this principle constitute a radical departure in method, but we know now that without it no progress in arithmetic was possible. And yet the principle is so simple that today the dullest school boy has no difficulty in grasping it. In a measure, it is suggested by the very structure of our number language. Indeed, it would appear that the first attempt to translate the action of the counting board into the language of numerals ought to have resulted in the discovery of the principle of position.[7]

Conceived in all probability as the symbol for an empty column on a counting board, the Indian *sunya* was destined to become the turning-point in a development without which the progress of modern science, industry, or commerce is inconceivable. And the influence of this great discovery was by no means confined to arithmetic. By paving the way to a generalized number concept, it played just as fundamental a rôle in practically every branch of mathematics. In the

[5] Smith and Karpinski, *op. cit.*, p. 51.   [6] *Ibid.*, p. 43.
[7] From Tobias Dantzig. *Number, The Language of Science*, p. 30. By permission of The Macmillan Company, publisher, New York, 1930.

history of culture the discovery of zero will always stand out as one of the greatest single achievements of the human race.[8]

While the abacus extended the usefulness of the number system and made possible elaborate calculations, it had the distinct disadvantage of being a thing quite apart from the mind that used it. The training of the mind which uses an abacus is not complete, because the processes of combination which such a mind uses are mechanical and external. The abacus served a useful purpose in that stage of civilization when the mind of man had not attained to a number system which is detached from all mechanical devices and yet possessed all of the virtues that the mechanical device contributes.[9]

The invention of the zero did not produce the principle of position; it merely provided for the appropriation of the principle by the written language of number. The abacus had always used the principle of position, but the abacus was a device outside of the individual — a mechanical device, not a language. By means of the zero it was made possible for man to take over the use of the principle of position and make it a part of his language of thinking and expression.

Let us state the importance of the zero in another way. The nine numerals of the Hindu-Arabic system were in use a long time before the zero was invented. The numerals could show number and hold position; they could not maintain positions, however, when the empty column existed in the case of a multitude of numbers that needed expression. An extra sign was needed to help the numerals to keep positions clear. The zero — the sign of the empty column — was invented, and it came into use as a device for filling up the spaces not occupied by the numerals.

[8] Dantzig, *op. cit.*, p. 35.
[9] From C. H. Judd. *Psychology of Social Institutions*, pp. 97–98. By permission of The Macmillan Company, publishers, New York, 1926.

VI. The Reception of the Numerals in Europe

The Hindu-Arabic numerals were introduced into Western Europe in the twelfth century, and were generally adopted as the means of notation and calculation by the sixteenth century. "The fifteenth century saw the rise of the new symbolism; the sixteenth century saw it slowly gain the mastery; the seventeenth century saw it finally conquer the system that for two thousand years had dominated the arithmetic of business. Not a little of the success of the new plan was due to Luther's demand that all learning should go into the vernacular."[10]

The Hindu-Arabic notation was very slow in making its way. The difficulty encountered was the confusion about the principle of position into which the use of the line abacus had led the European calculators. We have referred in a preceding chapter to this abacus, which used the lines to stand for the powers of ten and the spaces between the lines to stand for the half of such powers. The use of the spaces caused the true significance of the lines as representations of the powers of ten to be obscured. So, when the new system, which was built solidly and entirely upon this scheme of representations — that is, of powers of ten — was introduced, the slight obscuring of the fundamental idea was sufficient to retard its adoption for the period of four centuries. We may get some notion of the confusion that existed by noting the following explanation taken from an early English book:

Euery of these figuris bitokens hym selfe & no more, yf he stonde in the first place of the rewele. . . .

If it stonde in the secunde place of the rwle, he betokens ten tymes hym selfe, as this figure 2 here 20 tokens ten tyme hym selfe, that is twenty, for he hym selfe betoken tweyne, & ten tymes twene is twenty. And for he stondis on the lyft side & in the secunde place, he betokens ten tyme hym selfe. And so go forth . . .[11]

[10] Smith and Karpinski, *op. cit.*, pp. 149–150.   [11] *Ibid.*, p. 149.

When the Hindu-Arabic numerals were introduced into Western Europe, they were distinguished in the minds of most users by their most characteristic feature. No other system of numerals employed a zero. The zero was an interesting and striking peculiarity of the new system. A name for the zero came to be used to describe the use of the whole system: to *cipher* meant to use the system which had a *cipher* as a symbol. The masses judged the new system by appearances, and so they thought of the zero as a numeral; that is, as a sign for a number. It appeared to them that the zero was used like the other signs of the system; hence, it must be a numeral, standing for nothing.

VII. The Zero Is a Place Holder, Not a Numeral

The zero is the characteristic feature of the Hindu-Arabic system, because this system depends not merely upon numerals to show quantity, but also upon the positions in which the numerals are written. In this system the size of a group is indicated by position, and the number of the group by the numeral written in that position. Each numeral thus serves the double purpose of showing a number and of keeping the rest of the numerals in their proper places; the 2 in 521 shows 2 *tens* and puts the 5 in *hundred's* place. Suppose one has nothing to write. If that is all the purpose he has in mind, he writes nothing. There is no economy or common sense in writing something — the zero — for nothing. But suppose one has nothing to write in a given position, yet needs some means of keeping the numerals he does have to write in their proper places — for example, in writing *five hundred twenty*. One has no units to write. Why write zero for nothing? There is no need to indicate nothing by a sign, but there is need to put the 2 and the 5 in their proper places. The zero in 520 serves that important and essential purpose. One never needs the zero until he has to write the quantity ten, or certain quantities larger than ten. He needs it then to hold position. The zero is a place holder.

It is interesting to note that the original terms for zero did not mean a group of none. Both the Hindu term *sunya*, and the Arabic term *sifr* meant *empty*, or *void*. The sign, 0, was originally a sign for the empty column. It was left to the masses, who watched the use of the zero and who noticed only what their eyes could see, to convert the original and useful meaning of zero to nothing. There grew up a difference between the arithmetical (actual) use of the zero and the popular (apparent) use of the zero.

Teachers of elementary arithmetic might do well to take note of this difference, because failure on their part to note the distinction is responsible for the confusion children experience in employing the zero in computation. Children who are engaged in learning arithmetic must actually employ the zero for what it is intended and for what it is — that is, as a place holder. They will, of course, be confused somewhat by appearances, since the use of the zero looks like the use of a numeral. Let the teacher, however, fail to make the necessary distinction, or, what is worse, attempt to teach the children the apparent use of the zero as a symbol for nothing while neglecting entirely to call attention to the actual use of the symbol, and the confusion of the children will be worse confounded. As a remedy, the teacher often turns to better, more complete, and more skilful methods of teaching the apparent use of the zero; and the teacher just about as often finds himself in as much bewilderment about the failure of improved methods of teaching apparent uses as the children are in their attempts to convert apparent uses into actual uses.

In fairness, however, to the good intentions of teachers it must be admitted that the efforts to improve their methods of teaching the apparent uses of the zero are not without some measure of success. It often appears to teachers that the children will have to add, subtract, multiply, and divide zero just as they add, subtract, multiply, and divide when the nine numerals are used. So, as a means of preparation, the 'zero combinations' are 'taught.' There is much explaining and more drills. Through persistent effort, children finally learn to set down the approved answers when the zero is used. Since the actual use and meaning of the zero are neglected, what the children learn to do is necessarily barren of meaning. Their human minds are turned into machines for use in responding to the 'zero combinations' by giving what the teacher says are the correct answers. Like machines they learn to respond, but like machines they fail to think and to understand. Moreover, since the actual positional use of the zero is neglected in teaching the apparent uses, the children who finally learn how to respond with correct answers are not helped to keep the positions of the answers clear. If they learn about the importance of position, they learn it incidentally or as a separate and unrelated item.

VIII. The Zero in Later Mathematics

The reader of the foregoing statements that the zero is not a numeral, standing for nothing, may recall the frequent use of the zero as a numeral in later mathematics. The zero is used in later mathematics as a numeral, as a position on a scale, and as a division point between positive and negative numbers; and its use for these purposes is the same as the use of the nine numerals. All such uses, however, belong in the mathematics that has been developed out of *elementary* arithmetic. In the system of numeration that deals with the sizes and numbers of groups and with the various arrangements to be made of groups, the zero is unlike the numerals and has no use as a representation of no group, or nothing. Because it does not carry the idea of no group, it may not be classed with the numerals that stand for quantities, though its use may appear the same as the uses of the numerals. If the reader will reflect upon the uses the zero finally takes on in later mathematics, he will note that these are quite unlike any that are required in the

beginnings of arithmetic. Children of the beginning grades
do not study points on a scale; they study groups. They
do not deal with the relations between positive and negative numbers; they deal with the arrangements of groups.
They do not study the exceptions to the general laws of
combination that the zero as a numeral, and as representa-
tive of nothing, makes necessary; they study how groups
may be taken apart and how they may be combined. The
groups studied by beginners are actual groups of objects;
'nothing,' as a quantity, is an abstraction too far removed
from the world of actuality for their conception.

IX. The Merits of the Hindu-Arabic Numerals

The Hindu-Arabic notation is a superior system because
of its simplicity. It uses separate symbols to stand for those
number ideas that may be learned and handled as distinct
ideas; it uses the symbols to show the relations by which
one may conceive and handle those ideas that are not separate and distinct; it sharply distinguishes the idea of size
and the idea of number; it uses position to represent powers
of ten; it makes possible, and also strongly suggests, the
principle of dealing with tens just as one deals with units;
and it permits one to make use of all these advantages with
a minimum of conscious effort by keeping all relations clear
and in an ordered system. The merits of the system have
been indicated in our previous discussions; we shall have
occasion to refer to them again and again in later discussions.
It will be sufficient at this point if we will remind ourselves
that the Hindu-Arabic system finally appropriated to itself
all the advantages of the principle of position that had
developed in the use of counting devices and made these
advantages easily accessible to human minds by incorpo-
rating them into the written language of number. No longer
did the calculator have to demonstrate them to himself on
the counting board; he now possessed them as part of his
language of thinking.

CHAPTER VI

FRACTIONS

1. Ideas of parts and ideas of groups developed somewhat similarly.

2. The first fraction was a broken part of a thing, and it was thought of as a single part, or unit fraction.

3. The idea of the unit fraction was one relating to size. The idea of number was cared for automatically.

4. Sexagesimal fractions — sixtieths — cared for the idea of size automatically. Thinking with such fractions related to number of parts.

5. Uncial fractions — twelfths — were similar in character to sexagesimal fractions. In their use, however, attention was shifted back and forth between ideas of number and ideas of size. No certain way was provided for uniting the two sets of ideas in thought.

6. The use of fractions was uncertain, inexact, and confusing so long as size was considered to the neglect of number, as in unit fractions, or number was considered to the neglect of size, as in sexagesimals and uncials.

7. The Hindus combined the two sets of ideas. They provided the present way of representing both ideas at once.

8. Quite by accident, the decimal system of notation was appropriated for the representation of fractions. In the writing of decimals the numerals are written to show the numbers of parts, and their positions are used to show the sizes of parts.

9. The idea of percent is the idea of the hundredth part. It develops through the special study of hundredths.

10. The meaning of percent is clarified through consideration of the original meaning of "per centum" and of the derivation of the percent sign.

11. The idea of the fraction finds much practical use as a

means of stating the comparison between numbers; that is, of indicating one number in its relation to another number that may be more familiar.

12. Such practical use is in connection with one or another of the so-called 'three kinds of problems':

   (a) Finding the part, or percent, of a number;
   (b) Finding what part, or percent, one number is of another number;
   (c) Finding a number when a part, or a percent, of it is known.

13. Acquiring familiarity with the three kinds of problems is in the main the process of learning the distinctions between them and of looking for such distinctions.

I. PARALLELISMS BETWEEN IDEAS OF GROUPS AND IDEAS OF PARTS

At many points in their development ideas of groups and ideas of parts moved closely in parallel. Both had an ancient history. Both had their beginnings in perceptual experience. Both were inexact at the outset. Both underwent processes of refining and clarification that, in retrospect, seem extraordinarily slow. Both experienced through long centuries the solidifying influence of an inadequate written language. Finally, both appropriated as a common language the decimal system of notation, which makes possible an easy transference of thought from one set of ideas to the other.

As the history of numbers brings into relief the dominant features of ideas of groups, so the history of fractions sets off in clear perspective the essential characteristics of ideas of parts. The present chapter is intended, therefore, to present a brief sketch of the development of those ideas that are commonly called 'fractions' with the thought of thereby uncovering clues to explanations of the failures and successes of pupils in attacking this difficult chapter in their work in arithmetic.

II. What Fractions Are

Fractions are parts. The word 'fraction' derives from the Latin *frangere*, "to break." A part, or a fraction, of a thing was originally "broken off" the thing. Thus, pieces of bread were broken off the loaf just as a piece of candy is now broken off the stick and as a part of an apple is broken off when the apple is broken in two. In Medieval Europe, fractions were called "broken numbers," and sometimes "brokens." A fraction of a fraction, such as $\frac{1}{2}$ of $\frac{1}{4}$ was thus designated a "broken of broken." The Romans called their sixtieths "little parts." Their division into sixtieths resulted in their *partes minutiae primae*, "first little parts"; and their second division into sixtieths of sixtieths resulted in their *partes minutiae secundae*, "second little parts." From the two phrases come our familiar words 'minutes' and 'seconds.'

III. Unit Fractions

1. The First Fractions

The first fraction to which early peoples gave their attention was of the type that we now designate as a unit fraction; that is, "one part," though the term is now the carrier of more meaning than the original idea of part possessed. The first fraction was merely the broken off piece of a thing — a part of it, whether large or small. Size was, of course, distinguished from the beginning, though attention to size was but crudely comparative. The type of attention given and the type of idea resulting were of the sort manifested by the small child who distinguishes between a stick of candy and a piece of the stick or between the big and little pieces when the stick is broken in two. Though the older child and the adult may recognize the larger piece as two-thirds, say, of the original, each commonly regards it, not as two pieces, each the size of the smaller, but as what it actually is: namely, one piece. Thus did early man. Having at the outset no system of thinking to bring to bear upon broken parts, he regarded only the actualities. A part was a part, whether large or small, and each part was a unity.

As early man developed the art of counting, he was invested with a means of enlarging the meaning of his original idea of the part in the direction of what the term 'unit fraction' (a fraction of which the numerator is one and the denominator is any integer) now means to us. Counting provided a set of number names that enabled early man to keep in mind two or more parts into which a thing may have been divided. This set of names, combined with a recognition of the equality of sizes resulting from certain methods of division, made possible the creation of the idea of halves, thirds, fourths, etc. Thus, when a skin, or a collection of arrowheads, or any other item of property, was divided into two equal parts, and attention was given to one part as the equal of the other, the idea of the half was born; or, when the number of moons (months) during the rainy season was counted and the three were regarded as of equal duration, the idea of the third developed. Attention to equality of sizes and the possession of a number name, as a means of fixing attention upon the relation of each to the whole, completed the idea of the unit fraction — the half, the third, the fourth — by whatever name each was called.

2. Writing Unit Fractions

The correspondence between the unit-fraction idea and the number name that helped to fix its meaning was retained in the earliest written records. All that was needed was a sign to indicate the general idea of a part. This sign could then be joined with the appropriate numeral to indicate the size of the particular part to be represented. Such a method of notation was sufficient for primitive needs. Parts were thought of *one part* at a time; parts needed to be written *one part* at a time. Illustration may be drawn from the fractional notation of the early Egyptians.

The sign for a fraction used by the Egyptians was a crude ellipse. This sign indicated that a part was being shown. Just below the sign the numeral (sign) that indicated the size of the part was written. The illustration shows in the left column certain Egyptian numerals and in the right column the corresponding fractional expressions.

The only fraction not a unit fraction that the Egyptians could write was *two-thirds*. They apparently understood

///	three	⏢	one third
/////	five	⏢	one fifth
∩	ten	⏢	one tenth
∩∩∩	thirty	⏢	one thirtieth
∩∩ // ∩∩	forty-two	⏢	one forty-second

this fraction, and for it they used the special sign ⏢. All other fractions were thought of each as a *single part*, or unit fraction.

The method of writing unit fractions accomplished two results. First, it freed the mind for a more detailed and exact consideration of parts that were not equal divisions of the whole; second, it limited the consideration of such parts to their relations with unit fractions. When an Egyptian had eaten *a part* of his cake, for example, he had *a part* of it left, and he thought of this also as *one part*. Let us say that he had eaten a fourth of it. He now had this *one part* remaining.

He could write ⏢ to show how much he had eaten, but he had no way of showing by a single sign that *three-fourths* was left, because the part left was actually *one part*. There was no method of thinking *three parts* as a single part; that was too difficult an abstraction. True, the single part could be divided into three equal parts or the division could be carried through as a matter of thought. In such case, three parts resulted, the three parts were *separate* parts, and they had to be thought of, and written, as such: 𓏴 𓏴 𓏴; that is, as three unit fractions. Actually, the division was carried through, or thought through, so as to produce the smallest possible number and the largest possible sizes of unit fractions. The *three-fourths* part was divided thus:

with one half and one fourth resulting: 𓏲 𓏴. In similar manner, a part the size of *five-sixths* was represented 𓏲 𓏴; a part the size of *seven-eighths* was represented 𓏲 𓏴 𓏴; and so on. The fraction we would write as $\frac{9}{11}$, the Egyptians wrote as $\frac{1}{2}$ $\frac{1}{4}$ $\frac{1}{22}$ $\frac{1}{44}$; $\frac{5}{9}$ was written $\frac{1}{2}$ $\frac{1}{18}$; and $\frac{2}{43}$ was written $\frac{1}{42}$ $\frac{1}{86}$ $\frac{1}{129}$ $\frac{1}{301}$.[1]

Computations with unit fractions were, as we can readily see, matters of extraordinary difficulty. The reason was that the idea of the unit fraction was exclusively an idea of *size* of a single part, and did not admit into itself any thought of *number* of parts other than the understood thought of unity. Thought of number of parts required as many ideas of parts as the number under consideration. More than a single part could not be written as a single sign and, accordingly, could

[1] The clearest historical treatments of this and succeeding topics are to be found in the chapters or sections on fractions in the following:

D. E. Smith. *History of Mathematics*, II. (Ginn and Company, Boston, 1925.)

L. C. Karpinski. *The History of Arithmetic*. (Rand, McNally and Company, Chicago, 1925.)

Vera Sanford. *A Short History of Mathematics*. (Houghton Mifflin Company, Boston, 1930.)

not be carried in thought as a single part. The unit fraction concentrated upon *size*, but neglected *number*.

IV. SEXAGESIMAL FRACTIONS

The difficulties involved in the use of unit fractions led early peoples to the invention of a method of thinking and writing parts which in its essential feature was the extreme opposite of its predecessor. This was the method of the Babylonian and Greek astronomers of reducing their fractions to sixtieths and sixtieths of sixtieths. The first of these reductions, as indicated in a foregoing topic, gave us our *minutes*, and the second one of them, our *seconds*. This was the method of seeming to ignore *size* — that is, of so standardizing sizes that they could be readily carried in thought — and of concentrating upon *number* of parts.

Apparently, the use of unit fractions led to the conviction that a convenient method of dealing with number of parts was needed; and, apparently, the conclusion seemed to have been made that, since it was so extremely difficult to think of *number* when size of parts was represented, it would be equally difficult to think of *size* when *number* of parts was represented. The difficulty seemed to lie in the demand that the two essential features of the fraction, *size* and *number*, be thought of at once and each in relation to the other. At any rate, early peoples came finally to realize that attention needed to be given to number of parts, and when they did, they tried to dispense with size. They worked the size of any given part into so many 'minutes,' or so many 'seconds,' or both (not alone of the hour and degree, but of anything else); and then they proceeded to forget about parts and sizes in concentrating upon number of minutes and number of seconds just as they attended to whole numbers. Just as we do not have to think of 10 minutes, or 45 minutes, as parts of an hour, so early peoples were not compelled to think of parts and the sizes of parts when they used sexagesimals. Though they were actually parts, sexagesimals could be dealt with in computations as whole numbers were dealt with.

After the invention of sexagesimals, early peoples continued to use their unit fractions for ordinary purposes. They continued to think and write the *half, third, fourth*, and so on; but they could not use such parts as *four-fifths* and *five-eighths* as we do today. So when they had to think of parts of such sizes, they reduced them to sexagesimals. Instead of *four-fifths*, they thought of 48 minutes; and instead of *five-eighths*, they thought of 37 minutes and 30 seconds, or $37\frac{1}{2}$ minutes. Today we do not usually speak of *two-thirds* of an hour, but of 40 minutes. Today we seldom write $\frac{25}{72}$ of an hour, but 20 minutes and 50 seconds.

V. ROMAN UNCIALS

Although sexagesimals lent themselves readily to the exact computations of the astronomers, they were clumsy tools for common usage. The sixtieth part of the common things of life is too small a division for practical purposes. For example, there is no point in the measuring of butter and of cloth that are bought and sold in sixtieth divisions of the appropriate units of measure. Everyday usage requires a division into larger parts; that is, into parts with smaller denominators.

The Roman *uncia* was the result of such a division. The *uncia* was the *twelfth* part of the Roman foot and also the *twelfth* part of the Roman pound, and is the source of our English "inches" and "ounces." Likewise, it is necessary to keep in mind, the *uncia* was *the twelfth part of anything*. Here was a division, possessing the computational advantages of sexagesimals, small enough for convenience, and yet large enough to be readily perceptible. These advantages, however, were not put to use, and the common understanding of fractions was not greatly advanced. The reason was that the Romans continued to use unit fractions with their *uncials* in thinking of parts, and were apparently influenced the more by the limitations of both systems than by the advantages. Instead of learning to think both *size* and *number* together into single ideas of parts, they continued to attempt to forget number when considering size, and to forget size when considering number. All this seems to be indicated in the way they mixed the two contrasting sets of ideas in thinking, naming, and writing the fractions in common use. Below are given some commonly used fractions, their names, what the names meant, their symbols, and what the symbols showed.[2]

The Part	Its Name	Meaning	Its Symbol	What the Symbol Showed
$\frac{1}{12}$	uncia	twelfth	—	one twelfth
$\frac{1}{6}$	sextans	sixth	=	two twelfths
$\frac{1}{4}$	quadrans	fourth	= —	three twelfths
$\frac{1}{3}$	triens	third	= =	four twelfths
$\frac{5}{12}$	quincunx (quinque unciae)	five twelfths	= = —	five twelfths
$\frac{1}{2}$	semis	half	S	one half
$\frac{7}{12}$	septunx (septem unciae)	seven twelfths	S —	{ one half and one twelfth
$\frac{2}{3}$	bes (bi as)	two parts (two thirds)	S =	{ one half and two twelfths
$\frac{3}{4}$	dodrans (de quadrans)	one fourth away from one	S = —	{ one half and three twelfths
$\frac{5}{6}$	dextans (de sextans)	one sixth away from one	S = =	{ one half and four twelfths
$\frac{11}{12}$	deunx (de uncia)	one twelfth away from one	S = = —	{ one half and five twelfths

The confusion here in method of thinking is evident. Notice the last fraction, which we would speak, think, and write simply as *eleven-twelfths*. We would imagine that the Romans might have thought of it as *eleven unciae;* but instead, they thought of it as a unit fraction, namely, one *deunx*. Then, when they wrote it, they had to think very differently about it, because they wrote it as "a half and

[2] Smith, *op. cit.*, pp. 208–209.

five-twelfths." The way they mixed their thinking may be illustrated by reference to other fractions. Thus, a sixteenth part was called *semuncia sicilius*, "a twenty-fourth and a forty-eighth"; an eighth part was called *uncia semuncia*, "a twelfth and a twenty-fourth"; a three-sixteenth part was called *sextans sicilius*, "a sixth and a forty-eighth"; and a fifteen-sixteenth part was called *deunx sicilius*, "an uncia away and a forty-eighth."

VI. The Present Method of Writing Fractions

Slowly and gradually it was learned that there was little use in trying to forget the *number* of parts by leaving out the numerator in unit fractions, or in trying to forget the *size* of parts by leaving out the denominator in sexagesimals and uncials. If 'minutes' mean 'sixtieths' and 'inches' mean 'twelfths,' and if sixtieths and twelfths may both be shown by the writing of numerals with the sign for unit fractions, why not use numerals to show these and other sizes, when more than one part has to be shown? After a long, long time someone must have asked the question: "Why not a double use of numerals at one and the same time to show both size and number, which heretofore have been shown separately?"

The Hindus seem to have been the first to discover a way of using numerals to show both size and number of parts at once. More than a thousand years ago, the Hindus began to show the two by writing the figure for the one just under the figure for the other. At first, they omitted the bar: $\frac{2}{3}$; later, they used it: $\frac{2}{3}$. In early printing, the bar was often omitted, because of the difficulty of setting it up in type. Because of trouble in keeping the lines of type straight, denominators were often spelled; and, sometimes, fractions were shown by the numerals on their sides: $\frac{2}{3}$ for $\frac{2}{3}$, for example.

Since the Roman numerals were used in Europe up to four or five centuries ago, the Europeans, when they began to use the Hindu-Arabic numerals, and gradually to appropriate the Hindu form of the written fraction, mixed the two numeral systems. Thus, in a book on arithmetic, printed in 1514, fractions were printed in Roman numerals arranged in the form of the Hindu fraction: $\dfrac{I}{IIII}, \dfrac{I}{V}, \dfrac{II}{VI}, \dfrac{IX}{XI}, \dfrac{XX}{XXXI}$.

VII. Decimals

The idea of using decimals was another seemingly simple idea that actually was a long time developing. Some notion of the idea came from the use of sexagesimals. Like decimals, sexagesimals have a common base. Moreover, in writing sexagesimals, the parts are written in order of size from left to right, and, thus, the idea of the use of position is not absent. In preceding chapters, we have noted how the idea of writing tens, tens of tens, and so on, in different positions slowly led to the writing of the Hindu-Arabic numerals in different position to show different *sizes* of groups. Logically it was but a step, and a closely related one, to the thinking of tenths, tenths of tenths, and so on, and to the writing of these parts in different positions according to respective *sizes;* but actually it was a long time before the step was even thought of.

The idea of the decimal seems to have come pretty much by accident. The Hindus stumbled upon the idea almost a thousand years ago in their roundabout method of extracting the square root. They discovered that if a number is not a perfect square, its root might be approximated by finding the root of the number with an even number of zeros added and then dividing the root by 10, 100, 1000, and so on, according to whether the number of zeros added was two, four, six, and so on. Thus, to extract the square root of 2, six zeros were added. The root obtained, 1414, was then divided by 1000, giving $1\frac{414}{1000}$. The germ of the idea was also developed in connection with a method of dividing numbers by 10, 100, 1000, and so on.

In 1492, the arithmetic of Pellos was published. This book shows a method of dividing by tens, hundreds, and so on, and makes use of the decimal and the decimal point, although it gives answers in common fractions. Thus, to divide 587 by 10, a point was used to show what figures stood for the whole number in the answer and what one stood for the fraction, thus: 58.7, from which the answer was written, $58\frac{7}{10}$.

To divide 587 by 100, write 5.87; next, write $5\frac{87}{100}$.

To divide 397 by 20, write 39.7; divide 39 by 2; write the 1 remainder with the 7, making 17, the total remainder. The answer is $19\frac{17}{20}$.

Using the method of the arithmetic of Pellos with our present form of division, we would divide 16573 by 400, and 11791 by 3000, as shown:

$$41\frac{173}{400}$$
$$400\overline{)165.73}$$
$$16$$
$$\overline{5}$$
$$\overline{4}$$
$$\overline{173}$$
$$400$$

$$3\frac{2791}{3000}$$
$$3000\overline{)11.791}$$
$$9$$
$$\overline{2791}$$
$$3000$$

Six hundred years ago, Johannis de Muris indicated the square root of 2 thus: 1·4·1·4. He explained that the 1 to the left showed "units," the first 4 "tenths," the second 1 "tenths of tenths," and the second 4 "tenths of tenths of tenths." Thinking perhaps that such an answer might not be clear, he changed the answer so that it was in the final form of "twentieths of twentieths of twentieths," and also of "sixtieths of sixtieths of sixtieths."

In 1530, Christoff Rudolff made use of decimals much as we do today, using, however, a bar instead of a decimal point. Thus, to show 42.875, he wrote 42/875. In 1585, Simon Stevin published the first systematic treatment of decimal fractions, *La Disme*. In his book, *The Dime*, Stevin explained the use of decimals, and he used them as we do today, though he did not make use of the decimal point. In writing whole numbers and decimals, he used figures in circles to indicate positional values: ⓪ showed the place to be units; ① showed the place to be tenths; ② showed the place to be hundredths; and so on. Thus, to show 42.875, one or the other of the following forms was used: $\begin{smallmatrix}⓪&①&②&③\\42&8&7&5,\end{smallmatrix}$ or 42⓪ 8① 7② 5③.

After Stevin's time, as people began to develop the idea of decimals, they developed less confusing ways of writing them. Sometimes they used a comma between the whole number and the decimal; finally, they learned to use a point between the two. Thus, two and five-tenths was once written 2,5. Often the comma was used just to separate the whole number and the decimal, and other signs were used to indicate the fractions. Thus, in 1616, a number like 2.758 was written 2,7′5″8‴. Sometimes, when the comma was used, the writer would seem to forget the decimal form of notation, and would revert to the form of the common fraction. Thus, instead of writing 65.5, or writing it with a comma, 65,5, forms like these were used: $65,\frac{1}{2}$ and $65,\frac{5}{10}$. At times, the size of the fraction was indicated by numerals written under the numerator of the decimal. Thus, in a book written in 1685, the fraction .00438 was written $100000\atop438$. At other times, other signs for the decimals were used. Thus, in a book written in 1657, numbers which we write as 2.5; 6.75; and 14.085 were written as 25...(1); 675... (2); and 14085... (3). In parts of Europe today, the decimal point is placed in the middle of the line: 3·75.

VIII. The Importance of Position

The same rules apply in the writing of decimals as apply in the writing of whole numbers. In the writing of whole numbers, the *number* of ones or of groups is shown by the numerals, and the *sizes* of the groups, whether ones, tens, hundreds, or larger, are shown by the positions in which the numerals are written. In the writing of decimals, the *number* of the parts to be represented is shown by the numerals, and the *sizes* of the parts are shown by the positions in which the numerals are written.

IX. SIZE AND NUMBER

The foregoing paragraphs may be summarized in the statement that the fraction possesses two distinguishing features; namely, *size* of parts and *number* of parts, and that fruitful consideration of the fraction requires the study of both. Later discussion will indicate that the pupil frequently meets with difficulty in dealing with the denominators of fractions. Such difficulty is with the feature that both historically and in the experience of the pupil is the first to strike the attention. But because teachers and textbooks either take an understanding of size for granted, or neglect to stress the importance of size, or mislead the pupil in his consideration of size, much confusion results.

The pupil comes to the study of fractions after learning to deal with number. Perhaps, therefore, his understanding of number in the study of parts may be taken for granted. But not so the feature of size. He must be taught to think exactly as regards this feature. Very commonly the pupil is misled in his consideration of size by mistaken definitions forced upon him by teacher and textbook. It is the common practice to advance such definitions as the following: "The denominator shows the *number of parts* into which the thing has been divided." "The numerator shows the *number of parts* to be taken." In short, both denominator and numerator are said to show *number of parts*, which is only partly true; and then, in order to indicate a distinction where none has been made, a misleading phrase, like "to be taken," or "that you have," etc., is added to the definition of the numerator to becloud its meaning. After such definitions, the teacher wonders why the pupil, who at the outset had no trouble distinguishing halves, thirds, fourths, etc., proceeds to add two-thirds and three-fourths as follows:

$$\tfrac{2}{3} + \tfrac{3}{4} = \tfrac{5}{7}$$

The pupil, having been confused about *sizes*, or having had no systematic guidance in the recognition of *sizes*, or having been taught to treat them as *numbers*, knows very well that he can add 2 parts and 3 parts, and the result will be 5 parts. He proceeds so to add, as just indicated. Since the denominators in the addends possess a false meaning, he might just as well set down a false meaning (or any meaning) in the denominator of his answer.

The history of fractions reveals that the race made little, if any, progress in the development of ideas of fractions so long as size was emphasized at the expense of number, or so long as number was emphasized at the expense of size. The same revelation is to be noted in the case histories of pupils in the school. They make no progress in developing a working understanding of fractions so long as either distinguishing feature of the fraction is neglected in their thinking. *Pupils must be led to study size as well as number.*

X. Percents

1. The Idea of Percent

The idea of percent began to grow in the minds of people a long time before they began to think about the value and use of decimals. The idea was developed and used in connection with the levying of taxes, the grouping of soldiers, the charging of interest, and the computation of rates of gain or loss in trading.

The Romans levied some of their taxes in hundredths of the value of the property taxed, and they levied other taxes in parts that are closely related to hundredths. For example, when a slave purchased his freedom, a tax of $\tfrac{1}{20}$ of the purchase price was collected by the government; when a slave was sold, $\frac{1}{25}$ of the price received was collected; and when goods were sold at auction, a tax of $\frac{1}{100}$ was collected.

In the Roman army a company was composed of 100 soldiers. The company was called a *centuria*, a "century." Thus, a small number of soldiers were so many parts of the century, that is, so many hundredths.

In buying and selling, coins of small value were needed as well as coins of larger value. Frequently, the coins of small value, which were of metals of less value than gold and silver, were so made that it required 100 of them to equal in value the larger coin. Thus, today, there are 100 cents in our dollar, each a hundredth part of the dollar.

Interest for the use of money was charged at a certain rate. During the Middle Ages, the rate was named as so many coins for each 100 coins borrowed; and we find in the writings of 600 years ago such expressions as *20 p 100, X p cento*, and *VI p c°*, which meant 20 out of a hundred, 10 out of a hundred, and 6 out of a hundred. The letter "p" stood for "per," which means "by" or, as we use it, "out of"; "cento" is a form of "centum" which means "hundred"; and "c°" was an abbreviation of "cento." Today we would write the expressions as 20%, 10%, and 6%.

In order to determine his gains or losses on the goods he sold, a merchant would compute his rate of gain or loss on a hundred coins' worth of each kind of goods. Thus, to use our dollar to illustrate, if 8 dollars were gained on 100 dollars' worth of one kind of goods, and 10 dollars were gained on 100 dollars' worth of another kind, the gains would be thought and written as "$8 per cento," and "$10 per cento." Thus, the two rates of gain could be compared. The English still write and speak of per cents in the same way. The expression, "£6 per cent," meaning "6 pounds out of 100," is common. In America, we do not write "$6 per cent," but "6 percent"; and, instead of thinking "6 dollars out of 100," we think "6 hundredths." In computation we write 6% as .06, because we think of percents as hundredths.

It is often helpful, when the pupil has to find the percent of an amount, 6% of 300, let us say, to remind him of the older meaning, which is "6 out of a hundred." Thus, in determining 6% of 300, he may be encouraged to think: "If there must be 6 out of every hundred, and if there are 3 hundred, then there must be taken out 3 times 6, or 18." Of course, it is to be kept in mind that our present meaning of percents is hundredths; and that, to find 6% of 300, one may proceed to multiply 300 by .06.

2. The Percent Sign

The earlier form was "percento." Often, this form was abbreviated to "per c⁰" and "pc⁰." About three centuries ago, the abbreviation was frequently written as "per⁰̸" or "p⁰̸." From the latter abbreviation, we get our present form of the sign for percent, %, which is easier to write than the older forms. So long as one recognizes the sign, %, as an abbreviation for the expression that means "out of a hundred," or "hundredth," he encounters no danger of confusion.

Rates on bonds are often quoted as so much "per M̶," that is, "per mill," meaning "out of a thousand," or "thousandth." In Germany, the sign ⁰/oo is used for "per mill," the sign being patterned after the sign for percent, instead of being derived from the form of "mill." Baseball averages are printed in "percents." In such case, the term 'percent' is not properly used, because what is really meant is "per mill." Thus, if a player has been at bat 100 times and has made 30 hits, he really has batted 30 percent. This, however, is printed as .300, which is the same as .30 or 30%. But, because the term 'percent' is familiar, and the term 'per mill' is not, the batting average of .300 is usually read as '300 percent' instead of '300 per mill.' So, when we speak of a player's batting average as his 'percentage,' what we really mean is his 'permillage.' If a player has been at bat 4 times and has made 4 hits, we say that he has "batted a thousand." We should mean a thousand per mill, not a thousand percent.

XI. THE THREE KINDS OF PROBLEMS

Once the pupil has learned to deal understandingly with common fractions — that is, the fractions in common use, — he has little yet to learn in his study of decimals and percentage. In common fractions, he learns to deal with fractions of several different sizes; in decimals, he has to give attention to but three or four — namely, tenths, hundredths, thousandths, and occasionally ten-thousandths; in percentage, he needs t, give attention to but one, namely, hundredths. In decimals, all that has to be learned is the use of fractions, presumably familiar, in a new form of expression — that is, new for the expressing of fractions, not whole numbers — which also is presumably familiar. In percentage, all that has to be learned is the use of the hundredth, presumably familiar, in a new form of expression, which in reality is merely the abbreviation of an expression that is well understood.

As the idea of the fraction develops, the pupil finds use for it in so-called 'practical applications'; that is, both in comparing numbers and in stating the comparison between them. Whatever the manner of expressing the fraction, as a common fraction, as a decimal, or as a percent, the use of the idea in comparisons is exactly the same. The pupil's independence and confidence in such use depend upon his ability to distinguish the particular form, or kind, of application that is demanded by the practical situation.

The use of the idea of the fraction in finding and stating comparisons is to be recognized in what are commonly called "the three cases in percentage." In order to avoid the suggestion that such use is confined to percentage, and to emphasize the suggestion that the use is common to all three forms of the expression of fractions, it will be referred to throughout this book as "the three kinds of problems" in fractions, in decimals, and in percentage. The three kinds follow:

First kind: Finding the part, or percent, of a number
Second kind: Finding what part, or percent, one number is of another number
Third kind: Finding a number when a part, or a percent, of it is known

Learning the methods of solution is never difficult. The methods may be stated briefly, as follows: First kind, *multiply by the part, or percent;* second kind, *divide;* third kind, *divide by the part, or percent,* it being understood that computations involving percents require the changing of the percent form to the decimal form. Learning how to make distinctions between the three kinds of problems is the difficult task.

The pupil may be trained to make the necessary distinctions. He may learn how to notice distinctions if he is given training and practice in looking for them. The second kind of problem is easily distinguished from the other two, but the pupil is often at a loss as to which number to put into the dividend. Once he knows that the "number being asked about" goes into the dividend and has had practice in looking for such number, he may be expected, when he has distinguished the second kind of problem, to ask the question of himself, "What number is the problem asking about?" Looking for such number may not be the equivalent of finding it; looking, however, is a necessary prerequisite. Moreover, whenever the activity of looking is unsuccessful, it at least makes understandable the assistance the teacher may need to give.

The first and third kinds of problems are easily distinguished from the second kind, but they are not readily distinguishable from each other. Once the pupil has decided that the problem in question is either the first or the third kind, he may proceed with independence, if he has been taught the distinctions between the two. He may learn to think of the solution of the first kind of problem thus: "When a part, or a percent, is given of a number that *is given*, multiply by the part, or percent"; and of the solution of the third kind of problem thus: "When a part, or a percent, is given of a number that *is not given*, but has to be found, divide by the part, or percent." With such solutions in mind, the problem in question (first kind or third kind) may be attacked with an inquiry somewhat as follows: "Is the part, or the percent, that is given in the problem of a number *that is given*, or of a number *that is not given?*" The pupil may not be expected always to note the correct answer to his inquiry, nevertheless the making of such an inquiry points the pupil's attention in the right direction.

CHAPTER VII

THE DEVELOPMENT OF ARITHMETIC

ARGUMENT

1. The general adoption of the Hindu-Arabic numerals stimulated interest in the art of computation.

2. Interest in computation resulted, not only in unusual combinations of numbers, but also in newer and better methods of computation.

3. Interest in problems developed originally out of real and practical situations. As such situations were attacked and were provided solutions, interest shifted from practical considerations to the puzzle feature of the methods of solution.

4. For the sake of the puzzle element, problems came to be sought in fanciful and impractical situations.

5. Such ascendency of the puzzle interest confirms the point that a problem can provide a real interest even when its source bears no relation to reality.

6. The early interests in computations and in problems persist in present-day arithmetic, which divides into two parts; namely, computation and problem-solving. Ancient interests dominate the arithmetic of the modern school.

7. However, when ancient interests become too dominant, they produce critical reactions that are characterized by more or less sporadic enthusiasm. Chief among such reactions are:

    (a) The emphasis upon content and thinking, little as it was, in Warren Colburn's arithmetic of a century ago;

    (b) The elimination of outworn and useless topics of two decades ago in the interest of economy of time;

    (c) The selection of topics according to the criteria of social and business usage;

    (d) The tendency to motivate arithmetic through appeal to the immediate interests of pupils.

8. The method of elimination and selection that has been employed is the method of statistical analysis. As a consequence, the arithmetic of the schools has become an aggregate of number facts.

9. The following criticisms of present tendencies are offered:

(a) The method of statistical analysis results in an aggregation of facts that bears little relation to meaningful learning;

(b) Such analysis is that of an adult who has learned arithmetic, not that of a child who is learning arithmetic;

(c) The acceptance of useful number facts does not guarantee an understanding of their use;

(d) Understanding of use, if gained, follows learning; it does not precede learning as a motive;

(e) The criterion of present social and business usage does not take into account changing demands;

(f) The internal consistency within arithmetic is destroyed, and the subject is changed from one that depends upon the reason to one that depends upon the memory.

I. Purpose of Chapter

The present chapter has a twofold purpose. First, it will touch upon those high points in the history of arithmetic that appear to throw light upon the development of attitudes toward the subject. Second, it will seek an explanation of present-day attitudes, both as outgrowths of earlier ones and as determined by current influences. The effort will be made to discover the reasons why arithmetic, which appears to have begun as a systematic method of studying and dealing with groups, has developed in our schools into a drill subject composed of a multitude of skills.

II. COMPUTATION

1. Interest in the Process

The union of numeration and computation in the Hindu-Arabic system of notation, which made both processes an integral part of the written language of number, detached from mechanical devices yet retaining the virtues of a mechanical device, paved the way for the development of new interests in computation. Computations, such as multiplication and division, that theretofore had been carried through as additions and subtractions, respectively, now were made possible with the new place-system of numeration. With the new ability to carry through computations once looked upon as extraordinarily difficult, if not impossible, went the growth of new interests in computation.

Moreover, the new numerals provided a new interest in computation related to what may be called the speculative side of mathematics. From early times men had observed the strange properties that numbers possessed. They had at first associated these properties with magic; later, they undertook serious investigation of the principles underlying these properties. They observed the peculiar relations that existed between certain numbers; they studied the properties of prime numbers; and they on occasion organized in groups to determine the location of the last number. Though such speculations were the sport of philosophers, they were not entirely unknown to the popular mind. How greatly the popular mind has been impressed by speculations about number is indicated in the belief that still persists in the 'charm' of three, the 'magic' of seven, and the 'unlucky' thirteen. Because the new numerals were used to designate both units, tens, and powers of tens, a whole new series of unusual relations between numbers was revealed. Let us consider, first, how such speculations developed interest in computation, and, secondly, how interest in computation grew with the developing ability to compute.

2. The Magic of Numbers

The 'magic square,' shown herewith, distributes the first nine numbers in the squares so that they total 15 in whatever direction they are added. This square dates a thousand years before the Christian era. The square was copied by fortune tellers and soothsayers and used as a charm throughout the Orient. In the Middle Ages it was

4	9	2
3	5	7
8	1	6

used in many parts of Europe to drive away disease and to bring good luck. It is found in many recent Chinese books, and it is said that every fortune teller of the East makes use of it in his trade.

The properties of such magic squares have been the study of early mathematicians. Formulas for the building of magic squares of any given size have been evolved by the mathematicians of Japan,[1] and they have given their attention also to the building of 'magic circles.'

The 'strange' properties of numbers led to the invention of series of calculations like the following:

$$(a)$$

$$3 \times 37 = 111$$
$$6 \times 37 = 222$$
$$9 \times 37 = 333$$
$$\cdots$$
$$27 \times 37 = 999$$

$$(b)$$

$$7 \times 15{,}873 = 111{,}111$$
$$14 \times 15{,}873 = 222{,}222$$
$$21 \times 15{,}873 = 333{,}333$$
$$\cdots$$
$$63 \times 15{,}873 = 999{,}999$$

$$(c)$$

$$1 \times 8 + 1 = 9$$
$$12 \times 8 + 2 = 98$$
$$123 \times 8 + 3 = 987$$
$$1234 \times 8 + 4 = 9876$$

$$(d)$$

$$1 \times 9 + 2 = 11$$
$$12 \times 9 + 3 = 111$$
$$123 \times 9 + 4 = 1111$$
$$1234 \times 9 + 5 = 11111$$

$$\cdots$$

$$123456789 \times 8 + 9 = 987654321 \qquad 12345678 \times 9 + 9 = 111{,}111{,}111$$

[1] D. E. Smith and Y. Mikami. *A History of Japanese Mathematics* (The Open Court Publishing Company, Chicago, 1914). Ch. III.

$$(e)$$
$$9 \times 9 + 7 = 88$$
$$98 \times 9 + 6 = 888$$

$$\cdots \cdots \cdots$$

$$9876543 \times 9 + 1 = 88{,}888{,}888$$
$$98765432 \times 9 + 0 = 888{,}888{,}888$$

$$(f)$$
$$1 + 2 + 3 + 4 + 5 + 6 + 7 + 8 + 9 = 45$$
$$4 + 5 = 9$$

The foregoing calculations and others of like nature were early developments that retain an interest for the modern pupil in arithmetic. They are the forerunners of such modern curiosities as the following:

$$(g)$$

$$
\begin{array}{r}
105263157894736842 \\
\times\ 2 \\
\hline
210526315789473684
\end{array}
$$

Note in (g) that the same numerals appear in the product as in the multiplicand, but with the 2 moved from last to first place.

$$(h)$$

Set down the numerals 142,857 and multiply in turn by 1, 2, 3, 4, 5, 6, and 7. Note the same numerals appearing in the products with the exception of the last:

When multiplied by 1, the product is 142,857
When multiplied by 2, the product is 285,714
When multiplied by 3, the product is 428,571
When multiplied by 4, the product is 571,428
When multiplied by 5, the product is 714,285
When multiplied by 6, the product is 857,142
When multiplied by 7, the product is 999,999

The zero of the new system of numerals was itself a curiosity, and it influenced the development of computations that would produce curious arrangements of numerals and

zeros in the answers. An arithmetic of the tenth century
(Mahavir's) suggests the following interesting products, the
first (*i*) of which is called "the necklace of precious gems,"
and the second (*j*) "the royal necklace."

$$(i) \quad 14287143 \times 7 = 100010001$$
$$(j) \quad 142857143 \times 7 = 1000000001$$

The reader may wish to undertake the production of other
curiosities or other "royal necklaces." If he should make
any such effort, he will at least come to appreciate the large
amount of computation that is involved as well as the interest in computation that results.

3. The Prestige of the Computer

The fact that the numerals that stood for powers of ten in
the new system could be treated exactly like the numerals
that stood for units was not long in being discovered by the
medieval calculators. Having gained through experience a
knowledge of the multiplications and divisions of the smaller
groups, they proceeded to enlarge their knowledge and to
apply it to the multiplication and division of groups of tens,
hundreds, etc. Their efforts to devise efficient methods of
calculation, and the attractiveness of first one method then
another, as newer methods were devised, centered attention
upon calculation as an art of considerable importance in its
own right. So great did interest in calculation become, and
so wonderful did the manipulation of numbers appear, that
the calculator, whether clerk or priest, was looked upon as
one to command respect, as one set apart. He had the
admiration of lesser men as his due. In colonial and revolu-
tionary days, and even down to the immediate past, to be a
good 'arithmeticker' was to possess the chief qualification
of the good teacher. Indeed, in many of our schools today,
to be able to 'do his combinations' speedily and accurately
means that the pupil has qualified himself for promotion.

4. Typical Methods of Multiplying and Dividing

Let us consider some of the methods and procedures of multiplication and division that were adopted one after the other. Each method had its day, only to be succeeded by another, until our present methods were adopted. Each as it came along contributed its share of interest to the art of calculation.

As previous discussions have indicated, multiplication at first was performed as a series of additions or by means of duplation. Later, a method of decomposition was used for those multipliers that could be factored. For example, to multiply by 42, one multiplied first by 7 and then by 6. Various forms for keeping the partial products in position were used when the multiplier was not factored. The following are from the Treviso arithmetic of 1478: [2]

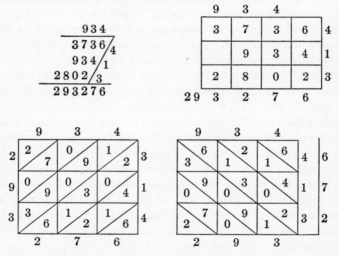

The multiplication shown in the four forms is 934 × 314 = 293,276.

[2] D. E. Smith. *History of Mathematics*, II (Ginn and Company, Boston, 1925), pp. 114–116.

Keeping in mind the easier multiplications, the following method of determining the harder ones was used:

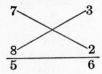

To multiply 7 by 8, the numbers with their complements to 10 were written. Then the products of the complements, 3×2, gave 6; and the difference of one factor and the complement of the other, $8 - 3$, or $7 - 2$, gave 5; thus the answer 56 was determined.

Division was at first performed either by successive subtractions or by 'mediation'; that is, successive halvings. Later, the factors of the divisor were used in succession: To divide by 24, one divided first by 4, then by 6; or first by 3, then by 8. The following will illustrate a few of the procedures used when the divisor was not factored:

To divide 900 by 8:

$$10 - 2)900\lfloor 90 + 18 + 3 + 1 = 112\tfrac{1}{2}$$
$$\underline{900 - 180}$$
$$180$$
$$\underline{180 - 36}$$
$$36$$
$$\underline{30 - 6}$$
$$6 + 6 = 12$$
$$\underline{10 - 2}$$
$$2 + 2 = 4, \tfrac{4}{8} = \tfrac{1}{2}$$

To divide 1728 by 12:

$$54$$
$$1728 \lfloor 144$$
$$1222$$
$$11$$

To divide 1728 by 144:

$$2$$
$$38$$
$$1728 \lfloor 12$$
$$1444$$
$$14$$

The following method is the forerunner of our present
method of long division:

$$
\begin{array}{r}
25)625 \underline{|25} \\
\underline{4} \\
22 \\
\underline{10} \\
125 \\
\underline{100} \\
25 \\
\underline{25}
\end{array}
$$

The method appeared in the fourteenth century and is
not unlike the method in use today.[3]

III. Problems

1. Interest in Problems

The arithmetic problems of early times, like those of the
present day, originated in the real situations of life; and,
like those of the present day, they took on modifications in
terms of the special interests they helped to create and in
terms of the special interests of the people who made use of
them. The length of time it would take for water flowing
through a pipe to fill a cistern, and the length of time it
would take an army to march a certain distance were, for
example, real situations in the lives of early peoples. They
were problems that on occasion possessed an intensely practical importance. It was necessary for the people of the
time to face the issues raised and to meet them to the best
of their knowledge and ability. As the issues were faced
from time to time and as solutions were reached by one
manner or another, interest shifted from the practical issues
involved to the logical issues. The use of a given method of
solution served to attract attention away from the practical
issue and to set the method up as a center of interest. The
method involved gradually grew in interest, and, in later

---

[3] See Smith, *op. cit.*, pp. 128–144.

years, when the original issue or situation had been superseded by newer ones, it influenced, for the sake of its own
preservation, the substitution of fanciful issues and situations for the original genuine ones. It happened, moreover,
that the people who had to face the original issues of the
practical situations met them through the use of certain
computational devices. Now, when such devices possessed
in themselves a peculiar and absorbing interest, it was bound
to happen that the original problems and methods of solution would absorb, or be influenced by, the interest in computation. Thus, a problem that once was real would develop
into a fanciful one, and a situation that once consisted of
simple number relations would develop into one with involved number relations.

Moreover, problems have always possessed a puzzle interest, which has manifested itself in many ways. One likes a
problem that mystifies a little or amuses. The puzzle provides a game to play; it suggests a matching of wits; it is
calculated to leave the solution, when once reached, still a
bit in doubt; its main business is recreation; it easily over-
shadows all interests that may be genuine and real; and,
when computation is difficult and uncertain, it readily takes
advantage of computational difficulties to add to its power
to mystify.

One who becomes absorbed either in the logic of his
method of solution or in the puzzle phases of his problems
easily ceases to be concerned with any practical value that
his problems may have. He quickly loses touch with the
real world, and, if he is a teacher of youth, he may forget
their immaturities and the closeness of their contacts with
reality. To him, the problem is the thing; to him, the
problem is the center around which all else must revolve;
to him, the problem is important in its own right only.
The fact that the logic of his method is a matter of importance often serves as a hindrance instead of a help in keeping
in mind the significance of its practical applications.

2. Illustrations of Problems

Following are some illustrations of the types of fanciful, computational, and recreational problems that absorbed the attention of early students of arithmetic:

> Say quickly, friend, in what portion of a day will four fountains, being let loose together, fill a cistern, which, if severally opened, they would fill in one day, half a day, the third, and the sixth part, respectively? [4]

From real origins, the problems soon passed into the pseudo-real class. Alcuin cites the case of a snail which took 246 years, 210 days, to get to a banquet; Mahavira has a lame man walk for three and one-fifth years at a time, and he pictures a snail crawling up a mountain. [5]

A man whose end was approaching, said to his eldest son, "Divide my goods among you thus: You are to have one bezant and a seventh of what is left." Then to his next son, he said, "Take two bezants and a seventh of what remains." To the third son, he said, "Then you are to take three bezants and a seventh of what is left." Thus he gave each son one bezant more than the previous son and a seventh of what remained and the last son had all that was left. Moreover, after this division, it developed that they had shared the father's property equally, although they had followed out his conditions. The question is, how many sons were there and how large was the estate? [6]

A lion is in a well whose depth is 50 feet. Every day, he climbs up $\frac{1}{7}$ of a foot and slips back $\frac{1}{9}$ of a foot. In how many days will he get out of the well? [7]

A mouse is at the top of a poplar tree that is 60 ft. high, and a cat is on the ground at its foot. The mouse descends $\frac{1}{2}$ of a foot each day and at night it turns back $\frac{1}{6}$ of a foot. The cat climbs 1 foot a day and goes back $\frac{1}{4}$ of a foot each night. The tree grows $\frac{1}{4}$ of a foot between the cat and the mouse

---

[4] L. C. Karpinski. *The History of Arithmetic* (Rand, McNally and Company, Chicago, 1925), p. 46.

[5] V. Sanford. *A Short History of Mathematics* (Houghton Mifflin Company, Boston, 1930), p. 218.

[6] *Ibid.*, p. 219.   [7] *Ibid.*, p. 207.

each day and it shrinks $\frac{1}{8}$ of a foot every night. In how many days will the cat reach the mouse and how many ells has the tree grown in the meantime, and how far does the cat climb? [8]

Another famous problem was the one concerning the number of grains of wheat that can, theoretically speaking, be placed upon a chessboard, one grain being put on the first square, two on the second, four on the third, and so on.

A Dutch arithmetician, Wilkens, takes the ratio in the chessboard problem as three instead of two, and considers not only the number of grains but also the number of ships necessary to carry the total amount, the value of the cargoes, and the impossibility that all the countries of the world should produce such an amount of wheat. [9]

The following problems are to be found in the arithmetics of the century just passed:

Three men lived together, one of them found he could drink a barrel of cider alone in 4 weeks, the second could drink it alone in 6 weeks, and the third in 7 weeks. How long would it last the three together? [10]

A cistern has 3 cocks to fill it, and one to empty it. One cock will fill it alone in 3 hours, the second in 5 hours, and the third in 9 hours. The other will empty it in 7 hours. If all the cocks were allowed to run together, in what time will it be filled? [11]

An arithmetic of our own day inquires of the sixth-grade pupil about the number of tons of stone Methuselah could have hauled in 900 years, working 300 days each year, to a city 20 miles away, on an oxcart that would carry $\frac{1}{2}$ ton of stone, provided his oxen travelled 2 miles an hour and he spent 10 hours a day travelling with them.

[8] *Ibid.*, pp. 207–208.
See also Smith, *op. cit.*, pp. 546–548.
[9] *Ibid.*, pp. 549–550.
[10] Warren Colburn. *Arithmetic upon the Inductive Method of Instruction* (Hilliard, Gray and Company, Boston, 1826), p. 225.
[11] *Ibid.*, p. 225.

The following problem, which never fails to evoke interest, is an illustration of modern problems of the "recreational" type:

Two clerks start in an office at the same time, one at a salary of $1000 for the first year and a raise of $200 each year thereafter, and the other with a salary of $1000 a year but with a raise of $50 every half year. Which has the larger income? [12]

IV. Logical Versus Practical Motives

There is a theory current in our schools to the effect that problems have to be 'real' problems, drawn from and applying to the practical side of life, in order to arouse the interests of pupils. The logical motive for attacking problems is frequently given no more than passing attention. Let a problem be drawn from the everyday experiences of people — preferably, of the pupils themselves — buying at the store, making change, determining the standing of a ball club, figuring the cost of a radio, working in the school garden, etc., and the worth of the problem is established beyond question. But let a problem be drawn from a fanciful situation, from one artificially produced for the sake of the lesson, from one which varies the slightest from reality, in order that an idea, or a number relation, or a principle of procedure may be illustrated and emphasized, and the problem is subject to severe condemnation. Is this true? Must the problem always be a real one? Must the situation that produces the problem always be actual? Which is the factor of central importance — the problem, or the method of thinking illustrated? Moreover, what kind of problems are effective in evoking and stimulating the interests of pupils? Which is the more successful in commanding the attention, the practical or the logical?

To the questions just raised we must withhold our answers, reserving them for a later discussion. Or, what is more to

[12] D. E. Smith and W. D. Reeve. *The Teaching of Junior High School Mathematics* (Ginn and Company, Boston, 1927), p. 390.

the point, let us suspend judgment about problems in arithmetic until we have made further progress in our discussions about the nature and development of the subject. We will do well for the present, however, if we will reflect that it was the logical interest in methods of procedure, rather than the practical interest in real situations, that determined the kinds of problems engaging the attention of arithmeticians for more than twenty centuries. In order to produce and to pass along the kinds of fanciful, unreal, mystifying, and computational problems that have just been illustrated, the arithmeticians of the past had to possess an interest that transcends the practical.

All this is intended, not as a plea for the abandonment of 'real' problems in our present-day classes in arithmetic, but as a plea for reflection upon the experiences of our predecessors.

V. Results of Ancient Interests

The two kinds of early interests just described; namely, interest in computation and interest in problems, have continued to the present day. They operated so long as to become what may be termed a racial habit of mind, a continuously transmitted state of mind, or attitude, or point of view toward the subject of arithmetic. However related the two interests were in the thinking of early arithmeticians, they finally developed as two separate and distinct interests. Computation, calculation, reckoning, was one thing; being able to understand and to solve the problem was another thing. Each interest had a peculiar fascination; each required, or seemed to require, a different attack; and each developed, as we have seen, from a different source.

We find in our schools today the results of these two kinds of early interests, which have been inherited from the past and which are being constantly passed along by teachers and by writers of textbooks. In our schools, computation is still one thing and problem-solving another; we first train

the pupil to perform the operations of arithmetic, and next
we teach him how to solve problems; the pupil first must
learn the 'number facts' and combinations, and then he is
expected to 'apply' them; each chapter of the textbook first
provides exercises for drill, and next some problems to be
solved; ability to compute is the first objective, and ability
to solve problems is the final objective. For the two kinds
of activities to be performed, or of things to be learned, or
of goals to be attained, we have succeeded in developing
different techniques of instruction. We have formulated
and seek to carry into practice two distinct methods of procedure — the one adapted to computation, the other to the
solution of problems. Computation and problem-solving
persist in our schools as separate activities and as distinct
interests.

This modern view of arithmetic, which separates the
subject into two distinct parts, may be the correct one.
Whether correct or not, however, we ought to recognize
that the view was determined by the accidents of early developments and has been handed down to us ready-made from
the past. If we can recognize the view as one that was determined by early enthusiasms, we may bring ourselves to the
point where we will be inclined to subject it to critical examination and analysis.

VI. Revolt Against Ancient Interests

1. Revolt Against Extremes

While the view that arithmetic embodies a double set of
interests still persists, there have been sharp and violent
reactions against the earlier tendencies to carry such interests to extremes. The first reaction began a century ago
with the publication of Warren Colburn's arithmetics. The
following enthusiastic account of Colburn's work, published
a half-century later, will convey an idea of his influence and
of the reaction he fostered:

Fifty years ago, arithmetic was taught as a mere collection of rules to be committed to memory and applied mechanically to the solution of problems. No reasons for an operation were given; none were required; and it was the privilege of only the favored few even to realize that there is any thought in the processes. Amidst this darkness a star arose in the East; that star was the mental arithmetic of Warren Colburn. It caught the eyes of a few of the wise men of the schools and led them to the adoption of methods of teaching that have lifted the mind from the slavery of dull routine to the freedom of independent thought. Through the influence of this little book, arithmetic was transformed from a dry collection of mechanical processes into a subject full of life and interest. The spirit of analysis, suggested and developed in it, runs today like a golden thread through the whole science, giving simplicity and beauty to all the various parts.[13]

The following quoted paragraphs trace the development of arithmetic from Colburn's day down to the beginning of the present century:

For three-quarters of a century after Warren Colburn published the first distinctively American arithmetic in 1821 there was a steady expansion of the content of the subject. Denominate numbers were dealt with in increasing variety; practical and theoretical problems accumulated and found their way into the textbooks. Drill exercises were given increased time in the school program. Arithmetic may very properly be described as a favorite subject in the district school which flourished during the middle of the last century. It is a subject in which definite problems can be set and in which the attainments of pupils can be accurately determined. Pupils and teachers alike accepted it as an important part of the school work and were satisfied to have it consume an appreciable part of the school day.

[13] Edward Brooks. *The Philosophy of Arithmetic* (Sower, Potts and Company, Philadelphia, 1876), p. iii. Quoted by G. T. Buswell and C. H. Judd, *Summary of Educational Investigations Relating to Arithmetic* (Department of Education, The University of Chicago, Chicago, 1925), p. 161.

During the later decades of the nineteenth century there came a general change in the conception of education. Society began to demand a broader type of schooling. The result was a general expansion of the curriculum. This expansion raised numerous questions as to the possibility of making room for new subjects by eliminating waste in the traditional courses of study. Education began to question every topic included in the curriculum.[14]

2. Elimination for Economy

The axe of elimination [15] fell upon the subject of arithmetic as well as upon other subjects in the curriculum. "Minimum Essentials," "Economy of Time," and the like were the catch phrases of educational discussions and writings. Such topics as the following were shorn from the curriculum in arithmetic in many of the schools of the country:

1. Long method of G. C. D.
2. Most of L. C. M.
3. Long, confusing problems in common fractions.
4. Long method of division of fractions. (Always invert and multiply.)
5. Complex and compound fractions.
6. Apothecaries' weight, troy weight, the furlong in long measure, the rood in square measure, the dram and quarter in avoirdupois weight, the surveyors' table, the table of folding paper, tables of foreign money, all reduction of more than two steps.
7. Most of longitude and time.
8. Cases in percentage. (Make one case by using x and the equation.)
9. True discount.
10. Most of compound and annual interest.
11. Partial payments, except the simplest.
12. Profit and loss as a separate topic.

[14] Buswell and Judd. *Op. cit.*, pp. 9–10.
[15] See *Fourteenth Yearbook of the National Society for the Study of Education, Part I.* (Public School Publishing Company, Bloomington, Illinois, 1915.)

13. Partnership.
14. Cube root.
15. The metric system.[16]

3. The Criterion of Social and Business Usage

The criterion for the selection of the topics to be included in the curriculum in arithmetic was social and business usage. Wilson, who has been a leading advocate of this criterion, defines it as follows:

> This principle insists that subject matter chosen shall be fundamentally useful from the standpoint of the needs of society. Interpreted in terms of child life, it means that the child shall see and understand reasonably well the usefulness of what he is learning. And this means that the child is able to organize into his own thinking and living the things upon which he is working in school. Broadly interpreted, the principle that school topics and subjects shall be useful in society means, on the one hand, that they shall not exceed adult usage, and, on the other hand, that they shall be adapted to the present thinking and understanding of the child.[17]

Again he remarks:

> . . . it is assumed that arithmetic in the grades is justified only on the basis of its utility in the common affairs of life. We learn the multiplication table, not to sharpen the wits or to comprehend a beautiful system, but to figure our bills, our taxes, or the interest on a note. Whatever arithmetic is given in the grades beyond the essentials required by social utility consumes time that could be used more profitably in other ways.[18]

[16] G. M. Wilson and others. *Connersville Course of Study in Mathematics for the Elementary Grades* (Warwick and York, Inc., Baltimore, 1922), pp. 13–14.
    See also W. A. Jessup, "Economy of time in arithmetic." *Elementary School Teacher,* 14: June, 1914, pp. 461–476.
[17] G. M. Wilson. "The present impasse in arithmetic." *Educational Method,* 11: November, 1931, 65–72, esp. 66.
[18] G. M. Wilson. *What Arithmetic Shall We Teach?* (Houghton Mifflin Company, Boston, 1926), pp. 1–2.

The method by which one uses the criterion of social utility to determine the curriculum is simple, though tedious and time-consuming. One first discovers what phases of arithmetic are being used by different social groups and what phases are not being used. The next step is to include the 'useful' and eliminate the 'useless.' Thus, if one discovers that Case III of percentage, for example, is not being used by adults, he discards that topic from the curriculum.

4. Motivation by 'Immediate Interests'

The revolt against ancient interests in computation and problem-solving has in recent years expressed itself in another way. One must not only eliminate the 'socially useless'; he must also include the 'useful' in terms of the immediate interests of pupils. The child must be made aware of, and he must be led to understand, the usefulness of the process or procedure that the school has set for him to learn.

> Instead of leading the child blindly through years of meaningless abstract problems, we have come to follow a child's interests and needs in selecting problems related to the home, the school, and the community. The method of presenting these conforms to the psychology of learning. The recognition of the instincts for play and activity and of the laws of interest, association, and habit formation are clearly shown in both subject matter and methods. Number concept, ideas, and process are built up through plays, games, dramatization, and motivated activities. At first, in the lower grades, problems growing out of the child's immediate environment build up and enlarge the application of number ideas and processes and aid as a background for the formal work. Later in the grammar grades community problems of a more complex nature give still wider scope to the mathematical training and lead the child out with a more efficient equipment into the world about him.[19]

[19] Katherine L. McLaughlin. "Summary of current tendencies in elementary-school mathematics as shown by recent textbooks." *Elementary School Journal*, 18: March. 1918, pp. 543–551, esp. 545.

Thus was the tendency as shown by the textbooks of the second decade of the present century, and thus the tendency persists in the textbooks of the fourth decade. It is very difficult for the uninitiated to recognize a present-day textbook in arithmetic by glancing at the topic headings. He finds such topics as "Bobby in Toyland," "A Day at the Seashore," "Playing Store," "A Game of Bean Bags," "Hitting the Target," "Getting a Hair Cut," "Our Fishing Trip," "The Peanut-Guessing Contest," "Valentine's Day," "The Whirligig Game," "In Alaska," "Down in a Coal Mine," and the like. The purpose of such topic-headings is evident. The arithmetic that the pupil has to learn is presumably too uninteresting in itself to make an appeal to pupils; consequently, it must be attached to matters that carry an interest in their own right. Or, the arithmetic that proves to be socially useful is presumably so lacking in logical motive as to require its attachment to matters that of themselves provide sufficient motive of the practical kind.

VII. Number Facts and Combinations

With the application of the axe of elimination to the curriculum in arithmetic, the second decade of the present century witnessed the advent of the educational statistician. The work of this expert in the field of arithmetic correlates strangely with that of the enthusiasts for child-interest and motivation. The reduction of arithmetic to its minimal essentials gave him an opportunity to employ his techniques in the development of the curriculum. His influence has made itself felt in the following manner.

Interest in the elimination of useless topics from the curriculum in arithmetic and in the reduction of arithmetic to its minimal essentials brought to the level of consciousness the fact that the subject is composed of a number of topics. What to include in the curriculum and what to eliminate were questions calling for analysis. The subject must perforce be divided into its parts, and these parts must be listed, labeled, numbered, and otherwise set forth, each as a separate and distinct entity. Arithmetic no longer could be considered an entity; henceforth it must be considered a composite of a multitude of details.

The analysis of arithmetic has led to the listing of 390 separate simple 'combinations,' 765 higher-decade additions, an equal number of higher decade subtractions, 40,095 two-digit divisions with single-digit quotients, to mention only a few. To be sure, not all the facts so listed are found to be 'socially useful.' Such may be eliminated, and the 'useful' facts retained in the curriculum. Since those 'facts' that are not 'useful' may be summarily dismissed from the curriculum, it follows that they have no logical connection with those that are retained for reasons of social utility. In other words, no relationship of any consequence exists between the 'facts,' whether 'useful' or 'useless.' Likewise, the 'useful facts' are of importance each in its own right — because of their 'usefulness' — not because of any relations that may exist among them. And so, because of the characteristics assigned to them, the 'number facts' must be taught to children each as a separate and distinct item of experience. One may find in the work of the school some strange and curious anomalies, but none more strange and curious than the union of the doctrines of social utility and of appeal to children's interests with the analysis of arithmetic into a multitude of unrelated details.

VIII. Criticism of Present Tendencies: Facts about Number Facts

With respect to the theory that arithmetic is a composite of many discrete isolated facts, it is important for one to consider (1) that an analysis of arithmetic into its parts may be entirely unrelated to the manner by which children learn the subject, and (2) that any such analysis is the analysis of the adult who has already learned the subject and is the product of adult interests rather than of children's interests. The adult may understand the relations between the various 'facts'; he may think of them either separately or in their relations; indeed, the fact that he has analyzed arithmetic into its parts indicates that he is conscious of arithmetic as a unity. But to suppose that children will be able to discover arithmetic as a unity when presented with the facts one by one is just as preposterous as to suppose that the ordinary man will be able to visualize the smooth-running automobile when shown a bolt here and a screw there. The mechanic who has removed these 'parts' recognizes them as distinct parts, to be sure; but he also recognizes them in relation to each other and in relation to the machine as a whole. He recognizes a separate use for each, but he is able to do so only because he recognizes that the machine as a whole requires a separate use for each. The separate uses are revealed, not by the parts themselves, but by the larger idea of unity that brings them together. The adult who is so enthusiastic about analysis might do well if, when analyzing arithmetic into its separate 'facts,' he would also make an analysis of the 'facts' themselves. If he is going to engage in analysis, he might be brought to question his procedure of analysis, if he would not stop with his analysis when he has reached the 'number facts.' Let us view a 'fact' from more than a single angle.

At least three facts about a 'number fact' are worthy of consideration. There is, first of all, the *existence* of the fact. "Three and two are five" is a fact that existed before the savage could count and that continues to exist, whether the child learns it or not. The child may be informed of its existence, and may accept its existence, as he accepts many other things, through his confidence in the superior wisdom and authority of the teacher. With such acceptance goes the second fact of major importance; namely, the *statement* of the number fact. How the number fact is to be stated is learned from the teacher. The manner of statement is a mere conventionality. Through practice, even the parrot

may learn the statement. The third fact of major importance is the *consciousness* of the number fact. At this point
intelligence plays a part, and at this point a contribution to
the child's intelligence may be made. Consciousness does
not of necessity follow the acceptance of existence and the
learning of the statement, since these two may take place
without any relation to 'consciousness' — in the sense of
'intelligent comprehension.' Consciousness, however, includes the other two. One may with propriety raise the
question whether a child can be made 'conscious' of a 'number fact' when it is so presented as to exist in his experience
merely as an isolated unrelated item. The experience of
teachers is very revealing on this point. They frequently
find that, after a pupil has accepted all the 'useful number
facts' and learned how to state them with ease and with
accuracy, he does not know what to do with them. They
frequently find, too, that he is more hopelessly confused
after he has learned many of the so-called 'facts' than he
was when he knew only a few of them.

With respect to the theory that the work in arithmetic
must be connected with games and plays and other children's interests in order that the learning may be motivated
by an understanding of usefulness, it may be well to remember that in the development of arithmetic the invention of
devices always preceded the necessity for their use. One
may reflect, if he wishes, that modern industrial society
would break down if the Arabic numerals and the methods
of thinking that they facilitate were suddenly withdrawn.
It is, however, more to the point to reflect that modern
industrial society did not come into existence until the Arabic numerals had been invented and accepted as a means of
number-thinking. Moreover, one may raise the question
how a child can be made 'conscious' of the 'usefulness' of a
process in arithmetic before he learns it. Suppose it does
relate to his interests, or what the adult views as his interests; how is it possible for the child to see and to understand

such relation before he has learned the process? What the process means, what its importance is, and how it may be used are learned only as the process is learned; indeed, they sometimes are not learned at all as the process is learned. How, then, can the usefulness of the process be made a motive for learning it? *One of the most striking and misleading fallacies current in our school procedures is the fond and uncritical belief that, once children have had explained to them the usefulness of learning, they will become eager seekers after truth.*

With respect to the theory that social and business usage shall determine the content of the curriculum, it will be well for one constantly to remind himself that this theory has worked hand-in-glove with the theory that arithmetic is a composite of isolated unrelated items. When usefulness is the criterion, any idea of a relation between topics and processes must be abandoned. When topics and processes may be included or excluded at will, any relationship among them must be decidedly unimportant. Moreover, a topic or process may not be 'useful' today, but may come into use ten years from today. What measures shall be taken to teach the topic or process after it comes into use to those people who have missed the instruction in the early years of their schooling?

The exclusion from the curriculum about fifteen years ago of Case III in percentage furnishes an interesting illustration of the fallacy of the social-utility theory. Because Case III was apparently not socially useful, it was eliminated from the curriculum in many schools, while Case I, which was found to be useful, was retained. The possibility that a study of Case III might enlarge the pupil's ideas of percentage in general and thus make him a more intelligent user of Case I was not considered. Moreover, in the midst of all the agitation about the 'uselessness' of Case III, American wholesalers and retailers very inconsiderately began to use it when they took up the practice of computing profit as a percent of the selling price rather than as a percent of the cost — thus, of course, bringing rapidly into use the procedure of finding a number when a percent of it is known.

The short-sightedness of the theory of social and business usage becomes apparent when one raises the questions: What makes a useful fact useful? Is the usefulness of a fact carried by the fact itself? Or is a fact useful only as the intelligent person finds use for it? One may discover in our schools many pupils who learn useful facts, but are unable to use them, and one may discover many pupils who are constantly finding use for the things they learn. Perhaps by reducing the curriculum to the useful and the practical we may neglect to impart many things that, though useless in social and business practices, may be of exceeding usefulness in the training of pupils. In physical education classes we teach the youth many plays and games. We do not expect him to find these quite so useful as he grows older; indeed, we expect him to abandon the games of childhood. The plays and games are taught, not because they are useful in later life, but because they furnish a training that will be useful. The arithmetical method of extracting the square root is certainly not a useful device in adult life. Most people have no occasion to use the device, and those who do have such occasion find it easier to resort to the table of logarithms or to the slide rule. Why, then, shall the school teach the extraction of the square root? It may be that the understanding of the method will give the pupil a clearer insight into the spatial relations of square measure.

IX. Computation and Problem-Solving, the Persistent Concerns

In outward appearance, the modern textbook differs markedly from textbooks of earlier days. In externals, modern methods of teaching differ markedly from those of our fathers' time. In content, the modern curriculum differs markedly from the curriculum of the past. Internally, however, the influence of the past still persists in the modern school. Computation and problem-solving were the interests of earlier days; computation and problem-solving remain as the interests of the present. The extremes to which earlier concern in computation and problem-solving were carried have led to sharp reactions in later days. The kinds of computations and the kinds of problems have undergone radical changes; but the changes have been changes in form and changes in procedure, not changes in the direction of effort. The interests of earlier peoples moved off at a tangent. Instead of moving back to the main road, we have for the greater part absorbed our energies in finding what seem to us to be better and more practical means of traveling along the side road. The following criticism, though severe and perhaps somewhat extreme, is not without reasonable excuse:

> For finally the student can never aid himself under this present system. Having no insight whatever into what he is doing, unable to reason and prevented from trying, he can have no assurance that his results are correct, and of course he can never correct them, in the proper sense, should they be wrong. All he can do is to substitute one dictated response for another. And so we reach the paradox that the science which for ages has been regarded as the best of all preparations for the use of the reason has come to be that section of the curriculum where the exercise of the reason is most effectually prevented.[20]

[20] McQuilkin DeGrange. "Statisticians, dull children, and psychologists." (*Educational Administration and Supervision*, 17: November, 1931), pp. 561–573, esp. 569–570.

CHAPTER VIII

METHODS OF THINKING

ARGUMENT

1. The sketch of the development of the number system in preceding chapters does not suggest that the child in school must develop his ideas of number according to the methods the race had to use. It merely describes the number system the child must learn.

2. The child must learn to think the arrangement of objects in the operations of addition, subtraction, multiplication, and division according to the pattern fixed by the race.

3. The issues and situations incident to number combination that confronted earlier generations now no longer exist.

4. Such issues and situations ought not to be artificially reproduced by the school for the sake of raising problems to be solved. To do so is to follow a procedure in which there are four fallacies:

    (a) the fallacy of time;
    (b) the fallacy of inferring the child's point of view from the adult's;
    (c) the fallacy of paralleling the learning situations of the child with those of the race;
    (d) the fallacy of inconsistency.

5. The perfection of the number system has removed the element of doubt from situations having a number phase.

6. Since a problem is a question involving doubt, when the doubt is removed from a question there is no problem.

7. To keep arithmetic as a set of problem activities is to withhold information and training in order to provide doubts. The school can hardly justify itself when it follows such antiquated methods of procedure.

8. The purpose of arithmetic in the school is to teach the

128

number system so that it will be understood, not to keep the system in doubt for the sake of problem situations.

9. An understanding of the number system is not to be derived from explanations that take their source from without the child's experience with number. Such explanations do not encourage self-confidence and self-reliance.

10. A true understanding is to be described only in terms of the development of general ideas on the part of the child. The organization of arithmetic, if perfected, provides a constant portrayal of such ideas.

11. The procedure of learning is neither one of listening to explanations nor one of trying to resolve the doubts from number situations that are left obscure, but rather one of developing a method of studying and attacking such situations.

12. The problems of arithmetic should not be treated as such, but as illustrations of ideas and methods that are more important.

———————

I. Relation of the Origins to Learning of Number

Before we turn to a discussion of the stages of development in number which the school should foster and through which the child should pass, it may be well to insert a word of caution. Our rapid sketch of the struggles of the race to create and bring to its present stage of perfection the system of number in use today is intended at no point to carry the suggestion that the child must develop his number ideas according to the same methods that the race has followed. Our sketch is intended merely to indicate some of the characteristics of the number system that society has perfected for its use and that it expects the child to acquire in order to take his place as a member of society; to trace the development of the various methods of attack that have been made upon the number situations confronting human beings, in order to discern, if possible, the methods that have been most effective; and to pave the way for a consideration of the place arithmetic has made for itself in the modern school and of the purposes of training in arithmetic.

It is easy to imagine a parallel between racial development and individual development, and to set up an argument that the conditions and situations that were instrumental in furthering racial progress should be duplicated in order to provide the motives and the settings for the progress of the individual. Indeed, as the preceding chapter has indicated and as our present discussion will show, it is extraordinarily difficult for the present to break away from the influences of the past and to make adaptations to present conditions. The attempt to duplicate the situations that confronted earlier societies in order to furnish the motives for learning in present society is, however, a distortion both of modern situations and of the conception of the true motives for learning. Though the child must learn the number system the race has evolved, the conditions that surround him are radically different. He has to learn in a short time what it took the race a long time to develop. He must be steered clear of the mistakes the race made. He must not be allowed the long periods of experimentation with inadequate methods of thinking that the race through accident had to experience. He is surrounded at birth by a perfected number system in daily use by the older generation, and throughout his formative years, if not his whole lifetime, he may profit through such experience; whereas the race enjoyed no such advantage because it was at all points confronted with the task of creating a number system and bringing it to perfection.

The only item in the parallel is the number system itself. Through blind trial extending over long centuries the race succeeded in creating and developing a number system; it is this same number system that the child must re-create and redevelop under the systematic guidance of the older generation. The race lacked guidance and consequently fell into many difficulties; the efforts of the child may be guided in the direction of the successful methods of attack that the race through trial and error finally came to adopt.

II. The Fundamental Operations

The operations of addition, subtraction, multiplication, and division, which are learned after one fashion or another by pupils in the early years of their schooling, may be referred to as illustrative (1) of the fact that the efforts of the race have fixed the pattern according to which the child must learn to think the arrangement of objects, and (2) of the fact that the issues incident to number combination that confronted earlier generations now no longer exist and should not now be artificially reproduced. With respect to the first type of illustration, it is to be remembered that the operations of arithmetic are grouping operations. To add and to multiply do not mean to increase, and to subtract and to divide do not mean to decrease. They all mean to regroup, and, when the quantity being dealt with is greater than nine, to regroup in terms of the standard group of ten. Let us consider these four operations in more detail.

First, addition does not mean to increase. Seven and eight are fifteen, yet a difference exists. The difference is, of course, not in the number of objects, because the same number remains throughout the activity of addition. In adding seven and eight we merely think the two groups together into a new arrangement. Starting with a chance arrangement, we think them into the standard arrangement of ten and five. The standard arrangement is more easily comprehended than the chance arrangement, because the former may be judged in terms of the group of ten, which is of standard size.

Second, subtraction does not mean to decrease. Fifteen minus eight equals seven. Here we begin with the standard arrangement. We rearrange the objects — if not actually, at least as a matter of thought — setting aside a group of eight and finding beside it a group of seven. Here, again, we deal with the same objects through the whole of the operation, finding them first in the standard arrangement of ten and five and lastly in the chance arrangement that is demanded by the situation at hand.

Third, multiplication does not mean to increase. Three fives are fifteen. We start with three groups of five and five and five. The standard arrangement is one ten and five. Six sevens are forty-two. The economy of the rearrangement is that in the one instance we have a certain number of objects in a chance arrangement, and in the other, the latter, instance the same objects are thought together in the standard arrangement. We simply clarify our thinking about them by standardizing the grouping into four tens and two. Economy is further illustrated by the necessity for comparison. Suppose, for example, we need to compare six sevens and five eights. In the original arrangements, comparison is very difficult and consequently subject to error. The standard arrangements, however, are easy to compare— four tens and two compared with four tens.

Fourth, division does not mean to decrease. Forty-two divided by six equals seven. In this instance, we merely translate the standard arrangement of a given number of objects into the arrangement demanded by the necessities of the moment. The question is, in forty-two, how many groups of six each? or in forty-two, how many do we have in each of six groups? Ten divided by one-half equals twenty. The process of division is not reversed. Ten is not increased to twenty. The question is, how many halves are there in ten? The answer is, twenty (halves).

There is nothing natural about the grouping of objects into tens. The writer remembers the little boy who described his wealth in the following terms: "I have a quarter, five nickels, three dimes, and seven cents." The boy was not aided by the suggestion, "How much do you have altogether?" The boy had already thought his money together, and had described the total. The suggestion of eighty-seven cents as a statement of the total was not helpful. The boy learned at a later date to group in tens, when the school had taught him the system of grouping that the race had perfected and made a part of his social inheritance.

III. OPERATIONS VERSUS PROBLEMS: SOME FALLACIES

With respect to the second type of illustration, to which allusion has been made, it may be suggested that there was a time when the methods of dealing with groups existed, if at all, as problems requiring study, the weighing of values, and critical judgment, and not as well defined and well understood methods of dealing with the quantitative situations of life. The time was, as our preceding chapters have indicated, when the manner of determining the size of a group raised grave and doubtful questions. One method after another was tried — giving attention to the individual members of the group, naming the members, one-to-one correspondence with tallies, etc. — but each method of attack left the question still in doubt and the problem of the size of the group still unsolved. The time was when the necessity of counting a large group called into play first one device then another, and, after employing the devices at hand, the enumerator was still in doubt about the group, and the group remained an unwieldy and unmanageable one. The time was when the fundamental operations of addition, subtraction, multiplication, and division called for the services of the expert, because the means by which large groups could be regrouped in the ways indicated were more or less a mystery to the common man. A herdsman may have faced the necessity of dividing his flock, for example, or a merchant his goods. The necessity may have been perfectly clear, but the manner of carrying through the division presented a problem. Solution could be attempted in various ways, but there was no means by which the solution could be reached with assurance. When a method of division was used and a solution gained, the solution was a doubtful one, and the original problem of how best to proceed still remained an unsolved problem.

Such problems as have been mentioned now no longer exist in civilized society. If one wishes to know the number in a group, he counts. If the necessity of arranging groups into larger ones, or of separating larger groups into smaller ones, presents itself, one knows exactly what to do and how to do it, whether the process demanded be addition, multiplication, subtraction, or division. Civilized society is in possession of methods of attack upon groups, methods of thinking their arrangement and rearrangement, that primitive society did not have. The methods of attack and the methods of thinking have worked to remove the element of doubt from the quantitative situations of life. With the doubt removed, the issues that confront one are no longer problems to be solved, but tasks to be performed.

It frequently happens, however, that the school undertakes to introduce the operations of addition, or of percentage, and the like by surrounding the child with the situations of life that seem to require the use of the operations next to be learned. The purpose is to provide a motive for learning. Let the child play the game of bean bags or be a clerk in the school store and in the course of time he will see the need of addition. The game or the clerkship becomes a problem that is unsolved until addition is learned. The game or the clerkship serves finally to direct the child's attention away from itself to the activity of addition, and this before addition is introduced. In other words, the attempt is made to withhold the introduction of addition until the child is brought, by some means or other, face to face with the problem of thinking things together in the orderly and systematic way that addition provides. Or, to state the matter in another way, the attempt is made to reproduce in the modern school the type of problem situation that in a primitive civilization slowly but finally led to the creation and use of addition.

There are at least four fallacies in such procedure.

One is the fallacy of time. The school life of the child is

too short to permit the duplication of the slow progress the race made in the perfection of our number system.

A second is the fallacy of assuming that the child's point of view with respect to the situations of games and plays may be inferred from the adult's point of view. The adult is perfectly clear on the point that both the bean-bag game and the clerkship in the store need for their perfection the use of the operations of addition; the child who has never been introduced to addition certainly does not possess the adult's superior point of view.

A third fallacy is the fallacy of paralleling the learning situations of the child with the learning situations of primitive people. The child is no doubt a primitive being in one sense of the term, but he does not live in a primitive society; and, what is just as much to the point, the school cannot reproduce the conditions of primitive life. Moreover, it is just about as senseless, though perhaps not as immediately serious, to deprive the child of society's mature ways of dealing with groups until he senses the need for them as it would be to deprive him of cooked foods and warm clothing until he arrives at the point where the need for these is clear.

A fourth fallacy is the fallacy of inconsistency. A situation is presented in order to enable the child to see it as a problem requiring addition, let us say, for its solution. Then having inferred that the child has sensed the problem just as the adult conceives that he should, he is moved at once to the learning of the process of addition that provides the solution. In the first place the child sees no problem; and in the second place, though he learns to add, he does not add as a means of solving a problem, however much the adult may insist that the process be treated as a means of solution, for without a problem there can be no solution. The result is that, when the child does learn to add, he is constantly misled in the use he might make of addition, on account of the insistence of the school that he treat the process as a solution when to him it is not a solution.

IV. The Removal of Doubt from Situations

The discussions of the foregoing paragraphs may be summarized in the statement that the creation and perfection of the number system have operated in the direction of removing the element of doubt from the quantitative situations of life. Quantitative situations, which at one time presented themselves as problems — that is, as questions involving doubt — are problems no longer, because the number system has provided clear and well-defined methods of attack upon the situations and has rendered them comprehensible and manageable. The number system has freed the mind from the necessity of dealing with quantitative situations as though they are problems, and thus has provided the opportunity for the mind to move out to new situations that heretofore have been foreign to experience. By providing a method of attack upon the simpler situations of life, the number system has made it possible for the mind to deal with more complex situations.

Illustrations may be drawn from the situations that provided some of the problems of earlier peoples. In the preceding chapter reference was made to the so-called 'problem of pursuit,' or the rate-time-distance problem. That was a real problem in the days of the Romans. A Roman legion, for example, would have to make a march of a given distance, reckoned in thousands of paces. In what time could the legion be counted upon to make the march and arrive at the designated destination? The answer in many cases was a rough approximation. Not being versed in the formula for computing the time from distance and rate, perhaps not having the formula raised to the level of clear consciousness, or not realizing its general applicability, the Roman officer in charge would give his answer in terms of what he could remember about the time consumed on former marches over different distances. He would approximate in terms of this isolated experience or that one, and his answer in each case would be slightly different. If the problem was a pressing one, his different approximations might serve to confuse rather than to aid.

It sometimes happens that one permits himself to speculate about rate-time-distance very much as the Romans had to speculate in earlier days.

One wishes to drive from Huntington to Wheeling, let us say. On the trip, when his mind is largely occupied with the business of driving, he may speculate as follows: "I can make the trip to Parkersburg in three hours; from Parkersburg on is a greater distance than it is to Parkersburg; I should make the distance from Parkersburg to Wheeling in four hours; it will take about seven hours to make the trip. No, the last time I made a trip, when I drove from Charleston to Glenville, which is about the same distance as from Huntington to Parkersburg, it required over three hours; so, it will require eight or nine hours to make the trip from Huntington to Wheeling."

Such speculations are, however, no longer necessary. When one is really concerned about time-rate-distance, he thinks somewhat as follows: "Ninety miles in three hours; thirty miles an hour; two hundred-ten miles; seven hours." Though one may permit himself to speculate idly about the relations between the conditions of such a situation as the one mentioned, he no longer has to do so. He has a method of attack ready at hand, which, when he wishes, or finds it expedient, to use it, removes all doubt from the situation. "If one can maintain an average speed of 30 miles an hour, in what time can he travel a distance of 225 miles?" is not a problem any longer. Though one may need to exercise care in making the necessary computation, he knows exactly what must be done to arrive at the answer to the question.

The 'cistern problem' of early times now no longer exists, though the conditions of the problem still remain and continue to confront the modern engineer on a scale many times as great. Water from one pipe will fill the cistern in six hours; water from a second pipe will fill it in four hours.

How long will it take to fill the cistern when water flows in through both pipes? Such was the situation in earlier times, but because there existed in the minds of earlier people no well-defined method of dealing with the situation, the situation created a problem. From their previous experiences with the flow of water into cisterns they could make one or more shrewd guesses for their answer, but in any case they had no positive assurance that their guess was correct until they checked their guess by trial and experiment. Moreover, if the conditions of the situation, such as the rate of flow in one pipe or the other, changed ever so slightly during the period of trial, they were thrown into still greater confusion about the guessed answers. Today the city engineer who has the facts about the city reservoir, the supply of water, the average daily consumption, etc., faces no such problem. Though the conditions are a hundred times more complex and on a scale a million times as great, no real problem exists, because the method of attack upon the conditions of the situation have removed the elements of doubt.

V. The Characteristics of a Problem

What we have been saying may be stated in another way. It is not the situation, nor the various conditions and elements of the situation, that creates a problem; nor is it even the necessity of dealing with the situation that creates a problem. The problem arises out of doubt about the way the situation must be handled. It is ignorance, or uncertainty, about the way the conditions should be dealt with that is the problem or that gives the situation the character of a problem. When this ignorance is removed, when assurance is substituted for uncertainty, when knowledge displaces doubt, the problem as such ceases to exist. This is only another way of saying that whether a problem exists depends upon the degree of intelligence possessed by the individual.

The same situation with identical conditions may confront

two individuals. It follows from what has just been said that to one the situation may present a problem, whereas to the other no problem may be presented. Let us illustrate. Two merchants, belonging to the same association of retailers, may decide to compute their gain as a certain percent of the selling price instead of as a certain percent of the cost. Each has decided to fix the prices of his articles so that the gain, which takes into account overhead and similar factors, is to be 40% of the selling price. What, then, should be the selling price of an article that costs $36? Here is a new situation, a new condition of affairs, facing the two merchants. To one it is a problem; to the other it is not a problem. How can the matter be explained? Identical situations — in one case, a problem; in the other, no problem.

The merchant who faces a problem in our illustrative case faces it because he does not possess a well-understood method of dealing with the situation. He does not thoroughly understand the relations between numbers that are expressed in terms of percent. His partial understanding is sufficient to enable him to recognize the right answer if and when he gets it, but he does not know how to proceed. He can think of several possible ways that may bring the answer, but he is not sure of any one way. He proceeds to guess, to try, to devise a rule-of-thumb method of solution. He guesses $70 as being the correct answer, but finds that $70 less 40% of $70 does not give the cost, which is $36. He may try $55, $65, and, finally, $60. The solution is finally gained through repeated trials. The merchant may next have to fix the price of an article whose cost is $21. He may recognize $21 as being $\frac{7}{12}$ of $36, and fix this price as $\frac{7}{12}$ of $60, but such a rule-of-thumb method is useful only so long as the figures $36, 40%, and $60 are remembered. When forgotten, or when a different percent of gain is desired, the problem is again to be faced by him.

The second merchant, who has no problem confronting him, has none because he knows and understands the method

of dealing with the situation. He is disturbed by no doubt
as to what should be done. All that confronts him is the
task of doing a little subtracting and a little dividing. He
can proceed with confidence from the first step to the last.

Both merchants proceed to the same results, but by pursuing different routes. The one solves a problem; the other
performs a task. The one is confronted by doubt; the other
proceeds to his task with confidence. The one expends
mental energy; the other conserves mental energy for situations that are more involved.

VI. THE PURPOSE OF ARITHMETIC IS NOT TEACHING HOW TO SOLVE PROBLEMS

The purpose of instruction in arithmetic may be stated in
terms of the service it renders. It has provided the race and
it provides the individual with a method of attack upon the
quantitative situations of life. It has removed, and it is
capable of removing, the element of doubt and uncertainty
from such situations. It has freed the mind, and it can continue to free the mind, from the necessity of dealing with
such situations as though they were problems. It has operated to conserve, and for the individual it continues to
operate to conserve, mental energy for more complicated
and more involved tasks. The purpose of instruction in
arithmetic is not to teach children how to solve problems;
the purpose is to provide them with methods of thinking,
with ideas of procedure, with meanings inherent in number
relations, with general principles of combination and arrangement, in order that the quantitative situations of life may
be handled intelligently and without doubt and uncertainty.
The purpose is so to order and systematize the child's
methods of dealing with combination and arrangement of
objects that he may go through life freed from the necessity
of confronting problems of an arithmetical nature. The purpose rests upon the assumption that the individual has a
higher function to perform in life than to expend his energy

in solving what were once problems in arithmetic but are problems no longer. He must be set free from the necessity of ever having problems in arithmetic to solve.

VII. The Relation of Present versus Past Conditions to Problem-Solving

In view of the present organization of the curriculum in arithmetic with its emphasis upon problems and problem-solving, what has just been said may seem heretical in the extreme. But we should remember that the school continues to emphasize problem-solving in arithmetic, because problem-solving was, and had to be, a major activity in the earliest developments of the subject. And we should remember further that arithmetic has come down to us from the past as a complete, unified, and simplified science, and is now no longer passing through the processes of development. When arithmetic was only a partially developed science — or rather when it was a composite of crude and unsystematic methods of dealing with groups — the quantitative situations of life were a series of problems to be solved. Now, with a unified and systematic method, or series of methods, of dealing with groups, the individual may become a master of quantitative situations. For the school to keep such situations on the level of questions involving doubt (problems) can mean nothing other than that the school deliberately withholds from pupils the superior methods of attack that society has created and brought to perfection.

The school can, if it wishes, present the task of determining the size of a group as a problem to be solved by the beginner. If it does, it withholds from him the method of counting for the sake of keeping him in doubt. The school can, if it wishes, present the task of determining the number of equal groups when the total is given and the size of each group is given as a problem to be solved. If it does, it keeps the child in ignorance of the meaning and uses of division as a method of arrangement in order to make the procedure to be chosen a doubtful one. The school can, if it wishes, keep the pupil in doubt about the meaning and uses of percentage; about the development, relations, and uses of weights and measures; and about the characteristics of the unit of square measure; and it will succeed in keeping the situations of charging interest for the use of money, of the computation of gain and loss, of denominate numbers, of determining areas, and so on, on the level of problems to be solved. Whether the school is ever justified in withholding information and training for the sake of antiquated methods of procedure is certainly seriously to be questioned.

It would seem to be the part of wisdom for the school to give the child training in counting before it sets the task of determining the size of a group; to teach the meaning and procedure of division before it expects the pupil to deal with a situation that requires the use of division; and to develop his understanding of percentage, weights and measures, square measure, and so on before it brings to his attention the varied situations of life that employ these ideas and methods of procedure. In order to live in civilized society as a useful member of the social group, the individual must be introduced to the devices and machines and procedures of civilized society, and this before he is called upon and expected to assume the responsibilities that fall to his lot. Shall the young driver of an automobile be allowed to face the situation of determining the side of the road to travel upon, courtesies of the road, and the like as problems to be solved? Shall he be permitted to drive until the need for rules of the road are impressed upon him by experience? Or shall he be taught the rules of the road from the beginning? If a drayman buys a new truck, shall he proceed to use it for hauling while he is still partially ignorant of its operation, or shall he inform himself of the way it should be handled before he undertakes to use it, in order that he may face no problem of operation while he is engaged in the serious conduct of his business?

The name 'problem' has come down from the past as the designation of the situation that formerly was a problem to be solved, but that has long ago lost its character as a problem.   When one speaks of 'problems' in arithmetic, everyone understands just what type of exercises is being mentioned.   Suddenly to change the name of the exercises would cause misunderstanding, especially among the pupils who have learned to use the old name.   Let the name be retained.   It is not the name that will cause confusion, but the incorrect manner of viewing the purpose of the exercises by the teacher.

VIII.   Old-Fashioned versus Modern Methods of Instruction

The discussions of the present chapter and of the preceding chapter have called attention to two apparently contrasting methods of instruction in arithmetic.   The contrast is often emphasized by the names that are given them.   They are often set over the one against the other by the names 'old-fashioned' and 'modern.'   The 'old-fashioned' method shows the pupils how to perform the operations of arithmetic; that is, teaches the 'number facts' in both simple and complex operations, and, finally, shows the pupils how to 'solve problems.'   The 'modern' method presents quantitative situations as 'problems' to be solved, and by devious ways leads from the 'problems' to the particular operations used in the process of 'solving.'   The former method shows procedures to be followed; the latter method undertakes to develop a feeling of 'need' for a procedure before the pupils are permitted to know anything about the procedure.   The former method withholds no information, at least, no 'useful' information; the latter withholds information for the sake of maintaining the 'problem' situation.   The former method is a piecemeal method that lacks unity; the latter seeks to establish a unity between the child's 'needs' and what he finally gets a chance to learn.

From another point of view, however, the two contrasting methods are very much alike. Both emphasize 'problems' in arithmetic to be solved, the one by showing the method and the other by withholding the method. Both emphasize the mechanical operations of arithmetic, the one by isolated drills and the other by presenting them as ways of getting answers to 'problems.' Both neglect the development of general ideas in arithmetic, the one by emphasizing the various processes as separate and unrelated things to do and the other by emphasizing the various processes as isolated methods of meeting children's needs which are sensed, if at all, as isolated needs. Both interpret arithmetic as a set of tools, each of which may be picked up and used for a particular purpose without any relation to the rest, and both methods show no interest in helping the pupil to fit together the various parts of arithmetic into a smooth-running machine of thinking.

Over against the two methods just described, our discussions suggest that arithmetic ought to become for the pupil a method of thinking that makes understandable the quantitative situations of life. The idea that he should understand what he is called upon to learn by studying the characteristics of the things themselves has been suggested. In this connection it may be well to insert a word of caution about the intent of the discussion of 'problems.'

The insistence that arithmetic ought not to be presented as a series of problems to be solved is not intended to carry the suggestion that the pupil is not to understand what he is learning. It merely suggests that there may be a way of getting him to understand a new step in arithmetic other than the method of presenting it as a means of solving a new kind of 'problem.' What has been said about arithmetic as a system, as a unified body of ideas, as a science, as a means of grouping by tens, and the like, should, perhaps, carry the suggestion that what the pupil has learned and understood about the steps already taken may be the best possible introduction to a new step that has to be taken. The unity within the subject itself, when the pupil is at all conscious of it, may be relied upon to lead from one thing to the thing which logically follows. Though the pupil will not be able to understand a new step until after he has taken it, his understanding of preceding steps, if given the chance, may throw some light upon the new step as he approaches it.

IX. EXPLAINING THE PROCESSES

Let us consider the means of developing the understanding of the pupil, first negatively, and next, in a positive way. Let us consider, first, how the teacher's efforts to help the pupil by means of explanations often lead to confusion, and, finally, how the pupil may be taught to rely more and more upon his developing ability to understand.

The importance of the pupil's understanding of the processes he learns to perform is generally recognized by teachers. To assist the pupil in his understanding, the teacher usually tries to explain each new process as the pupil comes to it. The effort meets with many failures. Often, instead of helping the pupil, the explanation attempted by the teacher stands out as an extra stumbling block for the pupil.

One criticism of the explanations of the teacher, and those of the book as well, is that they teach the pupil to depend upon the thinking of others rather than upon his own ability to think. When the teacher explains a process, the pupil must attend to that explanation; his scheme of thinking must pattern after the teacher's scheme; he must follow as another leads; his whole attitude must be one of dependence. As a consequence, the pupil is often quite as dependent upon the teacher's thinking and explanations (or upon those of the textbook) at the end of the course as he was at the beginning. The course in arithmetic thus misses one of its largest and most promising opportunities; namely, the opportunity of guiding the pupil in the direction of intellectual self-reliance and of fostering in him a growing feeling of confidence in the power and certainty and dependability of his own mental reactions.

Another criticism of the explanations of the teacher (and of the textbook) arises out of the fact that the occasion for each explanation is the pupil's difficulty and unfamiliarity with each new process as he comes to it. To the pupil, each new process usually appears entirely new. It thus appears that the new process must be explained in terms of its newness. As a consequence, each new process, which at first seems so different, is given a new and different explanation. The teacher and the book thus proceed to provide different explanations for the different processes, forgetful of the fact that the very newness of the explanation often renders it quite as difficult for the immature mind to grasp as the process that is being explained.

The trouble with new explanations for new processes is that the pupil is not encouraged to carry over from any one explanation or process any idea that may help him to understand the new process as he comes to it. The pupil is unable to see any connecting link between the different explanations or between the different processes. Each explanation appears to him just as new and strange as the process that seems to need explaining, because the explanation comes too abruptly and without any connection in the pupil's thinking with previous ones.

Worse yet, without any connection being made in the pupil's thinking between the various explanations that are given, they often appear to him as contradictory. A case in point is the explanation that the column to the right must be unbroken when adding whole numbers, and that the column to the left must be unbroken when adding decimals. Both are at fault because they are based upon what the pupil can see with his eyes rather than upon what ideas of relationship may be developing in his mind. Another illustration of contradiction is the explanations that are given of the apparently diminished result when one divides by a whole number and of the apparently increased result when he divides by a fraction. Such explanations are at fault because they are offered as explanations of apparent differences that the pupil can 'see,' and take no account of the fact that the same idea of procedure really appears in each process.

But, it may be urged, why not meet this difficulty by letting the teacher and the book provide consistent explanations. The answer is that explanations ought not to *originate* with the teacher and the book at all, but to develop from the pupil's own growing understanding of what he is learning. If he is learning arithmetic, he is learning a science that is consistent and interrelated in all of its parts. Knowing and understanding one thing enables the pupil, if some one will suggest the possibility to him, to make an intelligent attack upon the next process that must be learned. The answer is that if the teacher and the book would rely upon the internal consistency of the subject — the science of number — their explanations, rather the explanations they lead the pupil to make for himself, would be bound to be consistent.

The true criticism of the common type of explanation is that it comes from without the pupil's knowledge and experience in number — from the teacher or book — and not from within the system of ideas, called the science of number, that ought to be developing in the pupil's mind. There is some truth in the statement that when a pupil needs to have a thing explained, he is not helped by an explanation. Instead of explaining, the teacher and the book should endeavor to assist the pupil to explain the new steps he confronts more and more to himself and thus to rely more and more upon himself.

X. The Growth of General Ideas

Arithmetic is peculiarly adapted for such an endeavor. The *idea of ten* and the *idea of position*, for example, are two core ideas that run through it from beginning to end. Even

a glimmering of these ideas at the beginning helps the pupil
to recognize and rely upon them in the adding and subtracting of two-place numbers. 'Carrying' tens in addition,
subtraction, and multiplication, and division by two-place
numbers give opportunity for employing the ideas. At
every step, to and throughout decimals and percentage,
these same ideas continue to appear. Every step may provide the occasion both of illustrating and extending these
ideas in the pupil's mind, and of giving him an opportunity
to use what little he may previously have learned of them
as an aid in his attack upon new processes to be learned —
processes that at first may seem new, but that he may
quickly find to be very much like those he is familiar with.

Related to the ideas of ten and position — really a part
of them — are the ideas of *size* and of *number* (whether of
parts or of groups). Although these may be most evident
in fractions, they may be understood the better if one can
discover them running through the whole of arithmetic.
And fundamental to the whole of arithmetic are the ideas
of *combination of unequal and equal groups* in addition and
multiplication, respectively, and of *separation into unequal
and equal groups* in subtraction and division, respectively.

The various general ideas that may thus develop are called
by different names and may be distinguished as slightly different, each from the other. On the other hand, they all
are closely interrelated, and they are in reality the same
general idea of grouping by tens seen from different angles.
A glimmering of these ideas, or of the fundamental idea of
the group of ten, may be had from the beginning. Every
stage of the work may give the pupil increasing opportunity
to extend them and to use them in making clear what may
seem as new. They may serve to unify what otherwise is a
thousand-and-one separate things to be remembered. They
may help the pupil to develop a growing feeling of familiarity with what he is learning and with what is set before
him to learn, and a growing feeling of confidence and cer-

tainty in his methods of attack upon the new things he has
to learn. The constant recurrence of this idea or that —
the idea of ten, let us say — gives a feeling of familiarity
and confidence and certainty that is worth far more than
any mere skill the pupil may attain or any satisfaction he
may secure by obtaining correct answers. What little of
these central ideas of arithmetic even the dullest pupil may
grasp is just so much aid in making him into an independent
thinker. Once a pupil grasps a meaning or develops an idea,
he may be expected to gain an insight into number relations
independently of the class activities. The meaning or the
idea is an inner drive that stimulates the pupil and gives
him power to think for himself. Meanings and ideas are
dynamic facts of experience. Moreover, they shed light
back upon the experiences from which they grew and thus
give larger meanings to these experiences.

XI. Developing a Method of Attack

The importance of developing general ideas in arithmetic
may be illustrated in another way. In the study of fractions, the pupil encounters what we have termed the "three
kinds of problems." He meets the situation that requires
him to find the part of a number; a second situation that
requires him to find what part one number is of another
number; and a third situation that requires him to find a
number when a part of it is given. In decimals, the pupil
meets the same three kinds of situations; again in percentage, he meets the same three kinds. If no attempt is made
to have the pupil make comparisons, he may remember the
situations (if he does succeed in holding them all in mind)
as "nine kinds of problems." On the other hand, if comparisons and relations are emphasized from the beginning,
he will come to understand them as the "three kinds of problems"; and moreover he will understand their relations
and distinctions. Studying the "three kinds of problems"
in fractions helps in the further study of the same three

kinds in decimals and still more in their study later in percentage. As the pupil moves from one chapter in his arithmetic to the next, he is aided in handling the new chapter on a higher level of understanding by the use of what he learned about the same situations in the preceding chapter. He approaches the study of the new chapter with some ideas about the new chapter already formed and ready for use. A general method of attack is thus gradually developed.

Moreover, in the later stages of arithmetic, the pupil is required to study what are called the 'applications of percentage': interest, savings, investments, gain and loss, cost and selling price, insurance, taxes, etc. Each topic is new and unknown before it is studied. Each is in some degree a separate topic. Each may continue to appear as something entirely new and different. But, if the pupil approaches the study of each topic with an understanding of the "three kinds of problems" and of the relations and distinctions between them, he may be led to view the various apparently different topics, like interest, savings, and investments, each as further illustration of the same "three kinds of problems" he already knows about. Thus, in the study of interest, the pupil will learn about certain business practices previously unknown to him, and, what is more to the point, he will at the same time gain a better understanding of the old and familiar "three kinds of problems." Thus his general ideas will develop along with the gaining of new information, and thus his preparation for the study of succeeding topics will be strengthened. Such a procedure in studying brings into a single, unified scheme of thinking or method of attack what otherwise might easily be a dozen separate, distinct, and unrelated 'applications' of percentage.

Similarly, in the study of weights and measures, each new topic may appear as something new and different to be learned and as presenting some new information to be remembered; or each may be studied as a means of contributing to the pupil's general understanding of how people have proceeded in getting exact ideas of various kinds of things through the development of appropriate kinds of measures. The study of each kind of measurement may contribute its share to the pupil's idea of method of procedure and may serve to bring to clearer consciousness the idea that the thing to do is first to decide upon the unit or standard of measurement and next to apply it. Thus the approach to each new topic will be laid bare by the general ideas of procedure that preceding ones have helped to develop, and thus the learning of each new topic will become a procedure that is intelligent to the pupil because his previous studies have made clear a method of attack.

XII. The Nature of the 'Problem,' Properly Understood

Enough has been said about the purpose of instruction in arithmetic and about the importance of developing general ideas and methods of attack to indicate that the character of the exercise in arithmetic that is called a 'problem' should be revealing instead of obscuring. The purpose of the activities throughout is to help the pupil to understand, to enlighten him, to inform him about systematic ways of dealing with quantitative situations, to lead him to ideas of his own. To this end, processes and situations are demonstrated, analyzed, synthesized, discussed, illustrated. For the sake of illustration the teacher or the book describes an imagined situation, sometimes in complete detail, sometimes only partially, sometimes to its logical conclusion, and sometimes with the conclusion or answer omitted. The teacher and the book are in the habit of calling such an illustration a 'problem,' and the pupil has learned to call it a 'problem.' But it is not a real problem, because, if it is appropriate, it does not leave the pupil in doubt. It rather serves to throw light upon the process, or typical situation, or method of procedure, or idea that is under discussion from a different angle, and to give the pupil a different view of whatever is the central theme. Sometimes, as has been indicated, the teacher or book gives the illustration in complete detail; that is, the 'problem' is 'worked.' This is not to show the pupil 'how to work' the 'problem,' but to leave nothing of the illustration to chance. More frequently, however, the teacher or the book gives only a part of the illustration, leaving the pupil to supply the rest of it; that is, to 'work the problem.' And occasionally, the pupil is permitted to provide from his own experience, either direct or vicarious, the complete illustration. In any case, the 'problem' may serve to illustrate something that is of greater importance than itself; and it may serve with other types of illustrations to make clearer the topic that is being studied. *In sum, the 'problem' in arithmetic is in reality not a problem at all, but a type of illustrative exercise.*

CHAPTER IX

NUMBER AS A SCIENCE VERSUS NUMBER AS A PRACTICAL ART

ARGUMENT

1. The number system is a perfected science notable for its consistency and simplicity.

2. The type of progress exhibited by many pupils in the learning of arithmetic contrasts sharply with the characteristics of the number system.

3. Failures to learn the number system are to be explained by the fact that the system is analyzed for pupils into an aggregate of unrelated parts.

4. Drill has come to be the characteristic procedure in arithmetic. Drill has been mistaken for instruction, and accuracy and speed of performance have crowded out understanding from the list of goals that instruction is intended to seek.

5. The purpose of succeeding chapters is set forth: to describe the pupil's development in number-thinking.

Throughout the discussions of the preceding chapters there is to be noticed the constant intrusion of the contrast between what number-thinking has come to be as a highly perfected science and the accidental methods by which it is frequently taught and learned in the schools. On the one hand, number as a science is systematic and consistent; on the other hand, number as a practical art is often a series of rule-of-thumb procedures. Explicit attention to the contrast may well serve to introduce the discussions of the chapters that are to follow, since they treat of the possibilities of providing systematic guidance to the learning activities of pupils.

I. THE SCIENCE OF NUMBER

Through long ages of experimentation the race has perfected the number system that is in common use today. In the beginning, number ideas were the direct outgrowth of perceptual experiences, and as a consequence were meager in scope and relatively vague and indefinite. As time passed, systematic methods of giving attention to groups were created, and the substitution of these methods for the earlier accidental ones led to number ideas that were substantially exact and definite. These ideas were developed concurrently with the creation and development of number names, and they were made serviceable through the use of number names. In turn, the number names both suggested and made possible newer combinations of ideas that were farther and farther removed from direct experience. More and more, attention was withdrawn from perceptual discrimination and centered upon methods of combination. As a result, involved and unsystematic methods were gradually displaced by simple and systematic methods. The Hindu-Arabic system of notation has gradually displaced all other systems in civilized societies.

The Hindu-Arabic system is a decimal system. All numbers beyond nine are expressed in tens and in powers of ten. The idea of ten is the standard by which all chance groups and arrangements are evaluated. The necessity for expressing all quantities beyond nine in tens and powers of ten gradually impresses upon the mind of the individual the idea of ten as a standard and enforces the decimal arrangement as a method of thinking. The individual who learns the system quickly learns to think in terms of ten and to translate all chance groups and arrangements into tens.

The perfection of the Hindu-Arabic system of notation with its uniform standard for the expression and translation of all groups has made possible the discovery of many relations between numbers that hitherto had not been conceived. Many of these relations society has found to be of service in expressing the complicated phases of personal and business affairs and in thus bringing such affairs within the grasp of the inexperienced. Such relations have taken on the character of systematic methods of attack upon human affairs, changing them from situations involving doubt and uncertainty to situations easily understood and managed. Moreover, these relations have served to open up new sorts of personal and business affairs for the individual to undertake by making the quantitative phases of such affairs easy to understand.

The science of number is one of man's truly marvelous creations. Evolved, at first perhaps, as a tool to be employed by man in keeping account of his possessions, it has developed into a system of thinking whose perfection commands the respect of the most learned. It has become the language of precision, the medium of exact thinking and of concise and explicit statement, and the framework and pattern of modern scientific procedure. Since the time when the Hindu-Arabic numerals came into general use in western Europe less than four centuries ago, there has come to pass the industrial revolution, which has substituted the work of machines for the labor of human hands and exact science for blind trial. The formula, which is an explicit statement of the general laws of combination, has enabled the man of science to organize huge masses of often apparently unrelated phenomena into a single scheme of thinking, and thus to understand relations and to derive ideas that in turn lead to new discoveries and new instruments of human betterment. The achievements of modern science would have been utterly impossible without the science of number.

The science of number finds logical formulation and description in the school subject of arithmetic, which is offered in the elementary school as a means of training the pupil in methods of exact thinking. Through the study of arithmetic the pupil of the public school is introduced to the most fundamental of the sciences and to one of the most outstanding intellectual achievements of the human race.

II. The Failures of Pupils

Whenever the teacher begins to contemplate the beauty and the simplicity of the number system and the comprehensiveness and utility of its methods of procedure, he is brought sharply to a halt by a realization of the widespread and discouraging failures of pupils in the subject of arithmetic. To many pupils, this subject is baffling in the extreme. Instead of being simple and understandable, it often is bewildering and incomprehensible. Instead of helping pupils to gain methods of thinking and modes of attack upon the quantitative situations of life, it often appears as a means of inhibiting thinking and of beclouding quantitative issues. In spite of longer terms, better buildings, better equipment, and presumably better courses of study and better teachers, the subject of arithmetic remains as the rock upon which the hopes and aspirations of teachers and pupils continue to be wrecked. Not only do pupils fail in arithmetic; their failures are cumulative. Year by year pupils continue to fail, and the failures of given pupils become more and more serious. The two chapters immediately preceding have indicated a possible explanation of such failures. They deserve our further attention, however.

III. Unsuccessful Analysis

A century and a quarter ago Pestalozzi was engaged in the task of organizing instruction on the principle of proceeding from the simple to the complex. His plan was to divide and subdivide a subject into its minutest parts, and to teach these 'simple' parts to his pupils one by one. Thus, in reading, his pupils were expected first to learn letters, then syllables, then words, and, finally, phrases and sentences. In writing, his pupils had first to learn to make straight lines, curves, ovals, ellipses, one by one, and, finally, they were expected to combine these various parts of letters into wholes.

We have moved far from the piecemeal type of instruction advocated by Pestalozzi in our teaching of reading and writing. We remain, however, in the Pestalozzian period of meticulous dissection in our teaching of arithmetic. In this, the twentieth, century, our arithmetic is in the main in the early nineteenth-century period of development. This subject has been analyzed for the pupil into a multitude of combinations, processes, formulas, rules, types of problems, etc., and the pupil is taught each in turn as a separate item of experience. Often, when he has completed the course, he knows only those parts that he can still remember, and they all seem to him as separate and unrelated combinations, processes, formulas, rules, and types of problems to be solved. Finally, when his memory for these separate items fails him, he has nothing left to carry into his adult world but the remembrances of a series of meaningless, uninteresting, and unpleasant experiences that his classes in arithmetic seem to have provided for him.

Successful teaching in those subjects in which successful results are evident, and the success of some pupils in gaining an understanding of arithmetic as a unified system of ideas and modes of attack often in spite of the efforts of the school, furnish the strongest possible arguments against the time-worn method of artificially breaking a subject into parts and trying to teach the parts piecemeal and without logical and understandable relations. Instead of an artificial analysis, with haphazard methods of trying to take the pupil from parts to wholes — indeed, often of trying merely to teach parts without any relation to wholes — successful procedure is that of proceeding from wholes to parts to related wholes. Analysis is always necessary for study. Synthesis, which may build the parts into a related and understandable unity, is of paramount importance.

IV. The Resort to Drill

The present piecemeal organization of arithmetic leaves the pupil with no ideas of how to proceed except those that he may gain through verbatim memorization of directions and the blind following of formula and rule. There is little left for him to do but to follow the directions set for his guidance, and to practice following them until they stick in his memory. Moreover, there is little left for the teacher to undertake but to conduct the practice periods as effectively and as expeditiously as possible. Thus, drill has come to be the type of classroom procedure that is peculiar to, and characteristic of, arithmetic. Drill has come to assume an importance far in excess of its merits.

The importance of drill, the actual as well as the assumed, has led many writers and teachers to confuse drill with instruction, instead of distinguishing between the two, and to organize their teaching procedures as drill procedures. As a consequence, many pupils have failed to *comprehend* the combinations and processes they have mechanized through practice, even though they have mechanized the correct procedures; and many other pupils have mechanized roundabout and ineffectual procedures that extra amounts of drill have failed to correct.

Reasonable accuracy and reasonable speed, the standards for which have been set through numerous studies, are the proper goals of drill. But because drill has been confused with instruction, accuracy and speed are set down as the real goals of the school course in arithmetic by the textbooks and teachers' manuals in common use. When instruction is distinguished from drill, however, and kept in mind as the first step in classroom procedure, the pupil's understanding of processes becomes the primary goal of the school course, to which may be added the two goals already named. Arithmetic now becomes what the race has perfected and passed along and what society obligates the school to develop;

namely, a system of ideas, not merely a set of skills. The pupil's progress must be measured in terms of what he understands, not in terms of accuracy and speed. The modern world provides machines that can be used for computation, but none with the power of decision. Decision is a human activity, and the school may develop it.

V. The Task of the Next Chapters

The discussions to this point have indicated what it is that the child must learn in the school course in arithmetic, and have suggested certain methods of attack that he must be led to avoid and certain other methods of attack that have been successful in the development of number-thinking. The next chapters will undertake the task of describing the child's development in number. They will undertake to point out in some detail (1) how the child may develop number ideas through the systematic study of groups; (2) how his systematic studies may be directed, how the results he gains may be retained, and how his thinking may be gradually relieved from studies on lower levels and these be available for studies on higher levels by the oral and written language of number; (3) how he may be led to derive and develop general ideas of arrangement as outgrowths of his systematic studies; (4) how he may be led to the development of general principles of performance as outgrowths of the activity of giving attention to the similar procedure, the common element, that is appropriate in dealing with a variety of related situations; and (5) how his development of general ideas, general principles, and general methods of attack may be fostered by the school procedures that raise them to the level of consciousness from the very beginnings of his school course. In short, since preceding chapters have described the features of arithmetic to which pupils must give attention in order to learn, it now becomes the task of succeeding chapters to detail the step-by-step procedures that pupils must follow in learning.

CHAPTER X

THE STUDY OF GROUPS

Argument

1. The idea of number is the idea of the group. It is developed and clarified through the study of groups. Its nature is determined by the kind of study pursued, whether haphazard or systematic, incidental or planned.

2. The chapter describes the following methods of studying groups to ten:

    (a) Counting groups;

    (b) Comparing groups;

    (c) Taking groups apart and putting the parts together;

    (d) Emphasizing equal groups.

3. The general procedure suggested is as follows:

    (a) Teach the method of study;

    (b) See that pupils use the method.

4. Learning to count includes

    (a) Learning the number names in serial order;

    (b) Learning to discriminate objects;

    (c) Learning to use the number names as a means of discrimination;

    (d) Learning to give attention to the group as a whole.

5. The comparison of two groups involves at the outset: (a) counting both groups, (b) matching the two groups one-to-one, (c) counting the excess of one over the other. Later, the process may be chiefly that of counting the excess.

6. The language to be learned and used, both the oral and the written, is to express the comparisons the pupils make and understand. The language is not a substitute for ideas.

7. When groups are studied through (a) analysis and (b) synthesis, the pupils are to determine the answers by means of counting. The purpose is to enlarge ideas of groups. Learn-

ing the subtractions and additions that are related to the ideas
is a resultant of the study.

8. The language of arrangement, the oral and written
algorisms, is to be introduced as a means of expressing ideas
already gained.

9. The steps of progress in the study of groups through
analysis and synthesis are thus described: the pupils study
the arrangement of objects in a group

    (a) when the teacher makes the arrangement;
    (b) when the pupils make the arrangement;
    (c) when the pupils think the arrangement;
    (d) when the pupils think the arrangement with objects
        present only in imagination;
    (e) when the pupils think the arrangement with no objects
        present.

(The fourth and fifth steps are discussed in the next chapter.)

10. The same steps should be followed in the arrangement
of a group into smaller equal groups (division) and the combination of the smaller equal groups into the original one
(multiplication).

Foregoing chapters have made clear the points (1) that
the idea of number is the idea of the group, and (2) that
number ideas are developed by, and result from, the study
of groups. They have indicated that the concept of the
group, as distinguished from that of the objects that compose it — of their kind, size, shape, color, and so forth — is
the concept of number. The only importance of the objects
in the group, insofar as the idea of number may be concerned, is that they make the group what it is. The idea of
number is not concerned with objects; it deals only with
their arrangement. If there is one thing that stands out
more clearly than another in a review of the gropings of the
primitive mind after the idea of number, and of the subsequent development of number, it is that objects do not of
themselves furnish the idea, but that it grows only with the
systematic study of groups.

I. INCIDENTAL VERSUS SYSTEMATIC STUDY

The study of groups may be incidental, haphazard, and of the sort that accompanies one's ordinary, everyday experiences with groups of objects, or it may be an orderly, systematic study.   Both types of study lead to the development of number ideas — the former, to ideas that are inexact, vague, and indefinite; the latter, to ideas that are exact, clear, and definite.   Let us illustrate.

In each circle, numbered 1 and 2, is a group of objects. One glance at the objects in Circle 1 is sufficient to discover

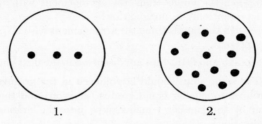

1.   2.

and to be certain of the fact that there are three objects in the group.   One glance at the objects in Circle 2 is sufficient to discover that there are several objects in the group.   Let the adult merely look at the second group of objects, focus his eyes upon first one, then another object, study the group from various angles, and all the conclusion he can draw is that the number is 'more' than the first group — 'several,' 'quite a few,' 'a lot,' 'many.'   He cannot tell exactly how many unless he takes the time to deal with the group systematically.   To determine exactly the number in the second group — that is, to become fully acquainted with the group — one must count (or deal with the group in some other systematic way).   Perhaps he can recognize a group of three, a group of four, and a group of five, and think the three groups together.   Whatever he does, he realizes that it takes much more systematic effort to apprehend a large group than it takes to apprehend a small one.

The young child, when he sees the two groups, forms ideas of them. He may, or he may not, know that there are three objects in Circle 1. His vague ideas of the numbers are expressed by such terms as 'not very many' or 'whole lot.' His ideas of the groups do not improve by handling them, dealing with them, or contemplating them haphazardly and unsystematically. His unsystematic comparisons will produce no more definite ideas than 'not as many,' 'more,' etc. The child must be trained in such systematic methods of viewing groups as the adult has learned to employ, before he can enlarge and perfect his ideas.

II. The Idea of the Group

The group of objects in Circle 1 can be exactly determined by the adult at a single glance, because he is able to give his attention at one and the same time to the whole group and to each of the objects that compose it. Since a group is determined by the objects that compose it, all the objects must be attended to. Moreover, all the objects, not merely as individuals, but as a group, must be attended to. The adult is not able at a glance to determine exactly the group in Circle 2; there are too many objects for him to attend to at once. He must take the time to give his attention, in one manner or another, to all the objects, and in addition, he must be equipped with the means of retaining what he learns about all the objects when he returns to a contemplation of the group as a whole. Knowledge of the group thus requires a double attention both to the group and to the members that compose it, and the ability to unite, or relate, the results of the double attention.

The difference between the idea of the group that the young child is able to form and the idea that the adult may gain cannot be explained by any difference in ability either to see or to examine the objects. Both can look at the objects and both can pay attention to the whole group. If there is any difference in the amount of sensory experience gained by a contemplation of the objects of a group, this difference is perhaps in favor of the young child. Experience with the group is, of course, necessary if one is to determine the number. But mere experience is not productive of the number idea as the adult knows and uses it. The experience one gains from his contemplation of the group must be organized experience. The method of organizing experience is the possession of the adult. The young child must be brought into possession of the adult's method if he is to be expected to gain number ideas which have the qualities of definiteness and exactness.

III. Methods of Studying Groups

It has been pointed out that, if the adult cannot at once give full attention both to the group as a whole and to each and every member of it, he carries through the double process piecemeal and step by step. He either counts — attends to each member one by one, and finally all together — or breaks down the whole group into smaller groups and then thinks the smaller groups together. His method of study is the combined method of analysis and synthesis; in one way or another, he takes the group apart, then puts it together. The fact that the double process may be entirely a matter of thought does not make it any the less an actual process.

Groups are studied just like anything else. To get an idea of a machine, of a situation, of a problem, one must first break it down into its component parts and then put the parts together in their proper relations. One may learn about a clock, for example, just by looking at the clock as a whole. One may learn much more about it, about what makes it run, about its reliability as a timepiece, and so on, if he can learn how to take it apart properly — that is, systematically and in an orderly way — and finally, how to put all the parts back together systematically and in an orderly way.

This chapter will mention certain methods of studying

groups that are pursued to some extent in the early grades. Each method of study is a method of giving attention both to the whole group and to the parts which compose it. Each leads to an enlarging and clarifying of children's number ideas.

Common observation of teaching practice and inferences from certain scientific studies[1] indicate that the methods of studying groups that are pursued in the primary grades are usually hurried and incidental, and that they are successful only to the extent that they are orderly and systematic. Brownell has accumulated a mass of evidence bearing upon the fact that children's difficulties in arithmetic result from a too-hurried transition from what he calls 'concrete number' to 'abstract number.' Judd's studies of counting reveal the process as an involved and systematic one, and indicate that sooner or later it must be learned in an orderly and systematic way.

The following methods of studying groups will be discussed: (1) counting groups, (2) comparing groups, (3) taking groups apart and putting the parts together, and (4) emphasizing equal groups.

1. Studying Groups by Counting

a. Should Counting be Neglected?   It is frequently argued in the manuals on the teaching of arithmetic that the school should teach the pupil to neglect counting. Counting is frequently mentioned as one of the common errors made by children in the operations of the fundamentals.[2]   There is no reason to believe, however, that children resort to count-

[1] W. A. Brownell. *The Development of Children's Number Ideas in the Primary Grades.* (Department of Education, The University of Chicago, Chicago, 1928.)

C. H. Judd. *Psychological Analysis of the Fundamentals of Arithmetic.* (Department of Education, The University of Chicago, Chicago, 1927.)

[2] G. T. Buswell. *Diagnostic Studies in Arithmetic.* (Department of Education, The University of Chicago, Chicago, 1926.)

ing when they add because they have had *too much* training in counting. They count because they have not learned better methods of adding. It will be pointed out in later pages that addition is a step in advance of counting, and that an understanding of the process of addition is based upon an understanding of processes that are simpler. One should not argue that the child should learn to walk without practice in crawling. The fact that short steps must be learned before longer steps can be taken does not argue that the longer steps should not be thoroughly mastered, nor does the importance of the longer steps argue for a neglect in the training in the shorter ones.

Our first-grade work in number, accordingly, is begun with some training to count and with practice in counting.

b. The Process of Counting. Beginners make mistakes in counting. Four of them may be cited.

1. Sometimes the number name is forgotten, or the names are used in the wrong order. The child counts, *one, two, three, four, five, six, eight, nine, ten, twelve, eleven.*

2. Sometimes the child fails to recognize the point where he has looked and so becomes confused. The adult often makes this error, especially when the objects are very similar or very close together. The failure here is one of discrimination.

3. Sometimes the number names and the discriminated objects are not properly matched. The eye runs ahead of the voice, or lags behind, and confusion results. When one counts the cars in a procession, for example, he does not merely say the number names, nor does he merely look at, or point to, or nod to, each individual car. He must do both, and he must do both at once. If he is careless in distinguishing the cars, he does not know when to cease giving the number names. If he distinguishes each car, but becomes mixed in giving the names, he counts inaccurately. Giving the number name and discriminating the individual car to which the given name belongs must be done together.

4. Sometimes the individual object is mistaken for the group. The child counts the ten fingers, stopping on the thumb of one hand. When asked, "how many?" (holding up and pointing to the thumb), he says, "*ten.*" He does not recognize that the name *ten* belongs to the tenth object counted only when it is thought of as a member of a group that includes all the objects previously counted.

When one counts, he does not study the qualities of the objects counted; he determines their *quantity.* To do this, he at once thinks all the objects counted as belonging together in a group and distinguishes each one from every other. The double act of grouping and discrimination is accomplished through an orderly and systematic reaction on the part of the individual. He resorts to pointing, or to nodding the head, as a means of discrimination, and he applies the number-name series that serves both to record his discrimination of each object in turn and to place it in a group with the objects previously counted.

c. Training in Counting. This process includes:

1. Training in the orderly use of the number names. The names must be learned in a series.

2. Training in the discrimination of objects counted.

3. Training in relating the number names and the discriminated objects; that is, practice in giving to each object in turn the number name that comes in orderly sequence.

4. Training in grouping; that is, practice in giving attention to the group as a whole as well as unit by unit.

Real practice in counting is the response to a definite question relating to quantity that either arises out of one's experience or is asked by another. Frequently, when the teacher directs, "count the books," the pupil will respond merely by giving the number names without much effort at discrimination, or, when he does discriminate with care, he arrives at the answer without giving attention to the *meaning of the answer.* The meaning of the answer, when one counts, is wrapped up in one's attention to all the objects counted — thought of together — in a group. In order to bring out for the child's attention the meaning of the answer when he counts, the teacher must so direct the pupil that he will be required to give attention to *each* object and *all* the objects together in a group. "Count the books" merely tells the child to do a thing that can be outwardly observed. "*How many* books are on the table?" is a question that only counting, with all that it implies, will answer. It is the type of direction that requires the fixing of attention upon a particular group. Do not direct the pupil to *count*, but give him the *question* that demands counting as a means of arriving at the answer.

d. Preliminary Testing. From one-fifth to one-third of the pupils at the beginning of the school year will be unable to give the number names to ten with complete accuracy and assurance. Most pupils will be able to give the names to ten, some far beyond ten. When they count objects, however, they often pay slight attention to the objects and as a consequence make errors of the second and third types named above. The teacher should not assume that the mere ability to give the number names in serial order is the ability to count.

The teacher's first task is to *test each pupil's ability to count.* This testing should be very informal. It may proceed as follows: Ask the children to count as far as they can. Ask them to count the pupils in a row, the books on the table, the chairs at the front of the room, the windows, etc.

As a guide to the types of teaching needed by individual pupils and by the class as a whole, *the abilities and difficulties should be listed.* These should be noted at the time when the pupils are tested, and tabulated in convenient form, as indicated at the top of page 169.

e. Counting to Ten. The preliminary activities of testing the abilities of the pupils give practice in counting to ten to those pupils who already have this ability and some training to the others who have difficulty. The weaker ones learn

Pupil's Name	Can Count Accurately	Gets Number Names Confused	Does Not Know Names	Fails to Discriminate	Needs Training	Needs Practice
John	to 10	10 to 15	15 to 20	No	10 to 20	1 to 10
Susan	to 15	No	No	Sometimes 10 to 20	15 to 20	10 to 20
Henry	to 6	6 to 12	12 to 20	6 to 10	1 to 20	1 to 10

through listening to the others, and they all get practice in repeating the number names in serial order. But since the training and the practice are incidental to the testing, it will be necessary to organize specific training and practice exercises in counting to ten. These the teacher may conduct as part of the exercises in counting to twenty.

f. Counting to Twenty. Following the preliminary exercises of the first few days, the work should proceed immediately to the extension of the pupil's abilities. Since most of the pupils can count to ten, at least insofar as saying the number names is concerned, they should be led at once to an exercise that is a little new and different — namely, counting to twenty. At the same time the pupils should be led to perfect their abilities to count, first to ten, then to twenty.

Be sure the number names are learned. The children learn these quickly through imitation and practice. Each child listens to the others repeating the number names and thus learns the names and their serial order. Individual children and the class as a whole are called upon to correct and to assist those who are inclined to get the names confused.

Saying the names should not be considered counting, merely preparation for counting. The names are needed in order to count, and so the names must be taught first. When the pupils can give the names in order, the pupils should be led to apply the names in counting. Mere practice in saying the names will help to fix them. Actual counting serves also to fix the names; hence counting should begin as soon as the names are learned. Indeed, the slower children can learn the names they do not know by listening to and imitating the actual counting of the other children.

Teach discrimination. The teacher must make sure that the children discriminate accurately the objects counted. Actually touching each object is a very positive means of discrimination. Pointing to the objects or nodding the head at the objects, one after the other, are common means. Giving the number name to the object, in counting it, assists to fix the discrimination as soon as it is made. The point for the teacher to keep in mind is that the child must *see* each object in the group, both as a member of the group and as distinct and separate from the rest of the group.

Give practice in counting. It should be borne in mind that the three types of training in counting that have been mentioned are received in coördination, and not necessarily one after the other. Practice in counting helps to fix the number names, gives practice in discrimination, trains in relating the names to the objects, and develops the idea that the name given to each object counted denotes the size of the group up to and including it. The idea of the group comes not through *telling* the pupil about it, but through the child's own practice in reacting to the group in a systematic way; that is, through *actual counting.*

g. Counting Exercises. In conducting the counting exercises, let the children count any set of objects in the room, pupils, desks, chairs, tables, doors, windows, erasers, blackboards, books, pencils, marks on the boards, etc. Let the children count in concert and individually, the better pupils helping the weaker ones at points of difficulty. Let the children count aloud, then quietly to themselves. When the children have counted a set of objects *to themselves*, if all give the right answer, have them count a larger group. If some give incorrect answers, have these children count aloud, one after the other, until the correct count is made.

When a child gives an incorrect answer, have him count aloud, pointing as he counts, to determine wherein he is at error. If he fails in giving the number names correctly, give him special help until he gets the names in order. If he has difficulty in discriminating, let him touch each object, counting slowly as each object is touched. Then have him count as he points, and later as he nods his head at the objects. Be sure that the practice exercises are not monopolized by the bright children. Give the slower children the larger share of the opportunities to count, allowing the brighter ones to count *to themselves* and to check the answers of the others.

Let the children count the marks, or dots, or circles, on one blackboard. "*How many?*" Let them count the marks on another blackboard. "*How many?*" Likewise, the marks on a third blackboard. "*How many?*" "Which board has the *most* marks?" "Are there *more* on this board or on that one?" Other words must be suggested frequently by the teacher and used constantly by the pupils until they become familiar, such as, *same, less, least*, etc.

h. Learning to Read and Write the Number Symbols. Since progress in arithmetic depends to such a large extent upon facility in the recognition and use of the language of number (both oral and written), the pupils of the first grade must from the very beginning develop an acquaintance with the number symbols.

As soon as the children have made a start in their counting exercises, introduce the symbols, 1 to 9 and 10 to 20, in connection with the number names. When the children have counted a group, of *eight*, let us say, write the symbol, 8; and so on until all the symbols have been written. Do not present a symbol, however, until the children have done something or had an experience — counting, for example — that provides a meaning to go with the symbol. Bear the following points in mind:

1. Stress the symbols 1 to 9, since it is upon the making of these symbols that the pupils must have immediate practice.

2. Introduce the symbols 10 to 20 incidentally as the occasion for writing these upon the board requires. The pupils may go as far as they are able in writing these at the beginning. However, practice in recognizing and writing these is to greater effect in connection with the teaching of their significance, as indicated in a later chapter.

3. Do not introduce the zero, 0, as such at this time. Practice in writing it may be given in connection with the writing of 10 and 20.

4. Introduce the symbols out of their serial order. Guard against the chance of suggesting the idea that 5 stands for the fifth object counted, 6 for the sixth object, and so on. As the pupils apprehend a group of six objects through counting them, write the 6 *to stand for the group*.

5. Give practice in recognizing the symbols. Give such directions: "Point to —— boys" (writing the symbol desired upon the board). "Count —— books" (writing the symbol desired), etc.

6. Give practice in writing the symbols. Such practice should be governed by the rules that apply to practice in handwriting. Make your own symbols large and plain. Show exactly how each symbol is made, in order that no pupil will begin by making the symbol backwards. Let the pupils make the symbols freely in the air, next on the board, and finally upon their papers. Make special efforts to get pupils to improve their writing by calling attention to possible improvements, such as making the last movement of the 2 a straight line and not curved under like the 3; the proper direction and right size of the loop of the 6; the right direction of the movements in making the 7, so there will be no tendency to make it backwards.

i. Summary. When one counts a group of objects, he engages in a systematic study of the group. He gives his attention to each object, one by one. He applies to each a name. The name serves the double purpose, first of setting the object off by itself as a separate entity from all the others, and second, of enabling one to think of it in connection with the ones previously named in the counting and with the ones that will be attended to next in the counting. The name serves both to set off and to combine, so that when one names the last object in the group, he has given it sufficient individual attention and has included it with all the rest to make the group. Counting enables one to give attention to all the members of the group and to the group as a whole. It leads to a definite idea of the group, which is an idea of number. By means of counting the pupil builds up ideas of the numbers.

2. Studying Groups by Comparing Them

a. The Results of Counting. The counting activities in which the children have been engaged have called their attention both to groups of objects and to the individual units of which each group is composed. In the process of counting a group of objects, the children were required to pay attention to the objects one by one, and finally to think of all the objects as being together in a group. The necessity of saying the number names in serial order in connection with the careful discrimination of the objects being counted called attention to the units that composed the group; the necessity of answering the question — "how many?" — centered attention upon the group as a whole. Thus, by counting eight objects, for example, referring to the whole group as *eight*, and recognizing and writing the symbol, 8, to stand for their answer to the question — "how many?" — the children have come to some realization of the meaning of *eight* and to some confidence in their ability to use *eight* with understanding. Their practice in counting has led them, moreover, to a reasonable proficiency in the use of counting to find out "how many?" Having learned to count, the children are now ready to *use* counting in number activities of a higher order than mere counting.

b. Developing and Enlarging the Children's Ideas of Number.

Before very long the children will be required to use each of the number ideas up to nine, in combination with the others, in what we call the combinations of addition, subtraction, multiplication, and division. They will be expected to be intelligent in their use of the number ideas in combination, to understand what they do when they add, subtract, and so on, and to have confidence in their ability to carry through the combinations successfully.

In order to use ideas with confidence, certainty, and understanding, a person needs to have the ideas fairly well developed in his mind. In the use of an idea in a given circumstance, one does not need to use all that he knows about it; he may need to use only one part or one phase of the idea. But the more he knows about the idea, the more certain he is in the use that he has to make. If the idea is very familiar, he can use it in this circumstance or that one, with perfect confidence in himself and with complete understanding of what he is trying to do.

Now, as a result of their counting activities, the children know something of the number ideas to *nine* or *ten*. They have started in their thinking the development of the ideas. They know the serial order of the numbers, and that is knowing a lot for beginners. They realize that *eight*, for example, is more than all that go before *eight*, and less than all that follow. They may know *eight* pretty well in its relation to *seven* and *nine*, but they are very vague with respect to the relations of *eight* and the other number ideas. And there is much about the idea *eight* with respect to the various groups that may compose it that they do not yet know. They may use *eight* with perfect confidence in counting, but they would be at a loss how to use *eight* in combination with other ideas. The idea of *eight* is only partly developed. It must now be clarified, and developed, and enlarged. By the use of the process of counting, the children need now, therefore, to be led to a further development of their number ideas.

In a very thorough study of the development of children's

number ideas, Brownell [3] has reached the conclusions that mere counting does not prepare for the study of the combinations, but that further attention must be given to the development of the number ideas if children are to be expected to employ them intelligently. He points out that counting is only one of the means that may be employed for the development of the number ideas, and that other means must be used if children are not to be handicapped in their later work.

In this and the two sections that follow suggestions will be made for directing pupils to a further study of groups of objects from one to nine.[4] Through counting the children have started to develop number ideas, because counting called their attention to groups. It will be expected that the children will now proceed to enlarge their number ideas through a further and more elaborate study of groups.

   c. *Developing Number Ideas by the Use of Groups of Objects.* In the study of groups, objects will have to be used for the purpose of demonstration. The teacher should be primarily interested in getting the pupils to study groups rather than objects. The objects will be presented, to be sure, but not for the purpose of calling attention to the objects themselves or to any of the concrete characteristics they possess, rather for the sake of directing attention to the ways the objects may be grouped. How the objects are arranged, or may be arranged, is what the pupils should be led to study. Since it is not possible in the beginning to call attention to grouping by means they will later learn, but do not now know, objects in various groups will be presented for study.

The objects need to be large enough to be easily seen and small enough to be easily handled. They ought not to be unusually attractive. Since number does not deal with ob-

---

[3] Brownell, *op. cit.*

[4] The same suggestions apply also to the study of a *group of ten.* But because the group of ten has a special significance, discussion of the ways it may be studied is reserved for a later chapter.

jects, but with the grouping or arrangement of objects, nothing should be introduced that will call attention away from the essential thing, which is their grouping, or arrangement. Therefore, the less attraction the objects have, the better suited they are to the purpose in using them here.

    d. Developing Number Ideas by Comparing Groups of Objects. Comparison is an important means of developing and clarifying the children's ideas about the sizes of groups. Thinking of one group in comparison with another serves to make both more understandable and usable. What is already known about each of the two helps to extend knowledge of the other. Through comparison the number ideas, which are already partially developed through attention to groups in counting, are seen in clearer perspective and from newer points of view. Through comparison the children are enabled to organize their experiences somewhat differently from what they otherwise would, and thus to enlarge their ideas through the newer form of reacting to their experiences.

    In the activities of comparing groups the children are required to give attention to two groups of objects, and thus to the two ideas that attach to the two groups, at once. They cannot give exclusive attention either to the one group or to the other. Attention must move from the one to the other, and back again; rather, attention must fix upon the relation between the two until the relation between the two has been definitely established. A new form of consciousness is developed that is not the same as the consciousness of either the one group or the other under comparison. This new relational form of consciousness is in a sense a new idea; but an idea nevertheless that intimately relates to the ideas that already belong to the two groups. In another sense the new idea of relation becomes a part of, and adds to, the ideas already in mind. Through comparison the children develop both a new idea and a connecting link between ideas that are already partially developed.

e. Developing Number Ideas by Matching Objects. The comparison of groups through a matching of the objects of one group with the objects of the other is not a new or a difficult experience for the children. When the oranges are passed at a party and each child takes one, but some are left in the dish, the children are at once aware that there are more oranges than there are children. Should it happen, when the oranges are passed, that there are not enough to go round, the inequality of the two groups is quickly apparent — especially to the children who have been left out in the distribution! When the children are called to their recitation chairs around the teacher, and each child takes a chair, the unoccupied chairs may be quickly noted. Or if, when all the children are seated and there are no extra chairs, the equality of the group of chairs and the group of children is apparent to any child who takes notice.

The type of comparison thus illustrated is known as 'one-to-one correspondence.' For each chair there is a child, for example, and for each child there is a chair. The chairs and children correspond, at least up to a certain point. Each chair represents a unit, and each child represents a unit. The correspondence between a unit of the one and a unit of the other, and the equality (or inequality) between the groups is easily noted.

f. Directing the Comparisons. It is to be understood that, while the teacher is to suggest and partially direct the comparisons that are to be made, the mental activities of making the actual comparisons are to be the children's own. The mental activity of comparing groups, as the teacher may suggest, may seem a little new and strange at first. It is not to be hurried. The teacher may suggest in a comparison of two groups a pairing of the units of one group with the units of the other until one group is exhausted, and may indicate by the proper question how the pupils may note the number in the larger group that is left unpaired. The process may be illustrated as follows:

Illustrative Lessons

1

The teacher indicates a row of pupils sitting at their desks, and asks, "How many children are in this row?" The children count, and answer (seven, let us say).

The teacher holds up five pencils, and asks, "How many pencils have I?" The children count, and answer.

The teacher asks, "Are there more children than pencils?" and, when the children have answered, asks, "How many more?" If the children can all answer, the teacher may summarize, as indicated later. If the children hesitate, the exercise may proceed, as follows:

The teacher says: "There are seven children in this row. I have five pencils. I will pass the pencils to the children." She gives each child a pencil until the pencils are gone. "How many of the children have no pencils?" The pupils can answer.

The exercise is now summarized. The teacher inquires, "How many children?" (Seven) "How many pencils?" (Five) "How many more children than pencils?" (Two) "Which is more, seven or five?" "How much more?" Finally, the teacher provides the statements, if the pupils do not already know how to give them: "Seven is two more than five," and "Five is two less than seven."

2

Five girls may be lined up in a row at the front of the room and three boys in a row close to them. Ask, "How many girls?" "How many boys?" "How many more girls than boys?" The teacher may suggest the pairing of the three boys with three of the girls, and when they have paired, indicate the two girls left unpaired. If the pupils need the demonstration of actual pairing, it may be carried out; if they can give their answers without it, it does not need to be used.

When it is clear to all the children that there are two more girls than boys, the exercise is to be summarized into the statements, "Five is two more than three," and "Three is two less than five." Likewise, books and pencils may be used to demonstrate one-to-one correspondence. In each book a pencil may be put, and the resulting inequality may be readily observed.

3

Eight dots may be made with white chalk and five dots with red chalk, thus:

● ● ● ● ● ● ●

● ● ● ●

The usual questions, "How many white dots?" "How many red dots?" can be answered by the children, because they can count.

The usual questions about "Which is the more?" "Which is the less?" "How many more?" "How many less?" are now given, and answered. Finally, the exercise is summarized, as indicated above.

Many other comparisons of groups of objects up to nine or ten with other groups up to nine or ten may be made in ways similar to these three illustrations. The teacher may suggest pairing, and in many cases cause the pairing to be made, to help those pupils who have to hesitate with their answers. When, however, the pupils can give their answers readily without such pairing, they should be permitted to do so. The point to be kept in mind is that the pupils must be permitted to do their own comparing. It is upon their own activities alone that a development of their ideas depends. The question, "How many more?" is usually sufficient to direct attention to the relation between two groups.

g. The Oral Language of Comparison. Comparison requires a language of its own. Such terms as *more* and *less, larger* and *smaller, longer* and *shorter, older* and *younger, farther* and *nearer,* and the like must be used both to direct the pupils' comparisons and to describe the comparisons after they have been made. In the earlier activities of counting, some of these terms have been used, and they are not entirely unfamiliar to children when they first enter school.

In calling attention to two groups of objects and directing the comparison of them, many questions and answers are used. At the close of a comparison, when the idea of relative sizes is perfectly clear to the children, the teacher provides the language that summarizes the idea of relation into a concise statement — "Five is two more than three," for example. As the work progresses, the children become able to do their own summarizing.

The value of the concise summary statement is due to the fact that it serves to hold in thought a comparison that has been very elaborate and time-consuming in the making. It helps the children to keep in mind what has just been done, and it serves later as a means of making a quick review.

It needs to be emphasized that such summary statements do not precede the thinking and the doing of a comparison. They follow. The idea of comparison must be developed first. Then, and only then, will the summary statement be of value.

Another point to be emphasized is that the summary statement, such as "Five is two more than three," is not given to be memorized at once. The bare statement can be memorized with ease without the children realizing what it is intended to describe. They can memorize words and neglect ideas. In time, as the ideas develop, however, the statements naturally will be memorized. Let meanings be insisted upon, and the memorizing will eventually take care of itself.

h. *The Written Language of Comparison.* Since the pupils are to learn gradually to depend upon the written language of number to aid them in their thinking, this language should be gradually introduced. Like the oral language, it is not, however, to be introduced in the beginning. It needs to follow the idea, because it should stand in the children's thinking as a way of expressing an idea already possessed by them.

At first the written form should be introduced as a substitute for the oral question. Finally, it may be understood as the written statement of a comparison after that has been thought out and understood.

As already mentioned, when inquiring about the two groups of dots on the board, the teacher may write, once the questions are asked and the answers are given. The teacher asks, "How many white dots?" and when the children answer, she says, "I will write the sign, or figure, to show eight. The teacher asks, "How many red dots?" and when the children answer, she says, "I will write the sign, or figure, to show five." She now has the figures written thus: $\begin{smallmatrix}8\\5\end{smallmatrix}$. She points out that the sign for the smaller group is written underneath.

The next question is, "Eight is how many more than five?" She writes the minus sign (−) beside the 5, and explains that this asks, "How many more?" when she asks about eight. She points out that a line is drawn so that the answer can be written underneath: $\begin{smallmatrix}8\\-\,5\end{smallmatrix}$.

Or, the question may be, "Five is how many less than eight?" In like manner the minus sign is written beside the 5, and is here explained as asking, "How many less?" when she is asking about five: $\begin{smallmatrix}8\\-\,5\end{smallmatrix}$.

The whole thing can be explained as asking a question without saying it aloud. The signs, $\begin{smallmatrix}8\\-\,5\end{smallmatrix}$, when one points to 8, or thinks of eight, ask "Eight is how many more than five?" When one points to 5, or thinks of five, they ask, "Five is how many less than eight?" When any two figures are written thus: $\begin{smallmatrix}8\\-\,5\end{smallmatrix}$, the question is, "How many more?" or "How many less?"

The pupils now proceed to get the answer. When they find it, the sign for it is written in its proper place, and the whole combination of signs is read as "Eight is three more than five," or "Five is three less than eight."

Illustrative Lessons

1

When the children have gained certainty and assurance in their comparison of number ideas through the actual comparison of groups of objects, they should be led to compare the ideas when they relate to things less tangible than objects. This will be a step in advance of what they have been doing, and the work should be attempted gradually, and never forced. For example, refer to actual situations, such as the following:

1. James is 6 years old. His sister, Lucy, is 9 years old. Who is the older? How much older?

2. Willie spent 10 cents for pencils, and 5 cents for candy. How much more did he spend for pencils?

The experiences of the children will contribute many similar situations that will make comparisons possible.

2

In the later stages of the work, when such questions are asked orally as, "Nine is how much more than five?" and in writing as,
$$\frac{9}{-5},$$
the children may be shown how to resort to finger-counting to arrive at the answer. When comparing five and nine, one assumes that he has counted to five, and then counts beyond five to nine, *on his* fingers, thus: *six, seven, eight, nine;* and notes that he has used *four* of his fingers to complete the count.

Of course, this is a very primitive method of making a comparison, and one that the pupil will need to forsake for better methods; but it is a step in advance of any method yet used, because it enables the pupil to *think* the comparison without objects other than fingers, by using his readily accessible fingers in place of the objects. If he never learns a better method, he will continue to use finger-counting; if and when he shall learn a better method, he will forsake his finger-counting. One need not fear the danger of finger-counting becoming habitual of itself; it becomes habitual only to the degree that no better method is learned. Provision will be made for the learning of better methods. Later, the pupil's thinking will be so short-cut and direct that he will have no need of finger-counting. Let him proceed *now* from the more concrete steps to finger-counting; let him use finger-counting as much as he needs to *now;* let him become proficient in its use *now* to answer the demands of thinking that are made upon him; let him be prepared by this step in advance of his earlier methods of comparison to move ahead to steps that are beyond it.

3

Move ahead from comparisons of the concrete — such as "How many more pencils are there here than books?" — to comparisons that are more exclusively thought comparisons, such as are required by the oral and written questions, "Eight is how many more than five," and $\dfrac{8}{-5}$.

i. Some Cautions to Observe in the Use of Comparisons. First, when a group of comparisons have been made, and the answers have been given and written like this:

$$\frac{\begin{array}{r}8\\-\,5\end{array}}{3}\qquad\frac{\begin{array}{r}9\\-\,7\end{array}}{2}\qquad\frac{\begin{array}{r}7\\-\,3\end{array}}{4}\qquad\frac{\begin{array}{r}5\\-\,3\end{array}}{2}\qquad\frac{\begin{array}{r}6\\-\,2\end{array}}{4}$$

be sure to erase the answers at the conclusion of the exercise. The pupils are not ready for memorizing the oral and written statements; rather, they may try to remember them in place of understanding them. If these oral and written statements are eventually to be used intelligently by the children in place of the ideas for which they stand, the ideas for which they stand must first be thoroughly mastered. The pupils are still beginners; they have as yet mastered nothing. They must be led slowly and gradually to mastery. The mere remembering of oral and written statements is not mastery. When the children reach the point where the ideas have become so familiar and so well understood that there is no need for them to return to the examination of concrete objects in actual groups in order to use them with certainty and intelligence, they will be ready for memorization. Indeed, if memorization is postponed to this point, there will be little need for memorization, because it will have slowly and gradually perfected itself in connection with the many thought activities that have been engaging the attention of the children.

Second, do not strive for completeness or absolute mastery of comparisons before proceeding to the activities that are suggested in the two sections which follow. In connection with the work suggested in those sections, let the study of comparisons be returned to. All number ideas are related, and all types of work leading to the development of number ideas are related. This section suggests one way to study groups. The next two sections (3 and 4) will suggest other ways. All are intended to lead to an enlargement of the children's ideas of groups. Let the different phases of the study of groups, then, be taken up, not as isolated phases, but as related phases.

In developing mastery of number ideas, the children will not master first one phase then another. Mastery will be gained along all related lines simultaneously and gradually. Each part of the work will help the other. The activities suggested here will help those to be suggested in the next sections. They, in turn, will reflect back upon those suggested here and give them added meaning.

j. Summary. By means of the activities that have just been suggested in Section 2, the children arrive at an understanding of groups that is more complete than any they had as a result of mere counting exercises. The study of groups has led to an enlargement of number ideas to nine. But the children are not yet ready to use the nine ideas in combinations. The activities of the two sections that follow are intended to lead to a further enlargement and development of the ideas to nine.

3. Studying Groups by Taking Apart (Analysis) and Putting Together (Synthesis)

Section 1 of our discussions has suggested how groups may be studied by giving attention one by one to the individual objects which compose them. Section 2 has suggested how groups may be studied by comparing one group with another. The present section, 3, will continue the discussions by suggesting how groups may be studied by means of analysis into the smaller groups of which each is composed and by means of synthesis of these smaller groups into the original larger ones. The purpose throughout is the same; namely, to lead pupils to enlarge, develop, and clarify their ideas of number up to nine.[5] Since the idea of number is the idea of the group, we must lead the children to a more systematic study of the group.

a. Number Facts versus Number Ideas. One may look upon the learning of arithmetic as the learning of separate number facts or one may view the process as the development in the mind of the learner of interrelated number ideas. Viewed from the former angle, the learning of arithmetic is little more than systematic memorization. Viewed from the latter angle, the process is that of an active mind that not only learns the various number facts but also understands their relations and seeks possibilities of their application. When number ideas are so developed, they may be applied by the learner in clarifying other number ideas he possesses and later in developing number ideas of higher order.

The point of view that will be maintained throughout these discussions is that pupils are to be set at activities that will lead them to *develop number ideas*, that the various so-called number facts are not merely *learned* by the pupils, but rather, *developed* by them as constituent parts of the number ideas, and that the development of the number ideas makes possible the *development* and learning of the so-called number facts *in their relations.* Consequently, the effort will be made to suggest the activities that will lead the pupils to think of *six*, for example, as five and one, four and two, three and three, etc., as two threes, three twos, as one less

[5] Really, up to *ten.* See footnote 4, p. 175.

than seven, etc., and not to separate in the instruction $\frac{3}{6}$ and $\frac{2}{6}$ merely because the latter has been suggested by some as being slightly more difficult than the former.

At every point the instruction is to be organized to the end that ideas will be developed and meanings gained. Learning arithmetic, thus considered, is not memorizing facts and manipulating number symbols on paper or on the board; it is, rather, the building of ideas out of ideas already gained and the acquiring and the relating of meanings; in short, it is an intellectual process. The processes of arithmetic, thus considered, are thought processes, not paper and pencil processes.

b. The Study of a Group of Six. Let the children's study of the arrangement, or grouping, of objects begin with a group of *six*. Such a group will be small enough for the pupils to deal with at the start, and at the same time large enough to present a challenge to them. Moreover, it leaves the smaller groups of *two*, *three*, *four*, and *five* for the pupils to deal with somewhat independently as soon as they have become familiar with the method of study.

Select six objects large enough to be visible to the entire class, but not too large to be easily handled. Pencils will serve the purpose.

/ / / / / /

1. "How many pencils have I here?" The pupils will determine by counting, since up to this point the activity is a continuation of their preliminary counting activities.

2. "I will now take two pencils away from the six and put them over here. Notice that I take two away."

/ / / /   / /

3. "How many pencils are left here?" The pupils determine.

4. Repeat the arrangement again and again, emphasizing

the facts that there are six pencils at first, and that, when two are taken away, four are left.

5. Call upon the pupils, one by one, to perform the activity, letting each child tell, step by step, what he does. Vary the objects used. Use sticks, books, pieces of chalk, tablets, etc.

6. Continue until each child is perfectly familiar with the fact, because he has seen it again and again, that when two is taken from six, four remains.

c. The Oral Language of Arrangement, or Grouping. When the pupils have observed the arrangement (of six) just described sufficiently often to understand it thoroughly, the teacher supplies the language that describes it: "Two from six is four." This the teacher supplies as substitution for the longer, round-about discussions, questions and answers, that she and the children have been using to guide their attention to the arrangement. This language can now be used by teacher and pupils in further discussion of the same arrangement, while it is being made, and as a means of describing it, after it has been made.

d. The Written Language of Arrangement. After the repeated process of arrangement has supplied the meaning, and after the oral language, "Two from six is four," has been connected with its meaning, the teacher supplies the written language: $\frac{6}{-2}$. This the teacher supplies to describe an arrangement while it is in the process of being made. In order that the connection that is made shall be between the written form and its meaning, and not merely between the written form and its oral expression to the exclusion of meaning, the children should be called upon to observe the writing of the form step by step:

1. "How many books are here?" Six. "I will write the figure for six to show how many."   6

2. "I take two away." "I write the figure for two $-\,2$

with this mark $(-)$ before it to show that I have taken two away." The children may be reminded, if they do not recall it themselves, that the signs, $\frac{6}{-2}$, also ask a question about 'more' or 'less.' Remind them, and at the same time point out and insist, that it also means "Two from six is how many?"

3. Now, taking the question, asked orally, "Two from six is how many?" and asked in writing, $\frac{6}{-2}$, the answer is found by observing, perhaps counting, the group that remains. The figure for the answer (4) is written in its proper place, as shown: $\frac{6}{-2}$.

$\quad\quad e.\ \textit{Use the Sign for Subtraction.}$ The sign for subtraction $(-)$ should be used during the first two grades. There must be something in the written form of subtraction to distinguish it from the form of addition, at least until the pupils have learned the process well enough to describe it by the word 'subtraction.' (Do not use the word 'subtract' in the beginning.) Call attention to the minus sign $(-)$, stating that it means 'to take away,' or that the number shown by the lower figure is to be taken away, and that it means 'from.'

$\quad\quad f.\ \textit{Read Upward.}$ In the expression $\frac{5}{-2}$, the reading should be upward. At first glance, this seems to be inconsistent with the manner of its writing, which is downward, and with the order of attending to the groups involved in the subtraction. One first attends to the group of five. Next, one attends to the group of two that is removed. But the removal of two objects is more than a single act of arrangement or a single act of thinking. One not merely takes away two objects; he takes away two objects from the five objects, and he must have the total in mind while removing the portion. The adult can, of course, just as readily think, "Five, take away two," as "Two from five;" but the child, if he starts with the former expression of his thinking, must remind himself, or be reminded, of the implication of the latter. So, if he starts with the former expression, he may be helped by including the latter, "Five, take away two *from five.*" In other words, the child, in removing the group of two or in thinking its removal, must go back in the process of thinking to the original group.

Moreover, the expression, "Five, take away two, three," is not a sentence; and if we insert the verb, the sentence is not in good form. If we substitute the word 'less' for 'take away,' we make a good sentence — "Five less two is three" — but we use a word that implies comparison of two groups when no comparison is undertaken.

We may dispose of the matter in another way. The writing of the simple combinations by the pupil in his early work is a matter of enough difficulty to require the reading of the expressions as a separate undertaking. He may write, "Five,

$$\frac{5}{-\,2}$$

take away two," -2, for example. This is one process. Now follows the actual thinking of the process, which is something different. He can just as well proceed, "Two from five is three" as "five take away two, three." Since the reading of the combination is different from writing it, it may be read in the manner that employs the simplest language, namely, "two from five is three."

g. Further Study of the Group by Putting Together. Now that the group of six has been arranged into a group of four and a group of two, the next thing to be done is to call attention to the process of putting the two groups together to form the original group.

1. "How many pencils are here?" **//**
2. "How many are here?" **////**
3. "I want to find out how many are two and four. I will *put them together* and see." The two groups are brought together.   **//////**

4. "How many are here together?"

5. "Two and four are how many?" If the children have been attending closely to the preceding demonstrations of arrangement, and are wide-awake to the fact that a *group of six* is being studied, they can answer at once. Otherwise, they can count.

6. The teacher presents the oral language to describe the arrangement of *putting things together:* "Two and four are six." The new, concise statement is now used by both teacher and pupils to summarize the discussions, and in answer to the questions they have been using.

7. The written language is now presented, $\frac{2}{4}$. The presentation is made step by step, as indicated above. As the pupils answer the questions about the two groups and about the final group when the two groups are brought together, the teacher writes first the sign for two, next the sign for four, finally the sign for six. In the process of writing, the teacher points out that the signs, $\underline{4}^{2}$, ask, "Two and four are how many?" and that the completion of the writing answers the question, thus: "Two and four are six." Notice that the expressions are written downward and are *read downward*. There are two reasons: (1) reading the *putting together* expressions downward helps to contrast them with the *taking away* expressions, which are read upward; (2) a slight advantage is claimed for downward adding in column addition.

8. With the objects now in a group of six, the double operations of *taking away* and *putting together* are reviewed:

"Two from six is four."
$$\begin{array}{r} 6 \\ -\ 2 \\ \hline 4 \end{array}$$

"Two and four are six."
$$\begin{array}{r} 2 \\ 4 \\ \hline 6 \end{array}$$

The purpose of reviewing the two operations together is both to bring them together in their relations and to fix attention upon their contrasts.

h. Continuing the Study of the Group of Six. The study of the group of six by means of analysis into smaller groups and of putting these smaller groups together into the original should continue. As the work progresses, the teacher may find that the demonstrations of the *taking away* and *putting together* exercises can be less elaborate than at first, because the children with some direction can carry through the necessary arrangements.

The arrangements of the group of six are now studied that lead to an understanding of the following oral and written descriptions:

$$\begin{array}{r} 6 \\ -\,4 \\ \hline 2 \end{array}$$
"Four from six is two."

$$\begin{array}{r} 4 \\ 2 \\ \hline 6 \end{array}$$
"Four and two are six."

$$\begin{array}{r} 6 \\ -\,3 \\ \hline 3 \end{array}$$
"Three from six is three."

$$\begin{array}{r} 3 \\ 3 \\ \hline 6 \end{array}$$
"Three and three are six."

$$\begin{array}{r} 6 \\ -\,5 \\ \hline 1 \end{array}$$
"Five from six is one."

$$\begin{array}{r} 5 \\ 1 \\ \hline 6 \end{array}$$
"Five and one are six."

$$\begin{array}{r} 6 \\ -\,1 \\ \hline 5 \end{array}$$
"One from six is five."

$$\begin{array}{r} 1 \\ 5 \\ \hline 6 \end{array}$$
"One and five are six."

i. Developing Ideas before Using Words and Signs. It will bear repeating that the foregoing oral and written descriptions should follow, not precede, the arrangements of the group of six they describe. The adult mind, in its number-thinking, has moved so far away from attention to concrete groupings, and has used the oral and written descriptions in place of the concrete groupings for so long, that it frequently mistakes the description for the thing it is intended to describe. Thus, the adult refers to a set of symbols, such as $\frac{2}{4}$, as a 'combination.' For all practical purposes of the 6 adult the reference is accurate enough. The symbols stand so completely for the combination they record, and the thinking of the adult is so far removed from the need of concrete demonstration, that they may with all propriety be called the combination. But in dealing with children who are in the midst of learning about the combinations, or arrangements, or groupings, of objects, the adult mind must bring itself to the level of the children's minds, and refrain from calling the sign for the thing the thing itself. Actually, the symbols, $\frac{2}{4}$, are not the combination, and the oral sen-6 tence, "Two and four are six," is not the combination. The combination is the actual process of combining, of the bringing together of a group of two and a group of four into a group of six, or the counting of a group of two and a group of four together in such a way as to discover that both together are six. *The symbols and the sentence describe what has been done.* The thing is first done, then talked about and written about. At the start the descriptions of the combinations, or arrangements, cannot properly be used as a substitute for the arrangements themselves. Later, when the children have acquired mastery through many repetitions of the actual arrangements, they may themselves substitute the oral and written language for the combinations the language describes. It must be borne in mind that such substitution must be made by the developing minds of the children, and that, when it comes, it must come as a result of gradual mental development.

So, let the teacher refrain from speaking of the signs, $\frac{2}{\underset{6}{4}}$, and the like, as the combinations and refrain from insisting that these signs, as 'combinations,' be learned. Children are so prone to memorize the oral and written descriptions of the combinations, instead of giving attention to the actual combinations, that the teacher should discourage, not encourage, them thus to memorize. Let the teacher be reminded that the children are *studying groups,* and that the oral and written statements of which we are speaking are useful only as they help the children to summarize and to keep in mind the various steps they *actually take* in the study of groups.

j. Progress of Pupils in Studying Groups. In the beginning pupils are entirely dependent in their study of groups upon the directions and suggestions of the teacher. They must gain independence. They must be thrown slowly and gradually upon their own resources. From the beginning, the teacher must plan to give them training in doing things more and more for themselves. Moreover, from the beginning, the pupils should be expected to make progress — very slow and gradual progress, to be sure — in their ability to give attention to the arrangement of objects without paying so much attention to the objects themselves.

Since the idea of number is the idea of the group, and not the idea of the objects, objects are needed in the beginning in order to provide an actual group for study. As the pupils become able, through study and practice, to give more and more attention to the group and to the arrangements of the group, objects may be used less and less. Finally, the objects may be dispensed with entirely.

The various steps of progress in the ability of pupils to give attention to arrangement are indicated in the following outline:

1. Attention to arrangement of objects when the teacher makes and describes the arrangement. This step has been described in the paragraphs dealing with a study of the group of six.

2. Attention to arrangement of objects when the pupils make and describe the arrangement.

3. Attention to arrangement of objects when the pupils do not actually make, but *think*, the arrangements, and then describe them.

4. Attention to arrangement when the objects are present only in imagination.

5. Attention to arrangement when no objects are present, employing the language of number to describe the arrangement, which is now entirely a matter of thought.

We shall proceed to describe steps 2 and 3, reserving for a succeeding chapter a description of steps 4 and 5.

k. Independent Work. Step 2 may be described as follows: Following the study of a group of six, as outlined in preceding topics, let each pupil have a group of six objects to study. The teacher directs the study by asking such questions, orally and in writing, as the following:

"Two from six is how many?" $\begin{array}{r} 6 \\ -\,2 \\ \hline 2 \end{array}$

"Two and four are how many?" $\begin{array}{r} 2 \\ \underline{4} \end{array}$, etc.

Each pupil arranges the objects in his group of six so as to demonstrate the arrangement called for and to determine the answer. When he has determined his answer, not merely remembered it, or had it suggested to him by another pupil, he may give his answer orally, or in writing, or in both ways, as required.

When the pupils are all familiar with the method of determining the answers to the teacher's questions about the group of six, they may next be given a group of three, four, or five, and permitted to determine answers to the teacher's questions.

The teacher asks, for example:

$$\begin{array}{r} 5 \\ -\ 2 \end{array}$$

"Two from five is how many?"

$$\begin{array}{r} 2 \\ \underline{3} \end{array}, \text{etc.}$$

"Two and three are how many?"

Each pupil determines his own answer and gives it as required.

In a similar manner the pupils proceed gradually to a study of a group of seven, of eight, and of nine.

l. Thinking the Arrangement. As the pupils make progress in the second step of their study of groups, they will develop a growing feeling of familiarity with what they are doing and with what is expected of them. Before long they will begin to become so familiar with the groups being studied that they can find and give their answers without having to go to the trouble of actually making the arrangements suggested. For example, when the question, "Two and three are how many?" is given, they will be able to determine five, by *thinking*, perhaps counting, the two groups together without actually bringing them together. They should be encouraged to move ahead to this step of *thinking things together* and *thinking things away*.

The familiar domino arrangements of semi-concrete objects (dots) is often found helpful in giving pupils training in thinking arrangements. Since they cannot actually move the dots, they have to think of them as being moved. The teacher presents the domino form, such as:

and asks, "How many dots are here?" and writes 3; "How many dots are here?" and writes 2; "How many dots are there altogether?" and writes 5.

When the pupils are ready for step 3, they may be instructed in the use of marks or dots on their paper or on the board. Thus, in studying the group of seven, the pupils may use seven marks on their paper

$$/ \; / \; / \; / \; / \; / \; /$$

In answering the question, "Three from seven is how many?" they may think the marks away by covering three of them with a finger and counting the number left.

m. Reviewing the Study of a Group. After a group has been studied, it should be returned to in frequent reviews. At first, the pupils answer the teacher's questions, "Four and two are how many?" $\frac{4}{2}$, "Five from six is how many?" $\frac{6}{-5}$, either by making the necessary arrangements of the objects of the group or by thinking the arrangements. Later, when the pupils have developed sufficient confidence in their ability, they should be instructed and given practice in 'telling the story' about the group. To tell about six, for example, the pupil tells (and demonstrates or not, as may be required) "One from six is five," "One and five are six," "Four from six is two," etc. Or, he may 'write the story,' as follows: $\frac{6}{-1}$, $\frac{1}{5}$, $\frac{6}{-4}$, etc. In connection with a review of six, what the pupils learned in connection with the exercises of comparison should be told and written: "Six is two more than four," "Six is three less than nine," etc., and $\frac{6}{-4}$, $\frac{9}{-6}$, etc.

In connection with the written review the point should again be emphasized that such a form as $\frac{6}{-4}$ means either 'more,' or 'less,' or 'take away.'

n. The Results of Studying the Arrangement of Groups. As

a result of studying the groups to nine the pupils develop
and enlarge and clarify their number ideas to nine. They
are thus prepared to handle these ideas in combination later
on in their work. Being more familiar with the ideas, they
can now use them with more assurance and independence.

Moreover, the pupils have learned (not completely, to be
sure) 36 'take away' arrangements and 36 'put together'
arrangements. These they have learned, not as separate
number facts, but in their relations to each other and in
their relations to the groups that they help to make familiar.
In the study of a group, the pupils have studied the various
ways it may be arranged. The various arrangements have
centered around the group, making it more definite and the
idea of it more usable. The idea of the group being studied
has, in turn, served to bind together in proper relations the
various arrangements. Thus, each has helped the other.
The arrangements give meaning to the group; the group
gives organization and system to the arrangements.

The written expressions of the arrangements that have
been made and studied are given below in a manner that
shows their relations to each other, and to the number ideas
that hold them together.

2	*3*		*4*			*5*			
2	3	3	4	4	4	5	5	5	5
−1	−1	−2	−1	−2	−3	−1	−2	−3	−4
1	2	1	3	2	1	4	3	2	1
1	1	2	1	2	3	1	2	3	4
1	2	1	3	2	1	4	3	2	1
2	3	3	4	4	4	5	5	5	5

6					*7*					
6	6	6	6	6	7	7	7	7	7	7
−1	−2	−3	−4	−5	−1	−2	−3	−4	−5	−6
5	4	3	2	1	6	5	4	3	2	1
1	2	3	4	5	1	2	3	4	5	6
5	4	3	2	1	6	5	4	3	2	1
6	6	6	6	6	7	7	7	7	7	7

			8								9			
8	8	8	8	8	8	8	9	9	9	9	9	9	9	9
−1	−2	−3	−4	−5	−6	−7	−1	−2	−3	−4	−5	−6	−7	−8
7	6	5	4	3	2	1	8	7	6	5	4	3	2	1
1	2	3	4	5	6	7	1	2	3	4	5	6	7	8
7	6	5	4	3	2	1	8	7	6	5	4	3	2	1
8	8	8	8	8	8	8	9	9	9	9	9	9	9	9

Notice that no zero combinations are shown in these written expressions. The use of the zero in the number system will be discussed in a later chapter. The child has no use for the zero until he comes to the study of ten. Hence there is nothing gained at this time by introducing the zero.

o. Use of the Terms 'Subtraction' and 'Addition.' In the study of a group, the pupils begin with the whole group together. The first thing that can be done with it is to separate it in some way. In each case, a smaller group was first *taken away.* This is the process of subtraction. Now, when the original group which is being studied has been separated into two smaller ones, the two smaller groups were *put together.* This is the process of addition. In each case, an addition arrangement followed its related subtraction arrangement.

During the activities just described in Section 3 the teacher has emphasized and the pupils have given their attention to the process of *taking away* and the process of *putting together.* The pupils have actually performed the processes again and again, and they have repeatedly *thought things away* and *thought them together.* Such activities have led to a development of the ideas 'take away' and 'put together.' Now, when the ideas have been gained, the teacher can offer the usual names for the ideas; namely, 'subtraction' and 'addition.' Now, the names need no explaining, because the pupils have already gained the ideas for which the names stand.

p. Directing Attention to Arrangement. It will be observed

that a given arrangement of objects into two groups — for
example, */// //* — may be described in either of two ways;
namely, "three and two are five," $\frac{3}{5}$, and "two and three
are five," $\frac{2}{3}$. The later use of such a pair of descriptions —
'combinations,' as they are commonly called — often influences the teacher to require their learning as isolated items
of experience. Their later use requires a mastery of each in
isolation. A given situation will require the use of one combination without any reference to the other one. For this
reason the teacher is sometimes in confusion whether to present them together or separately.

The nature of the pupil's work at this point solves the
question for the teacher. If the pupil is giving his attention
to a method of description as a fact of major importance,
he may be missing the idea of arrangement that he is supposed to describe. If he is giving his attention to an arrangement of objects, the different methods of description will be
thought of as belonging together. Their relation — indeed,
their similarity — will have more significance than their difference. It is not greatly important whether one says "the
pencil and paper are on the table," or "the paper and pencil
are on the table." The situation being described remains
the same. "Three and two are five," $\frac{3}{5}$, and "two and three
are five," $\frac{2}{3}$, are different only in form of expression. They
may be used to describe a single arrangement.

q. Thinking, not Memorizing, should be Encouraged. Let
it be repeated that the teacher should guard against the
learning of the language of arrangement as mere feats of
memory. If a pupil has difficulty in 'telling about a group,'

instead of merely suggesting the right words or showing him the correct written expressions, help him to work out his difficulty for himself. If thinking the arrangements without resort to the objects is too difficult, let him take the group of objects and actually arrange them in various ways, describing aloud and writing each arrangement. Next, let him attend to each arrangement and describe each without actually making the arrangement. The direction of effort should be to the end that the pupil will *think the arrangement*, not merely remember something to say and something to write.

r. Summary. The purpose of the activities described in this Section (3) is to lead children to develop and enlarge and clarify their ideas of the numbers to nine. Since the idea of number is the idea of the group, the children (1) have been taught how to study a group, and (2) have been directed into a more or less independent study of groups. Since the systematic study of a group is more effective than haphazard, incidental study, they have been directed in methods of studying groups systematically.

Through a development of their number ideas to nine, the children have received preparation for the later activities of using these nine ideas in combination. And they have not merely received preparation; they have actually learned to carry through, and to organize in proper relations, nearly half of the total of addition and subtraction combinations. Thus, their learning has demonstrated the fact that a step in arithmetic not merely prepares for the next step, but is in reality a good part of it.

4. Studying Groups by Emphasizing Equal Groups

By means of the methods of studying groups described in the two sections immediately preceding, the pupils enlarge and greatly clarify the ideas of the numbers, one to nine, that they had previously developed through counting, and in this process they learn many number facts in their relations and in connection with the nine ideas. In their activities opportunity also is afforded them to learn other and different number facts that serve the double purpose of enlarging the nine number ideas and of contributing to the development of the idea of groups. The number facts referred to are the few simple facts of multiplication and division that contribute to the ideas, four, six, eight, and nine.

a. Avoid Confusing Multiplication with Addition. It is probably better for the teacher in conducting the activities of arranging a group of eight into five and three, two and six, four and four, etc., merely to call attention in passing to the facts that four and four are equal groups than to attempt in the beginning to bring out the fact that in eight there are two fours in connection with the various facts of addition. Mathematically there is an intimate relation between "two fours are eight" and "four and four are eight," because both facts contribute to the pupil's idea of eight. Practically, however, there is a sharp distinction between the two facts, and the distinction is quite as important to learn as the similarity. The section immediately preceding makes clear the point that "two from five is three" and "two and three are five" must first be learned as separate and distinct arrangements before they can be learned together. It is the purpose of the present section (4) to emphasize the point that the related facts "two fours are eight" and "four and four are eight" must not be confused.

When one adds four and four he does not give special attention to the fact that the two groups are equal. He relates the process to those of adding two and six, or five and three, and so on, in which the groups which are to be added are not of the same size. If, when his attention is turned to the fact that in four and four the two groups are equal, he thinks of the combination as one of addition, he is compelled to view it as one of the very uncommon occurrences in addition. Indeed, the adding of groups of equal size is such an uncommon occurrence as to deserve no special recognition as such.

On the other hand, when one multiplies he does so because he is impressed with the fact that he is dealing with groups of exactly equal size. The equal size of the groups is a fact of major importance in determining to resort to the process of multiplying. Moreover, the exact number of the groups is a matter of special concern in multiplication, whereas in addition one pays little attention to the number of the groups to be added and is not assisted in the process by the little attention he does pay.

b. *Addition and Multiplication Are Indirectly Related.* The two processes bear to each other an indirect relationship. The fact that they both are useful in contributing to certain number ideas, not the fact that they are similar processes, is the reason why they should be put together as related processes. The accompanying figure may serve to illustrate the point. Processes (1), (2), (3), and (4) all contribute to the enlarging and enriching of the idea eight.

The Idea Eight

$$5\} \leftrightarrow \begin{cases}4\\4\end{cases} \quad 4\} \leftrightarrow \begin{cases}2\\4\end{cases}$$

$$\frac{3}{8} \quad \frac{4}{8} \quad \frac{4}{8} \quad \frac{2}{8}$$

(1)   (2)   (3)   (4)

They all are held together by the contributions they make to a common idea. Processes 1 and 2 are directly related because they are similar processes; likewise Processes 3 and 4 have a similar relation. Process 2 and Process 3 are similar only when and to the extent that one gives attention to the number of groups in (2) and to the fact that the groups are exactly the same size. Processes 2 and 3 belong together because they contribute to a common idea, not because they represent similar ideas of grouping.

c. *Teach Separately, then Relate.* There is no intention in the present discussion to suggest that all the activities of the preceding section (3) should be completed before those of this section (4) are begun. The arrangements "two threes are six" and "three twos are six" might just as well be learned before "four and three are seven," "two and five are seven," etc., as to be delayed until all of the arrangements of subtraction and addition that contribute to the ideas one to nine are learned. On the other hand, it is just as well to delay the arrangements of multiplication, provided they are finally made contributory to the number ideas one to nine. As frequently pointed out in foregoing discussions, it is the number ideas, not isolated facts of number combinations, to which pupils should give their attention from the beginning. The various facts of number combination should be learned, not in isolation, but in their relations as contributors to the number ideas. Neither false, nor strained, nor apparent similarities between the various arrangements should be appealed to. The pupils must learn to distinguish between them.

Whether the teacher introduces the activities of this section at the suitable points into the activities of the preceding section or keeps them entirely separate are not matters of great importance. The important points for the teacher to keep in mind are: (1) introduce the arrangements of multiplication that relate to the idea of six, for example, separate from those of subtraction and addition, and (2) when the arrangements of multiplication have been learned as distinct processes, relate them to the other arrangements that contribute to the idea six.

d. What to Emphasize. In conducting the activities that develop the arrangements of multiplication contributing to the ideas one to nine (and they are few in number), the teacher should call especially to the attention of the pupils two important things; namely (1) the fact that the groups dealt with are equal, and (2) the number of the groups.

It may be that the pupils will have difficulty in distinguishing between multiplication and addition. Complete understanding of the difference cannot be expected at once. Keep in mind that no effort should be made to teach them as one and the same process. In dealing with the arrangements of multiplication whose results are ten and above, the distinction will be much more apparent. It is important at this point in the course that a beginning be made in developing the understanding of the pupils.

Frequently the attempt is made to lead pupils to derive the idea of multiplication from the arrangements of addition; in other words, to teach multiplication as a special form of 'short-cut addition.' From the arrangement "three and three are six," the idea is suggested, or attempted, that "two threes are six," and so on. Such attempt serves to emphasize the similarity between the two processes, but fails to emphasize sufficiently the distinction.

Beginners in arithmetic seem to be able to note with little difficulty the similarity between addition and multiplication.[6] Questions relating to the two processes are asked in very similar terms, and both processes are 'put together' processes. Their chief difficulty is in distinguishing between the processes, and in avoiding being confused by the apparent and real similarities.

Another criticism of the method of presenting multiplication as 'short-cut addition' is that it unduly delays most of the multiplications that the pupils can otherwise readily learn. For example, the arrangement "three threes are nine" has to be postponed until the pupil learns to add a column of threes, and "nine sixes are fifty-four" has to be postponed until the pupil develops an ability in column addition that an understanding of the number system does not require. Many times pupils are found in the latter half of their fourth year with no more introduction to some of the simpler multiplications than purely memoriter exercises are able to give.

The contrast between the Roman and the Hindu-Arabic system of notation suggests another criticism. The Romans, 2000 years ago, when they wished to multiply, had to add. The system of numerals they had was a system of additions.

---

[6] C. H. Judd. *Psychological Analysis of the Fundamentals of Arithmetic* (Department of Education, The University of Chicago, Chicago, 1927), p. 88.

The Hindu-Arabic system, which we have, is a system of multiplications, as we have seen in a preceding chapter. It seems very strange, to say the least, that teachers often find no better method of teaching multiplication than the method of multiplication that was in general use twenty centuries ago.

   e. The Study of Groups from the Point of View of the Pupil. The necessity for further discussion and argument may be escaped if we turn our attention from a consideration of the problem of the teacher to a consideration of the task of the pupil. In the preceding section the question of whether addition comes first or subtraction comes first was avoided entirely by confining our discussion closely to the learning processes of the pupil. The topic under discussion was the study of the group by the pupil. When he has a whole group, and undertakes to study the whole group, the first thing he can do with it is take it apart into smaller groups. This is subtraction. Now, when he has taken apart the group being studied, he can next put the parts together. This is addition.

   Perhaps, if we keep our attention upon the things the pupil has before him to study, the whole question of how to introduce the idea of multiplication, including attention both to the number of groups and the equality of groups, will solve itself. Let us bear in mind that the pupil is not studying the so-called 'combinations' when he is engaging in the activities that have been described in Sections 3 and 4 just preceding. He is studying groups in order to build up in his mind clearer and more exact ideas of the groups. In the activities to be described in the present section, the pupil must continue to study groups. The study of the group, and the group as the center of attention, will determine both what the pupil learns first and the manner of his learning it.

   Let us review, for our own benefit, the important fact just cited that, when the pupil is engaged in the study of a group, the first thing he can do with the group is take it apart into smaller groups, and the consequent fact that the putting together of the smaller groups must, of necessity, follow after the taking apart.

f. The Sequence of Taking Apart and Putting Together. Let us suggest that emphasis upon equal groups follow the activities that have been described in the preceding section. Let us suppose that the children are reviewing what they have found out about a group of eight, for example. Each child has eight objects, and each in turn is answering a question by the teacher about eight:

"Five from eight is how many?"
$$\begin{array}{r} 8 \\ -5 \end{array},$$

"Six and two are how many?"
$$\begin{array}{r} 6 \\ \underline{2} \end{array}, \text{ etc.,}$$

or each child is telling or writing 'the whole story' of eight.

When such review exercises have been completed, the teacher may introduce the new kind of study somewhat as follows:

The teacher takes a group of eight objects — //////// — and makes the suggestion:

"Let us study something new about eight."

"How many pencils have I?" Eight.

"I would like to find out how many twos there are in eight. This is the way I can find out."

The teacher now separates the eight objects into groups of two.

"I want to find how many twos there are in eight, so I count out one two, and place them together here; I count out one two, and place them here; I count out one two, and place them here; and I count out one two, and they are here."

//   //   //   //

"How many are here?" (pointing to the first two)

"How many are here?" (pointing to the second two), etc.

By question and suggestion the point is emphasized that each group is equal.

"Now I have my eight separated (*divided* is just as familiar

a word, and may be used) into twos, and I want to know how many
twos there are in eight."

"Let us count the twos." (The twos are counted by teacher
and pupil — four.)

"Now, I know how many twos there are in eight. How many
twos are in eight?"

The children may answer "four." They should be instructed
to give the complete answer, which is "Four twos are eight."

The children now give attention, each to the eight objects he
has, and each answers the teacher's question, "How many twos
are in eight?" by actually making the arrangement himself. When
the arrangement has been made a sufficient number of times, he
may *think* the arrangement in order to answer the question.

In similar manner, the children proceed, when directed,
to find answers to such questions as the following:

> "How many fours in eight?"
> "How many twos in four?"
> "How many twos in six?"
> "How many threes in six?"
> "How many threes in nine?"

In the study of the group, the first question that can be
asked is a '*division' question*. The answer that is given is a
'*multiplication' answer*. Since the number of divisions possible in the study of the groups to nine is small, there will
be no need to introduce the terms 'division' and 'multiplication.' Later, when the pupil has opportunity to give
attention to a sufficient number of such arrangements to
develop their meanings, the terms may be introduced.

In connection with each of the arrangements that are
made necessary by the 'division' questions, the pupil may
be asked the corresponding 'multiplication' question. Thus,
following the question, "How many twos in eight?" and the
answer, "Four twos are eight," the question, "Four twos
are how many?" is asked. To this question, the same answer is given, "Four twos are eight." The pupils determine
the answer either by thinking back over what they have

just discovered in answering the 'division' question, or by putting together or thinking together the four groups of two to make eight. The new question — the 'multiplication' one — serves both as a review, and as a new view, of the arrangement being studied.

Give both kinds of questions, such as "How many twos in eight?" and "Four twos are how many?" Since both require the same answer, each strengthens the other.

g. Writing the Question and Answer. The pupils may be shown the written form of the division question, and how to write the answer when they have found it, or the written form may be delayed until later. There is a slight advantage in showing the form now, since it will be of service in later reviews, and the written form, being different from ones already learned, may help to fix distinctions.

After the pupils have learned to determine for themselves answers to such questions as, "How many twos in eight?" they may be shown how the question is written, thus:

$$2\overline{)8}$$

Let it be impressed that the written form asks, "How many twos in eight?" Do not call it "division," "divide," or describe it in any other way. Now, when they know what the question asks, show them where and how to write the answer.

$$2\overline{)8}^{\,4}$$
$$\underline{8}$$

As the 4 is written above, and another 8 below and the line is drawn, give the answer, "Four twos are eight."

The special written form of multiplication, $\frac{4}{8}^{2}$, ought not to be introduced until later. It would be of service in connection with but few arrangements, and would probably be confused with the written form for addition. Since the written form of division, $2\overline{)\,8}$, for example, asks all the questions needed by the pupils in their present study of groups, the written form of multiplication is not needed.

Let it be repeated that, when the written form is presented, it be presented as a *way of asking a question* — $2\overline{)\,8}$, "How many twos in eight?" — the answer to which the pupils can work out and give. If so presented, it will need no further explanation.

h. Counting by Twos, Threes, Fours, and Fives. An important, though somewhat incidental, means of drawing attention both to equal groups and to the idea of groups is the engrossing activities of counting by twos and fives. Children engage in these activities usually with no other motive than that of intellectual play. Just as the beginner in counting employs himself in counting everything — the buttons on his shoe, the people in the room, the dishes on the table — so the pupil who has learned to count by ones and discovers a new way to count by twos and fives takes special delight in these new methods. A little encouragement from the teacher is all that is needed either to initiate the activities or to help them along. Encourage the pupils, therefore, in their counting by twos to twenty and by fives to fifty, or even to one hundred. A good many of the pupils can quickly extend these activities to the counting by threes to thirty, and by fours to forty. Such activities, which are usually engaged in with keen interest, will frequently do as much to call the attention of the pupils to *groups* and to the *equality* of the groups as any device the teacher may use.

A *word of caution* may well be given at this point. It is important to be reminded that the pupil who merely uses the number names in counting by twos, for example, may be doing no more than repeating names. He may, or he may not, recognize the while that fourteen is two more than twelve and that two more than fourteen is sixteen. Earlier, in Section 1, it was pointed out that counting, to be an exercise that gives meanings to number names, must comprise at once both the saying of names and the discrimination of objects. Similarly, at this point, it needs to be made clear that counting by twos, for example, is not only saying the names, two, four, six, etc., but also distinguishing objects in groups of two and applying the names successively to the discriminated groups. Therefore, do not ask your pupils to count by twos when you suggest no objects to be counted. Let them count books, crayons, seats, pupils, etc., by twos until the ideas of relation between six and eight, twelve and fourteen, etc., are entirely clear. Afterward, it is permissible to let them merely say the number names as a means of fixing their serial order. Bear in mind that it is ideas and meanings with their related names that are to be gained, not the number names apart from the ideas and meanings they are intended to express.

IV. Summary

The activities which have been described in this chapter are the activities of studying systematically the groups of objects to nine. By means of such systematic study of groups, the pupils have built up and clarified and made familiar the number ideas to nine. They may now be called upon to learn the procedures of *using* these ideas in combination with each other. When they are introduced to the activities that follow, they will be able to use the number ideas, which now have become familiar, with confidence and understanding.

In connection with their study of groups to nine the pupils have been introduced to 36 combinations of addition, 36 of subtraction, 6 of multiplication, and 6 of division; and they have learned, with the exception of the 6 multiplication ones, the meaning and use of their corresponding written expressions. Thus, in the process of preparation for the study of combinations, the pupils have actually learned nearly half the addition and subtraction ones.

CHAPTER XI

PRACTICE FOR MASTERY

ARGUMENT

1. The 'problem' in arithmetic is a practice exercise. It should serve, not as an actual problem in which doubt is involved, but as an example, or illustration.

2. The general ideas in arithmetic develop through practice in recognizing them in familiar situations.

3. Later, when such ideas have been gained, understanding of new situations develops through practice in recognition.

4. 'Problem-solving' in arithmetic is, then, practice in the recognition (a) of general ideas in familiar situations, and (b) of new situations with which are involved the general ideas that now should be familiar. Thus, the double purpose of 'problem-solving' is distinguished.

5. In the selection of situations to provide the earlier kind of practice the criteria are (a) variety for the sake of breadth, and (b) absence of distracting elements for the sake of readiness.

6. The purpose of writing in problem-solving is to provide progressive reminders of the step-by-step procedure of recognition and computation.

7. Drill should be distinguished from instruction. It should provide more than practice in the use of the language of number. It should provide practice in thinking.

8. Drill should be delayed until the pupil understands what he should do. It should not seek the form of adult performance at the outset, but should be organized so that it may move ahead progressively to higher levels of performance.

9. The goals of drill are accuracy and speed. These results may relate to performance only, or they may be made to mean accuracy and speed in thinking as well.

10. Throughout the discussion, 'problem-solving' and 'drill' are treated as closely related steps of practice in thinking about the arrangement of groups, or amounts.

I. ATTENTION TO ARRANGEMENT

In the activities described in the preceding chapter, the pupils give their attention in studying groups to the arrangement of objects (1) when the teacher makes the arrangements, (2) when they themselves make the arrangements, and (3) when they think the arrangements. From step to step the pupils study the same things, but each step of the study is on a higher level, both of difficulty and of thinking required, than the one preceding. Now, having carried their study of arrangement to the level of thinking the arrangement, when the objects are present, the pupils should be led to take the steps of study that require the thinking of arrangement when the objects are not present. These we have designated as the steps of giving attention to the arrangement of objects (4) when the objects are present only in imagination, and (5) when no objects at all are present.

II. 'PROBLEM-SOLVING' AND 'DRILL'

The designations given to Steps 4 and 5 are not sufficient to enable one to distinguish the steps. It will be necessary to describe each in some detail. If one, however, uses the terms commonly employed to designate Steps 4 and 5; namely, 'problems' and 'combinations,' respectively, or 'problem-solving' and 'drill,' respectively, he has no difficulty in making the intended distinctions clear.

Although the common names for Steps 4 and 5 appear to set them off with sharp distinctions, the names in reality serve to emphasize distinctions that are more apparent than real. Steps 4 and 5 embody a continuation of the same kind of study of arrangement that was begun with Steps 1, 2, and 3. Throughout the first three steps the pupils studied the same thing; namely, arrangement; in the steps that succeed, they are to continue to study the same thing; namely, arrangement. Steps 1, 2, and 3 were exercises having a common purpose; Steps 4 and 5 are exercises having the same common purpose, but different in form. It is the forms of the exercises embodied in Steps 4 and 5 that strike the eye and that cause the steps to appear as different.

The terms 'problem-solving' and 'drill' have been used so long, and their use is so widespread, that one can hardly afford to drop them too abruptly. The terms will have to be retained in our discussions and given frequent use in order to avoid confusion. The effort will be made, however, to indicate that both 'problems' and 'combinations' are exercises for practice, and that both have a common purpose; namely, that of providing practice in giving attention to arrangement on levels higher than the ones necessary at the beginning of study.

III. Problem-Practice Exercises[1]

1. The Purpose of Problems

Problems are often called 'examples.' They are, in truth, 'examples,' or 'illustrations,' of matters that are more important. Often problems are considered in arithmetic courses as the center around which everything else revolves. Solving the problem and getting the answer often occupies the center of the stage. It is intended here that the problems have no such place in the scheme of things. It is the intent that the problems be resorted to in order to clarify an idea which the pupils have begun to develop.

In the preceding chapter the purpose in mind has been to get the children to develop their ideas of the numbers, one to nine, through the study of the arrangement of objects. The teacher has presented objects in various arrangements and has taken special pains to call to the attention of the pupils the arrangements so presented. The pupils have seen actual arrangements, and they themselves have made actual

[1] Note similar discussion in H. G. Wheat. *The Psychology of the Elementary School.* (Silver, Burdett and Company, Newark, 1931), Chap. IV.

arrangements of objects. Moreover, the pupils have at times, through the use of the language of number, *thought* the arrangement of objects without actually disturbing them. It is a further step in the pupils' development to *think* the arrangement of objects when the objects are present only in their imaginations.

In the problem "John caught 5 fish and gave Henry 2. How many did John have left?" the pupils are given a situation not actually present to the senses. The interest of the pupils is in the total situation, to be sure; they have, however, in the number relations — that is, in the rearrangement of the objects — a very special interest. Heretofore, the pupils have had before them five objects actually present and have laid aside two and observed three objects remaining. They have described the arrangement orally thus:

"Two from five is three," and in writing thus: $\begin{array}{r} 5 \\ -2 \\ \hline 3 \end{array}$. In the problem relating to John's fish, the pupils are compelled to think the rearrangement of the five fish. They can give little or no attention to the fish as individual objects. If the numbers were larger, they could not visualize the objects except in a vague, general, and indefinite outline of the whole group. Without giving attention to the fish, the pupils give attention to their division into two groups, employing the language of arrangement, which they have developed in connection with the actual arrangement of objects, to describe the arrangement now present only as a matter of thought. Because they have been guided through language to attend to the grouping of objects actually before them, they have learned to think in exact terms of a similar situation, not actually before them.

Moreover, dealing with a situation not actually present enlarges the pupils' ideas of arrangement. In the activities with objects, "two objects from five objects," for example, has been demonstrated repeatedly. The pupils have taken two crayons from five crayons, two books from five books, two pencils from five pencils, etc. Each succeeding activity has helped to fix in mind the fact, "two from five is three," and to give it a more general significance. It is merely a further step in practice to take two fish from five fish and have three fish remaining, when the fish are present only in the pupils' imaginations.

2. The Growth of General Ideas

The purpose of "problems" may be stated in another way. By means of such activities as were suggested in the preceding chapter which lead to the development of the facts of arrangement that are related to the ideas one to nine, the pupil is required to give his attention to certain definite and particular procedures in the grouping of objects. For example, the ideas of 'taking away,' of 'counting together,' of 'how many' when two groups are 'put together,' of 'equal groups,' and so on, are called to the attention of the pupils both by the teacher's demonstrations and descriptions and by the manner in which the questions of arrangement are stated. Thus, in a measure, the pupil learns not only how to take groups apart and how to put the parts together in a systematic way, but also something of the meanings of the processes he learns to perform. The names of the processes, to be sure, are not acquired; but, rather, something more important; namely, something of the ideas for which the names will come eventually to stand. The analysis and synthesis of groups introduce the activities of subtraction, addition, division, and multiplication before the corresponding terms are introduced. The children first observe and then perform the activities of taking away and putting together. These activities gradually take on meanings. Later, when the ideas become somewhat familiar, the terms 'subtraction' and 'addition' can be given. When the terms follow the ideas, they need no explanation. Or, in the study of a group of six, for example, the question is given orally, "how many twos are in six?" or in writing, 2)‾6, and the pupils first observe and then perform the activity of resolving a group of six into groups of two. They discover the answer, and learn to give it orally, "three twos

$$\begin{array}{r} 3 \\ 2\overline{)6} \\ \underline{6} \end{array}$$

are six," or in writing, 2)‾6. Thus the pupils learn the significance of the 'division' question, and how to find the 'multiplication' answer. In this way the ideas of division and multiplication begin to develop a long time before the common names for the ideas are given, and when the names are finally introduced, they need no explanation.

The importance of developing meanings in connection with processes being learned, and of understanding as a prelude to the habituation of processes, cannot be too strongly emphasized. It will be implied throughout our discussions as a fundamental principle to guide the organization of the course in arithmetic that, once a pupil grasps a meaning or develops an idea, he may be expected to gain an insight into number relations quite independently of the class activities. The meaning, or the idea, is an inner drive that both influences the pupil to think for himself and gives him power to do so. It works retroactively upon things already learned, giving them a new significance and a new interest; and it leads the mind to seek new truths that may serve to give it completeness. Meanings and ideas furnish a motive for learning, that, because it is logical and is intrinsically a part of experience already gained, transcends in the force of its influence any practical motive that is intrinsically a part of the world of experience not yet entered upon by the individual.

A fundamental fact about general ideas is that they develop slowly. The teacher does not give them. Their names do not necessarily carry them. They develop out of an ordered experience. They become familiar through constant contact. The teacher who has guided pupils through such activities as have been described in the preceding chapter realizes that the pupils have merely been introduced to the ideas of addition, subtraction, multiplication, and division, and that these ideas must be presented again and again if the pupils are to be expected to become familiar with them. Problem-practice exercises provide the meeting ground for the pupils and the ideas. By means of such exercises the pupils are given the opportunity of meeting the ideas again and again in a variety of familiar situations. Just as one becomes better and better acquainted with an individual to whom one has been introduced by meeting and recognizing him time and again in various circumstances, so the pupils develop an acquaintance with the general idea of addition, for example, by meeting and recognizing addition in various situations.

3. The Process and the Situation

Two elements of the problem-practice exercise in arithmetic may be distinguished; namely, the process and the situation. One may conceive of a problem as being one of four possible types: (1) the two elements may be familiar; (2) the two elements may be unfamiliar; (3) the process may be relatively unfamiliar and the situation familiar; or (4) the process may be familiar and the situation relatively unfamiliar. Types 1 and 2 are readily recognized as ineffective or impossible. For example, the problem of "John's fish" would be ineffective for the practice of pupils in the high school, and a problem giving the area of a square to find the length of a side would be impossible in the first grade. To be both effective and possible, the problem must be either Type 3 or Type 4. Consideration of Types 3 and 4 enforces a distinction between problems in the earlier stages, and problems in the later stages of the learning of arithmetic, that is, between a device that will illustrate an idea while it is being developed and one that will illustrate the idea while it is being applied.

4. The Purposes of Problem-Solving Distinguished

Foregoing discussions have indicated that the problem-practice exercise is useful for purposes of illustration. It will be necessary, therefore, for the teacher at all times to be very clear in his own mind as to just what the exercise is intended to illustrate. The teacher must have in mind the question: Is the exercise intended to serve as an illustration of a general idea of arrangement, such as addition (or, later on, percentage) or is the exercise intended to make clear by additional illustration a situation, such as square measure, interest, insurance, and the like? And the teacher's answer must be in accord with the state of the pupil's preparation and needs at the point where the illustrative problem-practice exercises in question are introduced.

Following such activities as are described in the preceding chapter, the pupil is prepared to profit by a number of suitable illustrations of the general ideas of addition and subtraction and perhaps by a few of the ideas of multiplication and division. The pupil is on no better than speaking terms with the ideas. He has met them only in the actual classroom situations incident to the study of groups. He needs now to have the ideas presented to him by a variety of situations that he can imagine in quick succession as a result of the oral descriptions of the teacher. He needs to enlarge his acquaintance with the general ideas by meeting them and recognizing them under many different circumstances. Since the general ideas are relatively unfamiliar and the purpose is to make them familiar, the situations that are described as a means of presenting the ideas for the pupil to recognize must be familiar situations. Since the general idea of addition, let us say, is a constituent of the total situation presented by the problem exercise, the situation, if a familiar one, will make the idea of addition stand out with sufficient clearness to be recognized. And since the situation is slightly different from any heretofore considered by the pupil, the idea of addition is presented from a slightly different angle. We may summarize by saying that the purpose of problem-solving in the earlier stages of the learning of arithmetic is to develop an understanding of the meaning and use of the fundamental ideas of addition, subtraction, multiplication, and division.

In the later stages of the learning of arithmetic, it will be important for the pupil to develop an understanding of a number of the practical situations of life that involve the use of number relations, such as weights and measures, savings, budgets, interest, and the like. Since these situations are not the familiar ones of his everyday experiences, but such as the circumstances of life in modern society require him to learn, it will be necessary for him to make special studies of them when the time comes. In all these situations, the general ideas of number relations appear as constituents. Now, if the pupil can approach a study of the situations with an understanding of the meaning and use of the general ideas, he may conduct his studies without handicap or hindrance, and with a good many suggestions as to the nature of the situations. The general ideas, if sufficiently clear, will help to enlarge acquaintance with the new situations. In the earlier stages, general ideas are developed through consideration of familiar situations. In the later stages — that is, when and if the general ideas have been developed — new situations may become the subjects of special study. The twofold purpose of the so-called 'problem-solving' activity in arithmetic must not be confused.

5. The Familiar Situation

Attention to the distinction between the earlier and later stages in the learning of arithmetic both indicates the importance of developing general ideas during the earlier period and impresses the importance of the use of familiar situations in the exercises of the earlier period. Consideration of the folly of attempting to teach new and unfamiliar situa-

tions before the general ideas of the processes that appear
in them have been learned suggests the importance of the
general ideas. Consideration of the need for general ideas
as a prelude to the study of unfamiliar situations suggests
the need for familiar situations at the outset as a means of
making the ideas clear.

Moreover, the need for variety of familiar situations is
evident. To enlarge his acquaintance with the general ideas,
it is necessary for the pupil to meet them as different situations, to come upon them from different views and in different garbs. Continuity of the one suggests variations of the
other. Since it is the general ideas that are the subjects of
study and that should be at the center of attention, the
situations that present them cannot well be continuous either
in form or subject matter. If one is interested in the situations as ends in themselves, he will see to it that they themselves make a continued story. Such situations as 'the bean
bag game,' 'a trip to the country,' 'the county fair,' and
the like, will be the subjects of study and discussion. If, on
the other hand, one is interested in the general ideas to be
developed, he will select first one situation, then a different
one, as illustrations of the ideas. He will see to it that the
situation of a given problem is different from the one preceding and the one following.

Finally, no elaborate statement of the situation in a problem will be attempted. Two things are to be kept in mind.
The first is that the situation should be a familiar one, in
which case it does not need elaborate statement. The second is that the purpose of the exercise is to center the
attention of the pupil upon an idea of arrangement, and not
upon the possibilities of the situation. One may, if he
wishes, add to the general enthusiasm in the situation by
giving it an elaborate and interesting statement. One may,
in such a problem as "John's fish," for example, describe at
length John's fishing trip and the exciting adventures John
experienced in catching the five fish, and he may stimulate

a lively discussion about fishing in general. Such a possibility offers its temptations to every teacher; it is so easy to digress from the work at hand, and so inviting to secure the interest and enthusiasm of the pupils, that one can hardly resist leaving the general idea of subtraction, for example, for an animated discussion of an imaginary boy on his vacation. But remember that the interest that may be aroused by such digressions is in every case extrinsic interest, not intrinsic interest in what should be the central theme of the exercise. The present writer has elsewhere brought together data showing that the effort to assist pupils in their problem-practice exercises by elaborate statements of the situations is largely misdirected and wasted.[2]

6. Ready Recognition Is Required

The point is often made that, in the actual and real experiences of life, one is confronted by very much more of the whole of a given situation than is presented in the terse, conventional statement of the problem-practice exercise, such as our discussion has recommended and such as textbooks usually offer. A very pointed presentation of this view is offered in an article by Brueckner from which the following paragraphs are taken:

> Many of the problems that arise in life can be solved only by the application of quantitative methods, involving not merely computation but also the consideration of important social and economic relations. For example, suppose that a sidewalk in a state of disrepair is to be replaced. The problem the owner of the property faces is, "How can this be done most economically and efficiently?" The typical verbal problem in arithmetic which presents this situation to the pupil might be stated as follows, "Mr. Andrews plans to build a sidewalk 5 feet wide and 45 feet long. How much will this

<hr/>

[2] H. G. Wheat, *The Relative Merits of Conventional and Imaginative Types of Problems in Arithmetic* (Bureau of Publications, Teachers College, Columbia University, New York, 1929).

cost at $2.25 a square yard?" In this statement the pupil is given all of the essential facts needed to get the answer to the question asked. He must decide on the processes to use and then perform the necessary computations. None of the important social and civic relations involved in the situation as it would develop in life are introduced in the statement of this typical verbal problem.

The questions that the property owner himself must face are much more far-reaching than those included in the above problem. Such considerations as the following arise in the typical situation: "Are there any legal restrictions on the type of sidewalk that may be laid, its width and materials of which it may be constructed? If so, why are there restrictions of this kind? Does the city build the sidewalk or must I secure a contractor myself? If the latter, how do I go about it to select a contractor? How do I secure bids on the work to be done? What information should I have concerning the reliability of the various firms which will guide me in selecting the firm to do the work? How can I be certain that the contract is correctly drawn? Are the bids too high? What investigations can I make which will enable me to find out if the bids are too high? In the absence of legal specifications how can I be certain that my sidewalk will be constructed according to sound engineering principles? After I have let the contract, need I check in any way on the extent to which the specifications in the contract are carried out? What steps will conclude the transaction? Does the city pay any portion of the cost of the sidewalk?" Similar questions are faced by the contractor in making out the bid so as to secure the work, in buying materials, laying the sidewalk, and supervising the work.[3]

The situation of sidewalk building takes us far beyond any activity suitable for beginners in arithmetic, but the manner of its discussion is illustrative of the kind of problem the teacher of beginners must face. Is the typical verbal problem of the cost of a sidewalk 5 feet wide and 45 feet

[3] L. J. Brueckner. "The nature of problem-solving" (*Journal of the National Education Association*, 21: January, 1932), pp. 13–14.

long at $2.25 a square yard suitable, or should the much more elaborate and complicated problem be the one for the teacher to present? The answer to this question must be determined by the purpose of the class exercise. If the purpose is to illustrate the relation between square feet and square yards or to illustrate the importance of being familiar with such relationship and of giving attention to it under a variety of circumstances, the verbal problem quoted is, along with many others of similar nature and purpose, suitable and appropriate. In that case, any introduction of the elements of legal requirements, of dealing with contractors, etc., would serve only as a means of distraction. If, on the other hand, the purpose is to introduce the pupil to the complicated problem of the property owner in building a sidewalk to meet the legal requirements of his neighborhood, the latter type of situation would be made the subject of study. In that case, the wise teacher would be perfectly sure of the fact that all the pupils had learned the relationship between square feet and square yards. In such case, the part of the situation relating to the size of walk and cost per square yard would in all probability appear in a form quite different from the one given in the quoted paragraphs.

In order to bring the illustration of the matter within the scope of the work of the beginning grades, we may consider the suggestion that such a statement as, "Frank had 1 penny and his mother gave him 4 pennies. How many pennies did he then have?" does not represent the total situation with which Frank is confronted. In the 'real life' experience, the situation confronting Frank might perhaps be something like this: "I have one penny and mother gives me four. How many more do I need to buy a sucker that costs two pennies and a pencil which costs five?" We are not concerned, however, with the real-life experience, but with the particular phases of real-life experiences that may be used for the purpose of contributing to the systematic training of the pupil in order that he may *move on* to real-life experiences on a level higher than those of childhood. We see the need for the development of the idea of a particular kind of number relation, and we provide for its abundant and varied illustration. We look beyond the pupil's present life to the time when he must be ready to give his attention with certainty and assurance to this and that type of number relationship, each as a rapidly passing phase of a larger and more involved total situation; we note that the usual life experience does not require an extended fixing of attention upon a particular fact of number relation, such as an elaborate statement of Frank's pennies might require; and so we provide for the pupil's training the type of illustration that demands a ready recognition of the general idea that it portrays. We remember that the exercises that are offered are intended to give training in the recognition of ideas; and so we select those that are varied for the sake of breadth and those that are tersely stated for the sake of readiness.

7. The Purpose of Writing

Frequently the efforts of the pupils to arrive at the answers to the questions raised in problem-practice exercises are guided in the direction of an excessive amount of activity with pencil and paper or at the board. Too often the pupils are required to engage in writing to such a degree that they quickly form the notion that problems are solved on paper or on the board. It is the too common occurrence for pupils to begin writing before they begin to think, and even to try first one operation, then another, without indulging in thought. It is important for us at this point, then, to get clear concerning the real purpose of the activity of writing in connection with the mental activity of finding the answer to a problem.

In the solution of a simple, one-step problem, the adult does not need to write. He solves it 'in his head.' In the solution of a problem of several steps, he needs to do some writing, but here again he solves it 'in his head.' He is able to take each step mentally, but he finds it necessary, in order to take several steps successively, to write the result of each step as a means of remembering it while he proceeds to the succeeding steps with an untrammeled mind. From step to step he writes the results of his thinking. What he writes is not the solution, but a more or less inadequate record of the solution. What he writes serves primarily as a reminder of what he has done mentally.

Likewise, the pupil in the first grade or the second grade solves his problems mentally and needs to resort to writing only to provide himself with reminders. It may be pointed out that writing is not needed in the *solution* of the one-step, single-process problem exercises that are there offered, and that it needs to be introduced only as a means of establishing the connection between the actual mental solution of problems and the written records of their solution. In the problem of Frank's pennies (Frank had 1 penny and his mother gave him 4 pennies), for example, no writing is needed, because the pupil needs no written reminder in adding 1 and 4. If, however, the problem involves more than one operation, such as column addition or two-place addition and subtraction, he will at the outset need to resort to writing to provide reminders both of what he has done and of what he needs to do.

In a problem which requires the adding of a column, such as 1

4

3, the pupil at the outset will need to write the column. In the first place, he will need to keep the quantities before his eyes in order to remember them. In adding 1 and 4 he may forget either to add the next quantity or what the next quantity is that he has to add. Accordingly, he writes the column; and although he does not write the partial solution secured by adding 1 and 4, he has the 3 before him as a reminder that more adding is to be done.

In a problem that requires a two-place operation, such as "there are 22 boys and 23 girls in the class," the pupil

22

will at the outset need to resort to writing, 23 . He first adds 2 and 3, and sets down that partial result, which stands as a reminder of what he has done. No effort is then needed to remember that partial result, because it is before him in writing and in its proper position; he is able to turn to the next requirement of the solution with a free mind. He now adds 2 and 2 and sets down that partial result in its proper position. The two partial results, set down in their proper positions, give him the answer he seeks.

In a problem that requires addition in the higher decades,

25

such as 3 , writing is not needed in the activity of determining the answer. The addition that is made ought to be a single process, like the adding of 5 and 3. Writing should not be permitted, except for the purpose of establishing the connection between the solution and the written record.

What has been said about the purpose of writing in the exercises with the simple one-step problems of the pupil's earliest activities applies with like emphasis to his later activities with problems of two and more steps. These later exercises are intended to give practice in recognizing the ideas of addition, subtraction, multiplication, and division when they appear as double and triple operations, etc. The real purpose of the exercises is to give practice in recognition of ideas. The pupil needs to write only enough of his computations to serve as a sufficient reminder of what he has done mentally at each step to permit him without hindrance to proceed to the consideration of succeeding steps.

8. How to Conduct the Practice

The purpose of the problem-practice exercise will bear repeating: it is to develop ideas by means of ready recognition of ideas in familiar situations. To this end, let the practice for the most part be oral practice; let the teacher or a pupil state the problem, and a pupil give the answer. When the pupils have had considerable oral practice, it will be time to show how the solution is recorded on paper or on the board. Only enough of the written exercise should be set down to establish the connection between the recognition of addition, say, in the problem of "Frank's pennies,"

$$\begin{array}{r} 1 \\ \text{and the way the solution is recorded, } 4. \\ \hline 5 \end{array}$$ If the pupils have

done in a satisfactory way the work suggested in the preceding chapter, written work will not be necessary until they have to deal with problems requiring column addition, addition of two-place numbers, etc.

When a problem is given, it should be stated twice at least. The adult who is confronted with a written problem reads it twice or more. He reads it the first time to grasp the import of the situation that is presented. (This may, of course, require more than one reading.) He reads it the second time (or finally) to recognize the numbers exactly. So, in presenting a problem, the teacher should read it to the class once in order for the pupils to grasp its meaning. (If one reading does not make the meaning clear to the pupils, read it again, and even a third time.) Permit no pupil to write a number during the first reading. Permit no writing until the pupils understand what is presented in the problem and what is required. When they understand, read the problem a second time (or finally) for them to get the numbers exactly.

Encourage a minimum of writing. If a pupil 'works' a problem without the need for writing, he has secured all the practice the problem is intended to give. Commend him for his accomplishment. Let him make a note of his answer (write it) if the oral answer is not desired. It will be necessary, however, as indicated above, for the pupil to write the quantities in dealing with problems involving column addition, two-place numbers, and the like.

Moreover, the pupils should be taught to *avoid unnecessary labeling*. A label in the written record of a solution is sometimes needed to serve as a reminder. When needed in the more involved problems of later arithmetic, it should be so used. In the simple, one-step problems of beginning arithmetic, there is no such need for labels. What the quantities stand for is comprehended without the labels. Moreover, the requirement of writing the labels serves to impress the mistaken notion that the solution of a problem comes through writing.

9. Summary

When the pupil has had sufficient practice in thinking the arrangement of objects to understand what he is about, he may proceed to practice in thinking arrangement when the objects are present only in imagination. He thus is enabled to carry his practice to a higher level. Moreover, he is provided practice in the recognition of certain general ideas of arrangement that appear in a variety of familiar situations to which he must give his attention.

Such practice in the recognition of general ideas in familiar situations is the so-called 'problem-solving' activity on the early levels of training. Later discussions will give further consideration to this phase of the problem-solving activity and also to the phase of the activity that is appropriate on the later levels of training.

IV. PRACTICING THE COMBINATIONS

1. Attention to Arrangement

In the activities of studying groups described in the preceding chapter, the pupils give their attention to the arrangement of objects (1) when the teacher makes the arrangements, (2) when they themselves make the arrangements, and (3) when they think the arrangements. In the activities, described in the preceding section of this chapter, the pupils carry their study of arrangement to a higher level.

They learn to give their attention to arrangement (4) when the objects to be arranged are present only in imagination. Now, in order to carry their thinking to a still higher level, the pupils must have practice in giving their attention to arrangement (5) when no objects at all are present. In this last step the study of arrangement is entirely a matter of thought. By means of the language of arrangement that the children learn and use in the four steps preceding, they fix their attention upon various arrangements and give them the proper descriptions.

2. What Practice Should Mean

Practicing the combinations often means — rather, it often degenerates into — mere practicing in writing the symbols and saying the appropriate words. Often the pupil will practice writing $\frac{5}{8}$, and saying "Five and three are eight," without giving any attention whatever to the idea of arrangement for which the expressions stand. When he does this, he receives practice, to be sure, but it is merely practice in using written and oral expressions, and not practice in thinking. Such practice leads in time to perfect memorization of the expressions, to their use with accuracy and speed, to mechanical perfection. Whether such practice has any value is a matter of serious doubt. About the fact that it produces harmful results, however, there can be no question. Pupils often learn to 'add' — that is, to go through the motions that bring the right answer, when the meaning of adding has escaped them entirely. They become mere adding machines, able to add when told, but unable to decide when and why to add.

The kind of practice the teacher should organize and conduct is not the kind that will be designed to bring the pupil into competition with an adding machine. The pupil can never hope to compete with the machine in doing the purely

mechanical things the machine is made to do. The kind of
practice the pupil receives should lead him to do the things
that are mental, not merely mechanical. For his own thinking, however, a certain degree of mechanical perfection will
be necessary. For example, he will need to be accurate in
his work, and he will need to work with reasonable speed.
But these are secondary to the all-important outcome of
being able to understand. Moreover, if the pupil understands what he is doing, and then practices what he understands in an understanding way, he will in time reach the
needed requirements of accuracy and speed. If we are going
to think of accuracy and speed as outcomes of practice, let
us think of them from the beginning in their proper relations with understanding, and in their proper sequence with
it; namely, (1) understanding, (2) accuracy, (3) speed.

3. Dangers to Be Avoided

In conducting practice with the combinations, the teacher
is constantly tempted to expect of the beginner the same
type of automatic response that the adult has learned to
give. The fact that a child can learn to write the expression, $\frac{5}{4}$, for example, with speed, and to speak the sentence,
"Five and four are nine," with no hesitation, constantly
suggests to the teacher the notion that the child can make
the same response as the adult. It is a case of a similarity
of outward responses suggesting a similarity of inward responses.

Through long experience with groups and their arrangements the adult has reached the point where his expressions
of the combinations are far removed from concrete experiences. He has built up so much meaning back of the expressions that the expressions have come to stand in place of
their meanings. Not only have the expressions themselves
become habituated, but the directions of one's thinking that

accompany them have also become habituated. Merely to give the expressions is sufficient for the adult. The child, on the other hand, has not acquired the long experience with groups and their arrangements that give the expressions of the combinations such abundant meaning. He has not been able to remove them very far from the concrete experiences for which they stand. Their meanings have just begun to develop in his mind, and they have by no means become habituated. So, if the child is required to give the written and oral expressions with too great speed and without some reference to the concrete experiences that make them meaningful, he is tempted to forsake their meanings entirely and to habituate the expressions merely as things to write and as things to say.

It will be necessary, therefore, for the teacher to make haste slowly. It is a fairly safe rule never to let the child write anything or say anything unless he first understands what he is doing. When a pupil is given a question, the teacher should see that he fully comprehends the question and thinks the answer before he attempts to give the answer. The teacher should constantly bear in mind that the child can memorize all the written and oral expressions perfectly without giving a thought to the arrangements for which they stand.

4. Rules to Follow

a. Make haste slowly. Do not strive for speed. As the pupil learns to think through an arrangement, and as he thinks through it again and again in the practice, he will gain speed in giving the correct responses.

b. Delay the pupil's response until he is sure it is the correct one. If the student of arithmetic learns to think before he writes, he will save an enormous amount of time usually required for erasures and for repeated trials.

c. Develop confidence. Let the pupil be sure he is right, then go ahead. Confidence, which grows with understand-

ing, is always better than mere skill. Let the activities of
this section follow the four steps in the study of arrangement
that have been described in preceding discussions, and the
pupil will be prepared to determine his own answers in the
practice of the fifth step. Let the pupil take what time he
needs to think the arrangement when no objects are present,
and he will be sure of his answers. He will not only carry
on successful work at the moment, but will also develop an
attitude that will be most helpful at succeeding stages of
his work.

d. Do not expect adult performance of children. If, when
the child is given such a question as -3, he resorts to the
9
actual arrangement of the objects that are before him, or
takes the time to imagine the arrangement, or counts off
his answer on his fingers, let him proceed to his answer in
his own way. Understanding of his answer and confidence
in it are the important results to be sought. If he seems
slow, have patience. Ask him the same question once more
presently, and ask it again and again. He may still be slow
in determining his answer, but he will gain in speed as practice continues. As he improves slowly through the right
kind of practice, he will learn to substitute better methods
for his earlier immature ones. It is a mistake for another to
try to do the substituting for him.

e. Insist upon attentive practice. Be sure the pupil gives
his attention to the question that is asked, whether given
orally or in writing. Let him take the time to understand
what is wanted and to determine what is wanted. His
response should be fundamentally a thought response, not
merely a verbal or a symbolic one.

f. Do not let the practice period drag. Start with good
attention, and stop before the interest lags. When a question is given, insist that each child *think* the answer for
himself and be ready to give it, if called upon. Call upon
different pupils for the answers.

g. Distribute the practice. Have a little practice each day. Drill upon a given combination, or group of combinations, very frequently at first, and less and less frequently as they are mastered.

h. Provide most practice at the points of difficulty. Observe the combinations that occasion difficulty. Let these be repeated with greatest frequency.

5. Practice Upon Number Ideas First

The exercises described in the preceding chapter are intended to lead to a development of the number ideas, one to nine. In the development of these ideas, the pupils have given their attention to various arrangements; that is, to various combinations. Drilling upon these ideas — upon the arrangements in their relations and as they contribute to these ideas — should precede the drills upon the arrangements in chance order.

In connection with the idea six, for example, let the pupils 'tell the whole story' of six, then 'write the whole story' of six. The 'whole story' is represented by such expressions as the following:

(a) Comparisons: $\dfrac{10}{-\ 6}$, $\dfrac{9}{-6}$, $\dfrac{8}{-6}$, $\dfrac{7}{-6}$, $\dfrac{6}{-5}$, $\dfrac{6}{-4}$, etc.

(b) Take away: $\dfrac{6}{-5}$, $\dfrac{6}{-4}$, $\dfrac{6}{-3}$, $\dfrac{6}{-2}$, $\dfrac{6}{-1}$.

(c) Put together: $\dfrac{5}{1}$, $\dfrac{4}{2}$, $\dfrac{3}{3}$, $\dfrac{2}{4}$, $\dfrac{1}{5}$.

(d) Equal groups: $2\overline{)\ 6}$, $3\overline{)\ 6}$.

In connection with written questions like those just shown the pupils may either answer orally or write the answers.

6. Practice Upon Combinations in Isolation

Practice upon the combinations in their relations to the ideas that hold them together should continue until they are pretty definitely fixed in mind. In connection with such practice, practice upon the combinations in chance order should gradually be introduced.

It will be necessary eventually for the pupils to be able to use any combination under any circumstance, without reference to others that may be related. For example, the pupil will need to add five and three and to do it immediately without reference to two and six, or four and four, etc. He will need, when he is ready for it, practice upon five and three in isolation; that is, without reference to two and six, etc. Exercises that provide for such drills in isolation should be conducted. Let each pupil give the answers orally, across the lines, sometimes forward, sometimes backward, up the columns, and down the columns; or let one pupil give the answers for one row or one column, and let another give the answers for the next, and so on. After sufficient oral practice, let the answers be given in writing. It is desirable to use printed, or mimeographed, sheets containing the exercises for the written practice.[4]

7. Practice in Thinking

Let it be repeated that the practice desired is practice in thinking, not practice in remembering. Train the pupils so that they will keep themselves from speaking or writing an answer until they have thought out the arrangement and are sure of their answer. Practice in thinking will gradually lead to the type of memorization that is useful, whereas practice in remembering may defeat its own ends, because the pupils may try to remember things to say and things to write. Such practice in remembering is always confusing. Practice in thinking the arrangements is slow work at first, but speed gradually comes. What is more to the point, the pupils finally automatize their *thinking*, rather than their words and symbols alone.

[4] The author's *Practice Books for Arithmetic*, Grade II to Grade VIII, inclusive (D. C. Heath and Company, Boston, 1936), provide such materials, particularly in the books for the earlier grades.

8. Drill Devices

For the sake of adding a little variation to the drills, it is permissible for the teacher to make use of some of the common drill devices, such as 'going up and down the ladder,' 'using the fish pond,' 'going around the circle,' 'finding one's way out of the maze,' and others of like nature.

The value of such devices, as indicated, is that they provide a little variety, or spice, or diversion, to the drills. They add flavor to the drills, as it were. Occasional resort to them is to be recommended. A few diverting measures in one's work are not to be condemned.

Such devices, however, must be used with care and caution. Just because they provide variety and diversion, they may prove to be too diverting. The child readily becomes enthusiastic about a new trick. He is apt to become so absorbed in it as to miss the lessons the trick is intended to aid. For example, the child is apt to become so absorbed in getting the largest possible number of answers from the 'fish pond,' or in the imagined difficulty of finding his way out of the 'maze,' that he will resort to the activity of trying to recite the answers to the combinations from memory. Instead of *thinking* the arrangement of objects that the question asks for, he may become absorbed in the competition provided by the game. If the pupils have learned to *think* the arrangements of objects, a little spice may be added to the exercises; too much spice, however, may spoil the exercises. If the children need to be diverted from the requirements of the exercises, it will probably be better to stop the exercises for a while and let them get some real diversion by playing a game that has no connection with the exercises than to mix game and exercises and have a poor quality of both.

9. Providing Variety

The kind of variety to be provided, when variety is needed, is variety of method that will ensure the same responses of thinking, not variety of method that will lead to different responses. The type of response to be secured is, as pointed out repeatedly, that of *thinking* arrangement.

Variety, to list a few suggestions, may be had by such means as these:

(1) 'Telling the story.'
(2) 'Writing the story.'
(3) Giving oral answers to exercises.
(4) Giving written answers to exercises.
(5) Using the blackboard or printed or mimeographed exercises.
(6) Using number cards. On the face of the card the question may be written and on the reverse the desired grouping may be indicated, thus:

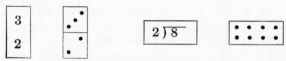

The reverse sides of the cards may be used for occasional reference, as needed.

(7) Illustrating numbers by distances. Additions and subtractions may frequently be illustrated to good advantage by directions of movement through spaces. For the beginner, the stepladder illustration may be suggestive. Let a ladder be drawn, nine steps high, with each step numbered. Let the activity be that of an imagined painter moving up and down the ladder while he is painting the side of a house. From the ground he moves up three steps. Next, he 'goes up' four steps. "How many steps up the ladder then?" "Now, he comes down five steps. Where is he?" "Now, he goes up six steps. Where is he?" And so on.

Indicate, before a question is asked, on which step the painter is standing. Be sure that is clear. Cover the numbers of the steps, and ask the question. When the answer is given, uncover the numbers so the answer can be checked.

It is to be remembered, whenever such devices are used, that the simpler the device the more quickly the pupil will understand its use and the less likelihood there will be that he will be distracted from his practice in thinking.

10. Summary

The present section deals with the activity of studying the arrangement of objects when the objects are not present. The activity is not unlike those previously described, except that it carries the study of arrangement to a new level. It, therefore, closely connects with, and depends upon, the activities of studying arrangement that precede.

CHAPTER XII

THE IDEA OF TEN: GROUPING BY TENS

ARGUMENT

1. Following the study of groups to ten, pupils must learn to think groups together and apart in a new way; namely, in relation to the idea of ten. Accordingly, this idea must first be developed.

2. The decimal system of notation requires the new and different method of thinking.

3. The place value of the numerals and the significance of zero as a place holder should be given consideration.

4. The so-called 'zero combinations' have no place in the elementary arithmetic of the Hindu-Arabic system.

5. Ten as a group should be studied in the same way that the groups preceding it have been studied (see Chapter X).

6. The use of ten in the writing of the 'teens and other two-place numbers should be learned. The significance of the ten's position should be called to attention.

7. The significance of the nine numerals in ten's position should be demonstrated objectively by groups of ten.

I. The Results of the Previous Study
by the Pupils

The activities in which the pupils have been engaging up to this point have been described as *thoughtful* activities — activities of giving attention in a thoughtful way to groups and to arrangements. To the extent that their activities have been thoughtful, the pupils have gained certain well-defined results. These we may enumerate briefly as follows:

1. Through the systematic study of groups to nine — by counting, by comparison, and by taking apart and putting together — the pupils have developed and clarified their number ideas to nine. By now, these ideas have become

238

definite. Each is an idea of importance in its own right as well as in its relations to the others, and each has become so well known that it can be used with confidence and independence.

2. In the systematic study of each group to nine the group has been arranged in various ways — taken apart and put together — and the arrangements have been noted, studied, thought, described, and stored in memory. These arrangements were learned in their relations, reviewed in their relations, and finally, reviewed one by one in isolation. Moreover, by means of problem-practice exercises the pupils have had practice in recognizing the ideas of arrangement that go by the names addition and subtraction, as they appeared as integral parts of familiar situations.

By means of their earlier counting exercises and later through comparisons, the pupils have acquired in some degree the idea of ten. The group of ten has been studied by counting it and by comparing it with smaller groups. Moreover, to the degree that the counting exercises have gone beyond ten, the pupils have gained other ideas. They have had some practice in counting to twenty, perhaps beyond twenty, and they have had some practice in writing the signs or figures for the number ideas, ten to twenty.

II. The Next Step

In an earlier discussion the mistake was pointed out of trying to take children too rapidly and abruptly from the activities of counting to the activities of using number ideas in combinations. It was pointed out that the pupils need to develop and clarify their ideas to nine before they can be expected to use them in combinations with understanding and independence. Accordingly, the systematic study of groups to nine was undertaken, which has led not only to a development of the ideas, but also to some training in their use in combination.

Now that the pupils have developed their ideas to nine

and have learned nearly half of the addition and subtraction combinations of these nine ideas, it would seem that the next step is the one of learning the rest of the combinations of the nine number ideas.

Learning the rest of the combinations would, indeed, be the next step, were it not for the fact that the pupils must learn to deal with groups and with arrangements that exceed nine in a way that is quite different from the way they have been dealing with the groups and arrangements that do not exceed nine. From now on, the pupils must learn to group and to arrange objects, or to think such groups and arrangements, *in a new way — new* to them, at least. So, before they are led to undertake the learning of the rest of the combinations of the number ideas they have been learning, they need first of all to become acquainted with this new way of dealing with groups and arrangements of objects.

III. The Written Language of Number

The practice of expressing the number ideas in writing — that is, by signs, symbols, or figures — serves two purposes. In the first place, the writing serves as a record of thinking after it has been carried on. When one has counted a group of fifty objects, for example, or has come by some other means to an idea of this group, he can write down as a record the result of his thinking, thus, 50, or L, or fifty. As a record, each is as good as the other. Instead of having to carry the result in memory, he can turn to the record — 50, or L, or fifty — and note what he has once done.

Secondly, the writing of a number idea may serve, not only as a reminder of *what* one has thought out, but also as a reminder of *how* he thought it out. It may serve to record not only the *results* of thinking, but also the *manner* of thinking. Recording *results* aids the memory; recording *manner* of thinking aids later thinking, makes later thinking easier. Let us illustrate.

The sign, L, records fifty, but it does not show how one arrived at the idea. The sign, 50, records fifty, and shows how one has built up his ideas to get fifty. 50 shows five tens. One may hold in mind that L stands for five times X, but one does not need to remember that 50 is five times 10. The relation between 50 and 10 is shown in the way 50 is written. The Roman sign, C, stands for one hundred, but it does not *show* ten tens. The Arabic sign, 100, both stands for one hundred, and shows ten tens.

In the Arabic system of writing numbers, there are nine signs, 1, 2, 3, 4, 5, 6, 7, 8, 9. Each stands for a separate group. Although the groups are related in various ways, the signs do not show the relations. One has to carry these relations in his mind. In the writing of the number ideas beyond nine, the same nine symbols are used in various ways, not to show different unrelated groups, but to show tens and groups of ten. *Everything beyond nine is written as so many tens.* Instead of having different symbols for ten, fifty, one hundred, and five hundred, and so on, one uses the same symbols to write these ideas as he has learned to use in writing the ideas to ten. The symbols still are written in the same way and may be handled in the same way. They record the different ideas *by the position* in which they are written.

The symbol 1 written in ten's place means 1 ten — 10.
The symbol 5 written in ten's place means 5 tens — 50.
The symbol 1 written in hundred's place means 1 hundred — 100.
The symbol 5 written in hundred's place means 5 hundred — 500.

To write eleven, one writes two 1's, 11. The signs, 11, may look like two 1's, but they do not stand for two 1's. Position must be considered. The signs, 11, show 1 *ten* and 1. The signs, 55, show 5 *tens* and 5; 505 show 5 *hundreds* and 5, and so on. Such considerations as these are of special significance in the training of the pupil, because they emphasize the mode of thought that he should learn.

IV. The Use of a Place Holder

To write five hundred thirty-seven, one writes 5 in hundred's place, 3 in ten's place, and 7 in unit's place — 537. To write five hundred, one writes 5 in hundred's place — 500. Since one has nothing else to write, he must use some means of putting the 5 in hundred's place. The zeros, 0 0, hold ten's and unit's places. To write five hundred seven, one writes 5 in hundred's place and 7 in unit's place. The symbols written are 5 and 7. Suppose he writes it thus, 5 7. So written, it is confusing. One needs a sign to put 5 in its proper place. The zero does it, thus — 507. In writing a large number, 2463, for example, in which every place is filled by the sign for a number, one does not need a place holder, because each number sign holds its own place. But in writing a large number, 2060, for example, in which every place is not filled by the sign of a number, one needs something to fill up the places and hold them. The zero serves as a place holder. That is the use it has in our number system. That is the use the pupils need to learn.

V. The So-Called 'Zero Combinations'

If pupils are taught the real meaning and use of the zero, they need not try to learn the various meaningless and misleading expressions that usually go by the name 'zero combinations.' They will have no use for such expressions, either in connection with their day by day experiences with groups or in their later study and use of the number system.

The pupil has no need for a sign for 'nothing.' If he wishes to write nothing, he writes nothing; that is, he does not write anything. If, in dealing with groups, he observes no group, he needs to pay the fact no further attention, and therefore, he does not need to say anything, or to write something, about it. To illustrate, if there are five marbles in one hand, and none in the other, the pupil knows at once without further consideration that the total is five. He knows it perfectly well before anyone tells him that "five

and nothing are five," and shows him how to write $\dfrac{5}{\underline{0}}$. If he
5

sees that none are taken away, that the marbles are not disturbed, he realizes the fact at once. No further inquiry is necessary. He does not need to be asked, or to ask himself, "nothing from five is how many?" The fact is so well known that it does not require oral or written description.

Learning the expression, $\dfrac{5}{\underline{-0}}$, is learning to express some-
5

thing that is so obvious as to need no expression.

Moreover, the writing of a 'zero combination' gives the appearance of expressing and describing an actual arrangement when none has been made. Suppose there are five objects in one hand and none in the other. Let the expres-

sion, $\dfrac{5}{\underline{0}}$, be written. The expression apparently describes an
5

arrangement of the objects that has been made, or thought, when in fact no arrangement has been attempted. The pupil is asked to describe something that has been done with the group when it is perfectly clear that nothing has

been done. True, the pupil may learn to write, $\dfrac{5}{\underline{0}}$, and to
5

say, "Five and nothing are five," but he will be learning to use a meaningless and misleading set of expressions, which, though pretending to express something, expresses nothing.

When the pupil comes to dealing with tens and groups of tens, he will have no use for the zero except as a place holder. In his operations with tens, he may find what appears to be a 'zero combination' in one or more of the columns. For example, in the additions shown it appears that a 'zero combination' must be dealt with in the two unit's columns. In both, the zero is first observed and then neglected. In the

$$\begin{array}{r} 25 \\ \underline{30} \end{array} \qquad \begin{array}{r} 25 \\ 30 \\ \underline{43} \end{array}$$

first, one notices five represented in the unit's column, and that is all he finds represented. In setting down below the line the number represented, he sets down what he sees. In the second, one notices five and three represented in the unit's column, so five and three are thought together as eight. The zero is neglected because it is something that does not influence the arrangement to be performed or to be thought. The zero, being used as a place holder, is attended to as a place holder.

Zero combinations have been giving pupils unusual difficulty for the past twenty years. About twenty years ago, they began to appear in tests, and pupils were confused by them. The remedy used for the difficulty was that of 'teaching' these zero combinations, or trying to teach them. Teachers have tried to explain them, but, since they mean nothing, explanations have added to the confusion. The remedy suggested here is to omit them, both from the teaching and the testing, since they are both meaningless and useless. Their uselessness will be indicated from time to time in connection with the discussions of operations which *apparently*, though not actually, employ them.

VI. The Importance of Ten

The importance of the idea of ten has been indicated. Its importance is unique. No other group is used in the same sense. When one is dealing with groups smaller than ten, he deals with separate groups. When he deals with groups larger than nine, he deals with them as tens. Everything beyond nine is stated as ten, or some grouping or arrangement of tens.

In expressing the ideas beyond nine in writing, one learns to resort to the use of position. In one position a figure represents units; in another, tens; and so on.

In number-thinking, one thinks of groups to ten and then thinks of groups by tens in exactly the same way.

The idea of ten is an idea of paramount importance: every

activity that can be used to get pupils to develop it must be used. As the pupil makes progress in his arithmetic, he will make understandable progress to the extent that he is familiar with ten and is conscious of its use and importance. Each succeeding activity, up to and through the study of decimals and percentage, will require the pupil to employ his idea of ten and to depend upon the position of the figures he writes as he thinks, and each succeeding activity may serve to enlarge his idea of ten and his use of position. The beginner cannot learn at the outset all he will need to know about ten and about position. He will have the chance to learn more and more about them as he employs them in succeeding activities. What is important now is that he be made conscious of the ideas of ten and of position so that he will have something *in his own mind* to rely upon as he moves along to succeeding stages of his work.

VII. STUDYING THE GROUP OF TEN

The work begins with a systematic study of the group of ten. The object is to enlarge and clarify the pupil's idea of ten. The methods are the same as the ones the pupil has learned to employ in studying the groups to nine.

1. Enlarge the Idea of Ten by Comparisons

By means of the activities of comparing, such as are described in Chapter X, the pupils may enlarge their idea of ten. Let a group of ten be counted, and compared with a group of eight, seven, nine, five, six, etc.

When actual comparisons have been made and described by the oral and written language of comparison, let the pupils answer such questions as:

"Ten is how many more than eight?"
$$\begin{array}{r} 10 \\ -8 \\ \hline \end{array}$$

"Ten is how many more than seven?"
$$\begin{array}{r} 10 \\ -7 \\ \hline \end{array}$$

"Ten is how many more than nine?"
$$\begin{array}{r} 10 \\ -9 \\ \hline \end{array}$$

2. Take Apart and Put Together Arrangements of Ten

With a group of ten objects, say, pencils, before each of the pupils, the teacher asks such questions and gets such replies as these:

"How many pencils have you?"

"Take three away. How many are left?"

"Tell what you have done." "Three from ten is seven."

$$\begin{array}{r} 10 \\ -3 \\ \hline 7 \end{array}$$

"Write what you have done."

$$\begin{array}{r} 3 \\ 7 \\ \hline \end{array}$$

"Three and seven are how many?"

By similar questions, the attention of the pupils is called to the various arrangements that can be made with ten objects, and the pupils learn to describe each arrangement both orally and in writing.

Following are the written expressions of the arrangements of ten that the pupils learn to make and to describe:

$$\begin{array}{ccccccccc} 10 & 10 & 10 & 10 & 10 & 10 & 10 & 10 & 10 \\ -9 & -8 & -7 & -6 & -5 & -4 & -3 & -2 & -1 \\ \hline 1 & 2 & 3 & 4 & 5 & 6 & 7 & 8 & 9 \end{array}$$

$$\begin{array}{ccccccccc} 9 & 8 & 7 & 6 & 5 & 4 & 3 & 2 & 1 \\ 1 & 2 & 3 & 4 & 5 & 6 & 7 & 8 & 9 \\ \hline 10 & 10 & 10 & 10 & 10 & 10 & 10 & 10 & 10 \end{array}$$

$$\begin{array}{cc} 5 & 2 \\ 2)\overline{10} & 5)\overline{10} \\ \underline{10} & \underline{10} \end{array}$$

It will be noted that there are nine new arrangements of subtraction and nine new arrangements of addition. These, added to the ones the pupils have already learned, make a total of 45 arrangements of each.

Practice continues by having the pupils *think* the arrangements in answer to the teacher's questions, by having them tell and write 'the whole story' of ten, etc. Finally, the arrangements are practiced as they are made to appear in chance order. The exercises for practice are conducted as described in the final section of the preceding chapter. These include the 45 combinations of addition and the 45 combinations of subtraction.

The teacher should not neglect requiring the pupils to give attention to arrangements of ten objects when the objects are present only in the imagination. Exercises such as those suggested in the preceding chapter should be conducted.

"Jimmie had 10 pieces of candy. He gave away 6 pieces. How many pieces of candy had he left?" etc.

"Sarah has 7 red stamps and 3 blue stamps. How many stamps does Sarah have?" etc.

"Janie picked 10 roses. She tied them together into bouquets, putting 2 roses together in each bouquet. How many bouquets did she have?" etc.

As in the activities suggested in the preceding chapter, so here let the pupils each in turn suggest 'problems' dealing with ten. The objects in the room, their experiences at home and on the playground, buying at the store, etc., provide the materials for many 'problems' that both they and the teacher can give. It will be well, too, in giving 'problems' dealing with ten, to give problems dealing with nine, eight, seven, and so on.

3. Study Ten in Combinations to Nineteen

Through the study of the various possible arrangements of the group of ten and through the activities of comparing the group of ten with smaller groups, the pupils have developed a fairly definite notion of ten as a group, and the symbol, 10, has acquired more definite meaning. The pupils now need to learn more about the ideas, eleven to nineteen, than their previous practice in counting has taught them, and, at the same time, they need to learn more about ten and its use. The first step is the development of some understanding of the relation between the idea of ten and the ideas, eleven to nineteen. Attention should be called to the relation, both as it is demonstrated by the teacher and as the manner of expressing the ideas in writing makes use of and illustrates the relation.

4. Emphasize the Group

Illustrate by the grouping of objects, first, the fact that groups of objects smaller than ten are each thought of as a single group; and second, the fact that groups of ten and of more than ten are each thought of as a group of ten and so many more, as the case may be.

Show a group of five, or seven, or eight, or nine objects. Point out that, when counted as five, let us say, they are put together or thought together all in one group. Put the objects together in one group. Point out that the group is expressed by one figure in writing, 5. Make the same illustrations again and again with other groups to nine, inclusive. Show that each is put together or thought together as one group, and expressed in writing by one figure: 1, 2, 3, 4, 5, 6, 7, 8, or 9.

Next, show a group of ten objects. Point out that they, too, are put together or thought together as one group. Point out that such a group is thought of as one group of ten, but that this group is expressed in writing in a different way. Point out that there is no figure, or sign, for ten, but that *the place where a figure is written* is intended to show ten in writing. Write 10 and compare it with the symbols 1 to 9. Show the place where 1 is written. Point out that the 1 is in ten's place and that it means, not 1, but 1 ten.

Point to the zero in 10 as something that puts the 1 in ten's place. Repeat the fact that to write ten, one has no new or different sign for it, as he has for the numbers one to nine, but has to make use of 1 written in ten's place. "I will write ten by writing 1 in ten's place." Write 1. Ask if that shows 1 ten. "What must I do to put the 1 in ten's place, so that it will show 1 ten?" Let the answer be emphasized that *the 0 is written to put the 1 in its proper place.*

Next, show a group of eleven objects. Have the pupils count them. Point out that such a group is thought of, not as a single group with all the objects together, but as a *group of ten* and one more. Arrange the objects as a group of ten and one more. Point out that the number is to be thought of as ten and one, and that the number is expressed in writing as one ten and one. Write 11. Point out that while 11 looks like two 1's, it does not mean two 1's. *Emphasize the importance of position.* Point out that 11 is written with 1 in unit's place to show one, and 1 in ten's place to show 1 ten; that 11 shows 1 and 1 ten. Referring back to the group of ten and one, or one and ten, called *eleven*, speak of the one as one, and of the ten as one ten. Let this matter be referred to again and again. Let the pupils write 11 and explain what each of the 1's stands for. Ask:

"What does 11 show?" "One and one ten, or one ten and one."

"What is 11 called?" "Eleven."

"Eleven is how many more than ten?"

"Ten and how many more are eleven?"

Point out that the way eleven is written shows that eleven is one more than ten, and that ten and one are eleven.

In similar manner, show groups of ten and two, ten and three, etc., to ten and nine, and explain what the symbols 12 to 19 show in each case.

Let this work be reviewed again and again.

"Write nine and ten together." "19."

"What does 19 show?" "Nine and one ten, or one ten and nine."

"What is 19 called?" "Nineteen."

"Nineteen is how many more than ten?"

"Ten and how many are nineteen?"

"In the figures 19, what does the 9 show?" "What does
the 1 show?" "Why does the 1 in 19 show 1 ten?" "Write
1 ten by itself." "10." "What is the zero for?" and so on.

Let the practice continue until the pupils are able to see
in 15, for example, not a symbol that represents fifteen objects all in one group, but a symbol that represents fifteen
objects grouped as one ten and five.

5. Groups of Tens

In order further to impress the fact that in arithmetic
one must think in terms of ten, the pupils should be introduced to the method of thinking in groups of tens, to the
system of writing the symbols, 20 to 100, and to the significance of these symbols as written. This will include some
counting, some writing and reading of the symbols, and
some demonstration of the groups for which the symbols
stand. It should not be necessary to explain the meaning
of every set of symbols from 20 to 100 or to demonstrate
objectively every idea represented by them.

It is to be assumed that the pupils, through the various
objective demonstrations and activities previously described,
have already developed some fairly definite notions of the
group of ten and of thinking of numbers beyond ten in relation to ten. The pupils should now be given an opportunity
to extend these ideas, to enlarge upon them through their
active employment. It is possible to demonstrate every idea
from ten to one hundred through the use of objects in groups
of tens. It should be kept in mind, however, that while
some demonstration is necessary to set the pupils to thinking, continued demonstration may retard their progress in
thinking. One advantage of the system of using the symbols the pupils are now to learn is that, through emphasizing
a common method of grouping, the system makes continued
use of detailed representation unnecessary. Enough demonstration needs to be provided by the teacher to give the

pupils the idea of method of grouping. When the pupils have developed the idea, they should be encouraged to think the method of grouping that is used.

6. Use Objects in Groups of Ten

Toothpicks are cheap and easy to handle as objects for the demonstrations. Count out ten groups of ten each, and slip a small rubber band around each group of ten to hold them together. Do this before class to save time. When the class assembles, call attention to the bunches of toothpicks. Give each pupil a bunch, or have them passed from pupil to pupil, with instructions to count the toothpicks in each bunch. Let the pupils report the number — ten — in each bunch as it is handed back.

"How many bunches of toothpicks have I?" Ten bunches.

"How many toothpicks in this bunch?" Ten. Write 10.

"Here are two bunches of toothpicks; ten here and ten here, or two tens. This is the way to write two tens, 20."

"Here are three bunches; ten here, ten here, and ten here, or three tens. This is the way to write three tens, 30."

"Here are four bunches —" and so on, until all the tens from 10 to 100 are written.

Hold up five bunches. Ask how many. Have a pupil point to the figures that show five tens, 50. Point out that the 5 in 50 is in ten's place, and shows 5 tens. Continue with six bunches, nine bunches, two bunches, etc., until the pupils have clearly in their minds that 60 shows six tens, 90 shows nine tens, and so on.

Summarize by showing how the toothpicks may be counted as one ten, two tens, and so on to ten tens.

Now, teach the names of two tens, three tens, etc., if the pupils do not already know them: twenty, thirty, and so on to one hundred. When the pupils have learned the names, have them count the bunched toothpicks: ten, twenty, thirty, and so on.

Give the pupils practice in associating the symbols both with their names and with what they stand for:

> 10 is called ten; it means 1 ten.
> 20 is called twenty; it means 2 tens.
> 90 is called ninety; it means 9 tens.

7. Review Groups Already Learned

For the sake of proper associations, let the numbers ten to nineteen be reviewed. Have the symbols written and their meanings discussed. For example, let the children point out that 15 shows 1 ten and five, that 10 shows 1 ten, and so on. Do not have a written expression until the children have given it its common name; for example, 15, fifteen; 10, ten, and so on. What each expression actually shows should always be associated with what it is commonly called.

8. Lead to an Extension of the Idea

Suppose the discussion is upon 16. The pupils call it sixteen, and point out that it shows 1 ten and 6. Substitute 2 for the 1 in ten's place.

> "How many tens do the figures show?" "Two tens."
> "What is the whole number shown?" "Two tens and six."
> "What is 26 called?" "Twenty-six."

If the pupils have difficulty in arriving at the name, twenty-six, point to the symbol, 20, which should be before the pupils on the board. Ask, "how many tens?" and when the answer is given, get the name, twenty. Return to the figure, 26, and give it its name. (It is to be kept in mind that the important thing for the pupils to get in mind is the significance of 26; namely, two tens and six. The name, twenty-six, can be fixed in the exercises of counting or otherwise.)

It may be well to vary the exercise just described. If the original discussion is upon 16, substitute 0 for 6. Have the figure read, and its value told. Now substitute another sign for the 1 in ten's place; for example, 2. "How many tens are shown?" ("Two tens.") "What is this called?" ("Twenty.") In like manner, substitute other symbols in ten's place, until the pupils recognize 30, 40, 50, etc., not merely as thirty, forty, fifty, etc., but also as showing three tens, four tens, five tens, etc.

Or, demonstrate the idea, twenty-six, by two bunches of toothpicks and six loose ones. Show the two bunches. "How many toothpicks?" ("Twenty," or "two tens.") Write 20, to show twenty, or two tens. Point out that the 2 is in ten's place to show two tens. Ask what the zero is for.

Now, show the two bunches and the six loose picks.

"How many here?" "Twenty," or "two tens."

"How many are here?" "Six."

"How many do I have altogether?" "Twenty and six," or "twenty-six."

"This is the way to write twenty-six; I write six (6) in unit's place, and two (2) in ten's place — (26). This (26) shows two tens and six, or twenty-six."

"When I write twenty, I write two (2) in ten's place. Do I need a zero (0)? Why?"

"When I write twenty-six, I write two (2) in ten's place, and six (6) in unit's place. Do I need to write a zero (0)? Why not?"

In like manner, other numbers are demonstrated and expressed in writing.

9. Exercises

Exercises such as are indicated by the following forms should now be conducted until the pupils have fixed the idea of *ten's place* and of the significance of numbers in *ten's place*.

28 is —— tens and —— (*units* or *ones* understood, but not necessarily named)

73 is —— tens and ——

69 is —— tens and ——   (*units* or *ones* understood, but not
     and   necessarily named)
5 tens and 6 are ——
3 tens and 2 are ——
9 tens and 5 are ——

The teacher may either follow the forms in an oral exercise with the pupils or state the questions indicated and have the pupils fill in the blanks in writing on paper or at the board. The written exercise should predominate, inasmuch as the *ten's position* is indicated only by the written form.

10. Develop a Number Chart

As the work proceeds, develop a number chart to 100 upon the board, and let the pupils make one at their desks. Assisted by the pupils, the chart may be begun, writing the symbols to 20 as follows:

	1	2	3	4	5	6	7	8	9
10	11	12	13	14	15	16	17	18	19
20									

At this point review the significance of 10, 20, 30 to 100 and write these in a column below the 20. Now review the numbers 21 to 29 writing them in the 20's row. The chart now has the following appearance. Its completion should be left largely to the independent activities of the pupils, while the teacher, of course, directs their efforts.

	1	2	3	4	5	6	7	8	9
10	11	12	13	14	15	16	17	18	19
20	21	22	23	24	25	26	27	28	29
30									
40									
50									
60									
70									
80									
90									
100									

As this number chart develops, it should be returned to in frequent reviews. The teacher may point to a number, 47, for example. The pupils should give the name, *forty-seven*, and tell the meaning; namely, it is 4 *tens* and 7.

11. Point Out the Significance of the Zero

While it is not to be expected that pupils at the stage of development represented by the work now being described will be able to arrive at a complete understanding of the significance of the zero, something of its importance and use may be pointed out to them. The zero is not a symbol for a quantity. Its use is merely to hold a position. When 25 is written, the 2 represents 2 *tens* because it is in *ten's* place. It is the second position to the left, because the 5 in *units* (or one's) place holds it there. Now, if we have no units to write, we must have some sign to take the place of units in order that the 2 may be held in the second, or *ten's*, position.

No elaborate explanation of the use of the zero is to be recommended. The significance may be discerned in part as the pupils have impressed upon them, through the various activities described in the foregoing pages, the facts that 25 is 2 *tens* and 5 and that 20 is 2 *tens*, and so on. It is impressed upon them from the beginning that 11 is not two one's, but 1 and 1 *ten* or 1 *ten* and 1. As the work proceeds, the teacher should indicate that 10 is 1 *ten*, that 20 is 2 *tens*, and so on.

12. Emphasize the Ten's Position

Coincident with the pointing out of the use of the zero as opportunity affords, the place *where the tens are written* should be emphasized. This the pupils have had called to their attention *indirectly* in all the work that has been suggested in this chapter. The suggestion now made is that the teacher should take advantage of every opportunity to call the matter to the pupils' attention *directly*. This should be only in connection with the regular activities that lead

to the development of the idea of tens and (let us repeat)
only as opportunity affords. As with the zero, this particular idea of form of written expression of number ideas should
develop only in connection with the development of the number ideas.

The idea of ten, the significance of the zero, and the
importance of position will be called into constant and
ever-increasing use as the pupil moves forward through the
various steps of arithmetic. The general ideas named develop gradually; but as they develop, they throw light upon,
and make intelligible the many phases of the various processes with whole numbers and fractions that the pupil will
be called upon to learn. Moreover, they will serve, to the
extent that he develops them, to knit together into a consistent scheme, or system, all the various processes that at
first glance appear to be so different each from the other.
Thus, what the pupil is beginning to learn now will, when extended and enlarged and clarified in succeeding grades, take
him through the later stages of his learning up to, and including, decimals and percentage.

VIII. Summary

By means of the activities described in this chapter, pupils
first become acquainted with the group of ten in its relations
to smaller groups; and second, they begin that development of the idea of ten that may serve to throw light upon
and to make clear all subsequent work in arithmetic. The
present activities reveal to pupils for the first time something of the unique importance of the group of ten as a
standard by which all other groups are evaluated. The activities give pupils their first introduction to the number
system they must learn.

CHAPTER XIII

EXTENDING THE NUMBER IDEAS

ARGUMENT

1. Through objective demonstration and practice pupils may learn that tens are added and subtracted just as units are added and subtracted.

2. Such demonstrations and practice give opportunity for further emphasis upon the significance of ten's position and the use of the zero.

3. They extend the practice on the simple additions and subtractions to higher levels.

4. Additions and subtractions in the higher decades serve to extend practice to higher levels.

5. The relations to the simpler additions and subtractions should be made clear. The goal is understanding, not merely skill.

6. The higher-decade additions chosen for practice should be those that are useful in column additions and in multiplications.

7. The higher-decade subtractions are intended merely to extend the pupil's practice.

8. Column addition provides for an extension of practice to a new level.

9. The new type of addition should be understood before practice begins. To this end, objective demonstration of the process is recommended.

I. REVIEW OF PREVIOUS STUDY

If the activities described in the foregoing chapters have been carried through thoughtfully and systematically, they have resulted in enlarging and clarifying of the children's number ideas to ten, and in attaching a special significance

257

of the idea of ten. In the development of these ideas, the children have studied groups and have given thoughtful attention to the various arrangements of these groups. Around each number idea as a center of reference, they have learned the arrangements, or combinations, that relate to it. They have learned in their relations 45 addition combinations and 45 subtraction combinations and have given some attention to 8 combinations of equal groups. Moreover, they have learned to deal with the idea of ten in a special manner, and to think of ten and of the method of grouping by tens as these give meanings to the numbers from ten to one hundred.

It will be well as a prelude to the activities suggested in the present chapter to take the pupils through a rapid review of what they have already learned. Such a review will be very useful, because the pupils will be called upon, in undertaking the activities now to be suggested, to make use in ways that are new and different of the ideas they have developed and of the arrangements they have already learned. The review will make easier their introduction to the new activities. The new activities, in turn, will provide new associations for the arrangements the pupils have learned and new uses for the ideas they have acquired. The new activities will be discovered to be not entirely new and different, but in reality means of extending and enlarging the uses of what the pupils know. The new activities will thus provide a new and different kind of review — in a sense, a new view of things already familiar.

II. Adding and Subtracting Tens

1. Purpose of the Activities

The purpose of the activities described in this section is to introduce the pupils to the idea that tens may be dealt with in exactly the same way as units. As the pupils gain this idea slowly and gradually, they will slowly and gradually discover that they are in possession of the key that serves to unlock the mysteries of later arithmetic. They will discover, as they make progress in succeeding activities, that tens are multiplied just like units and divided just like units, that one multiplies by tens and divides by tens just as he multiplies and divides by units, that hundreds, thousands, tenths, hundredths, etc., are added, subtracted, multiplied, and divided just like units, and so on. As they move forward to the more and more complex processes of arithmetic, which in comparison with the simpler processes are more and more difficult, they may find themselves in better and better possession of the idea that throws light upon complex processes and makes them understandable. Thus, by gaining possession of the idea that will make the later processes easy to understand, the pupils may find as they proceed that the apparently more and more difficult processes may be attacked by them more and more effectively and successfully. And thus, instead of needing more and more explanation and direction as they move forward to the later complex processes of arithmetic, the pupils may in reality be able to get along with less and less explanation and direction. By being trained from the beginning in method of procedure and method of attack, they may learn to rely upon their gradually developing ideas to explain the newer processes to them and to give them direction about how to proceed.

Specifically, the present section will show how to introduce the pupils to the fact that tens are dealt with just like units by instructing them and giving them practice in the addition and subtraction of tens. Having learned to add and subtract units to the extent of being able to put together and take away groups relating to the ideas to ten, and having been introduced to the idea of ten and its importance in connection with numbers larger than ten, the pupils may now proceed to the processes of adding tens and subtracting tens.

2. Use Groups of Objects to Demonstrate

For the sake of illustrating what the pupils have to learn, the teacher may resort to the use of toothpicks in bunches of ten, as were used in the demonstrations of the preceding chapter.

Pass around several bunches. Have the children count the picks in each bunch, so that they will be clear that there are ten in each.

Place the bunches before the pupils and ask: "How many bunches are here?" "Eight," let us say.

Remind the pupils that each bunch is a bunch of ten.

"How many picks are here?" "Eighty, or eight tens."

"Let us write eight tens, or eighty."

"Now watch as I take away five tens, or fifty."

$$\begin{array}{r} 80 \\ -50 \\ \hline 30 \end{array}$$

Write 50 with the minus sign (−) before it, and draw a line to show that fifty, or five tens, is to be taken away from eighty, or eight tens.

"How many are left?" "Three tens, or thirty."

Write 30 in its proper place.

Review the activity with eight picks, taking five away and leaving three. Repeat the activity with eight bunches (tens), taking away five bunches (tens) and leaving three bunches (tens). Emphasize the similarity between "five from eight is three" and "five tens from eight tens are three tens."

$$\begin{array}{r} 8 \\ -5 \\ \hline 3 \end{array}, \quad \begin{array}{r} 80 \\ -50 \\ \hline 30 \end{array}.$$

Make impressive the point that tens are subtracted just like units. Again state the question, "Fifty from eighty is how many?" in writing,

$$\begin{array}{r} 80 \\ -50 \end{array}.$$

Point out that the 8 is in ten's place, and means 8 tens, that the 5 is in ten's place, and means 5 tens. Subtract. The pupils know that the answer will be 3 tens, but let it be emphasized. Show that the subtraction is just the same as "five from eight is three," but that the 3, since it means 3 tens, must be written in ten's place. Write the 3 in the answer,

$$\begin{array}{r} 80 \\ -50 \\ \hline 3 \end{array}.$$

"What is wrong with the answer? I have subtracted, 'five from eight is three,' but I want the 3 to show 3 tens. What must I do?" "You must write a zero (0) to hold the unit's place and to put the 3 in ten's place."

Write the zero in its proper place.

Point out, when such a question is given, $\dfrac{80}{-50}$, that one notices that he has to take away tens, and he knows ahead of time that the answer must be written in ten's place. So in order to put the answer in ten's place, he writes a zero (0) in the beginning, and then goes ahead and subtracts tens just like units — "five from eight is three" — and writes the 3 where it belongs.

Let the pupils practice a number of subtractions at the board and on their papers. Let them explain why they write the zero (0) first, and how they subtract the tens.

60	90	50	80	70	40	100
−40,	−30,	−20,	−10,	−60,	−30,	−60, etc.

Return to the bunches of picks for further demonstration — five bunches and three bunches, for example. In a manner similar to that used in demonstrating the subtraction of tens, illustrate the addition of tens. Encourage the pupils to think of the five bunches and of the three bunches, as five tens and three tens, and to write them as 50 and 30.

"How many are fifty and thirty?" $\dfrac{50}{30}$

Let the pupils count the five bunches and the three bunches together to get eight bunches, and demonstrate the point that in adding 50 and 30, one adds the tens just like units, "five and three are eight," and writes the eight (8) in ten's place to show eight tens, or eighty.

Point out, when such a question is asked as, $\dfrac{50}{30}$, that one notices that he has to add tens, and he knows ahead of time that the answer must be written in ten's place. So in order to put the answer in ten's place, he writes a zero (0) in the beginning, and then goes ahead and adds the tens just like units — "five and three are eight," and writes the 8 where it belongs.

Let the pupils practice a number of additions at the board and on their papers. Let them explain why they write the zero (0) first, and how they add the tens.

40	30	50	60	30	20	10
50,	70,	20,	40,	20,	70,	50, etc.

Illustrate the performance of the operations in such combinations as $\begin{array}{r} 78 \\ -46 \end{array}$, as follows:

Let the 78 be represented by seven bunches of picks and eight loose ones. Point out that the first operation, "six from eight," means six picks taken from the eight. Let them be taken away and two are left. Write 2.

Point out that the second operation, "four from seven," means four tens from seven tens. Let four bunches be taken away, saying, "Four from seven is three." Three (tens) are left. Write 3 (in ten's place). Since 2 has already been written, it will put the 3 (tens) in its proper place.

Illustrate the performance of the operations in such combinations as, $\begin{array}{r} 46 \\ 32 \end{array}$, as follows:

Let the 46 and the 32 be represented by four bunches of picks and six single ones, and three bunches and two single ones, respectively. Point out that one first adds the units, "six and two are eight," illustrating by putting together and counting together the six picks and the two picks. Write 8.

Point out that the next operation "four and three" means four (tens) and three (tens), and that one adds, "four and three are seven," and knows that the answer is seven tens. Illustrate by putting together and counting together the four bunches and the three bunches. Write 7 (tens) in its proper place. The sign previously written (8) puts the 7 in ten's place where it belongs.

3. Teach the Pupils to Extend Their Ideas

Objective demonstration of thinking groups of ten together and thinking them apart should be continued until the pupils get the idea that tens are added and subtracted just like units. The purpose of the demonstrations is to get the pupils to thinking about the arrangements of groups just as they have already learned to think about the arrangements of objects. When the purpose has been accomplished, the demonstrations should cease, and the pupils should move ahead to the activities of using and extending the knowledge they have gained in preceding lessons.

Questions requiring the arranging of tens should be asked and answered both orally and in writing. The pupils will be able to answer the questions, "Twenty and thirty are

$$20$$

how many?" and $\underline{30}$, without resort to writing. They will need to have sufficient practice in writing the answers to the additions and subtractions of tens to associate the written expressions with their proper meanings.

Questions requiring the arranging of tens and units should be asked and answered in writing. Such arrangements as,

$$25 \qquad 75$$

$\underline{43}$ and $\underline{-41}$, need to be written, because each involves two steps in thinking. The pupils first must deal with the units as units, and next must deal with the tens as though they were units. When the units have been arranged in thought according to the directions the question gives, the answer needs to be set down, because the pupils will be unable to hold it in memory while they perform the next arrangement

$$5 \qquad\qquad 9$$

asked for. Having learned to add, $\underline{3}$, and to subtract, $\underline{-4}$, and to set down their results in writing, they can proceed

$$55 \qquad\qquad 99$$

with equal ease to add, $\underline{33}$, and to subtract, $\underline{-44}$. They can quickly see that the tens are dealt with just like the units.

4. Emphasize the Use of Zero

In the addition and subtraction of two-place numbers, the zero appears in combination with signs for the numbers. Attention should be called, as indicated in foregoing illustrations, to the zero, not as a sign for a number idea or for a group that may be arranged with other groups, but as a sign that *holds a place* and keeps the positions of the numerals clear in the written expression of number ideas.

Some illustration of the manner of presenting the use of the zero has already been given.

In combinations like the following, $\underline{40}^{25}$ and $\underline{-50}^{78}$, show, in the case of the unit's column that one has five in one group, but does not add anything to it; or that one has eight in one group, but does not take anything from it; and that one still has five in the one group and eight in the other. So starting with five or eight, and letting the five alone and the eight alone, one still has five in the one example and eight in the other. So 5 is written as the answer to the one and 8 as the answer to the other.

Since the zero (0) can be considered as a symbol for quantity, only in a sense that is highly abstract, do not undertake to call attention to what are sometimes called the 'zero combinations.' In the experience of the child they do not exist; and in the experience of the adult, the zero, as such, in addition and subtraction, is neglected. The zero, being a mere *place holder* in our system of notation, does not affect the sum or difference one way or the other, and it should not be called to the attention of children, in so-called 'zero combinations,' as though it did.

In combinations like the following, $\underline{-54}^{84}$, $\underline{-28}^{78}$, etc., point out in each case, starting with four and taking four away, etc., that no units are left, and no figure to show units is to be written; but since tens are next to be taken from tens, leaving tens for an answer, the answer must be *written in ten's place* in order to show tens. Therefore, in order to place the answer, when one gets it, where it belongs, one first writes a zero (0) in unit's place to put the answer where it belongs. Thus, the pupils may subtract: "Four from four is nothing." (There is no number figure, no numeral, to be written, so one writes 0 to make the next figure show

tens). "Five from eight is three." The three is written (3)
under the 5 (tens) and 8 (tens) to show 3 (tens) left. The
zero (0) already written makes the 3 show three tens.

5. Practice Exercises

In the practice exercises that should follow, no carrying in
addition or subtraction should be involved. In the exercises that use the 36 addition and the 36 subtraction combinations relating to the ideas to ten, such as, 25, -62,
$\overset{43}{25}$, $\overset{95}{-62}$,
etc., no carrying is possible. The practice should involve
the use of the 9 addition and the 9 subtraction combinations
that relate to the idea of ten. Carrying may be avoided by
taking care to place all such combinations in the ten's col-
umn, thus: $\overset{43}{62}$, $\overset{36}{71}$, $\overset{108}{-65}$, $\overset{105}{-23}$, etc.

The practice of the pupils should be progressive. It
should be practice in thinking as well as practice in written
expression. In the beginning the work should be slow and
deliberate. Let the pupil 'think ahead,' explaining step by
step what he is doing or, when he has finished an example,
let him explain step by step what he has done. Let the fact
that tens are added and subtracted *just like units* be stressed
again and again; and let the pupils explain again and again
the use of the zero *to hold position*. Finally, when the pupils
are perfectly clear in their own minds as to what their work
means, the practice may be speeded up by a gradual reduction of the 'thinking out loud' and of the explanations required. Finally, the pupils should add or subtract in each
column in exactly the same way — *just like units* — and read
their answers by giving the usual names, thus, fifty, twenty-
seven, sixty-five, eighty, etc.

6. Summary

The activities that have been described in this section are
the activities of using what the pupils have learned in the

gaining of new knowledge and understanding. The various arrangements of addition and subtraction that relate to the ideas to ten are used in both old and new ways. Combined with the idea of ten, whose development had already begun, these arrangements have been used as arrangements of units and arrangements of tens. The pupils have learned that tens are added and subtracted "just like units," they have learned to put some reliance upon *position* as an aid in thinking, and they have gained practice in simple arrangements. They may now proceed to further practice of the simple arrangements as they appear in new forms and with new uses.

III. Additions and Subtractions in the Higher Decades

1. Results of Previous Activities

By means of their previous activities the children have developed somewhat definite ideas of groups to ten, together with some notion of the special importance of the group of ten. They have learned the various arrangements that build up and relate to the ideas mentioned, and they have learned special uses of these arrangements in connection with the activity of grouping by tens or of thinking objects as arranged in groups of tens. They have practiced the arrangements mentioned, both as simple arrangements and as arrangements of groups of tens. The pupils are now ready to gain further practice with the arrangements they know in connection with a further extension of their ideas.

2. Two Kinds of Practice

The teacher of beginners does not expect mastery all at once, but the teacher does expect that the pupils will make progress in the direction of mastery. In order that the pupils may finally master the arrangements they have learned, they need practice — practice in making them, practice in thinking them, and finally, practice that will release thinking for other things.

One kind of practice is repetition of the thing in the very same way it was learned. Another kind of practice is repetition under new, though somewhat similar, conditions. The first kind of practice is necessary in the beginning; the second kind of practice carries thinking to new and higher levels. The activities of the preceding section illustrate this second kind. Having learned to add two and three, for example, the pupils gained practice not only in adding two and three when objects were being thought together, but also in adding two and three when groups of tens were being thought together. The activities to be outlined in the present section will give further opportunity for practice of this kind.

3. Higher-Decade Addition

Our Arabic system of expressing numbers in writing and of using them in thinking as groups of tens has been discussed. It is a *decimal* system. The numbers are thought and written in *decades*. Those below ten are in the lowest decade. Those from ten to ninety-nine are in the higher decades.

Additions such as "two and three are five," "five and four are nine," etc., are known as the simple additions. Additions such as "twenty-two and three are twenty-five," "sixty-five and four are sixty-nine," etc., are known as the higher-decade additions.

Higher-decade addition is necessary both in column addi-

$$\begin{array}{c} 8 \\ 7 \end{array}$$

tion and in multiplication. In the column $\underline{4}$, one first makes

$$8$$

use of his knowledge of the simple combination, $\underline{7}$. He next adds 15 and 4. The answer, 19, is in the same decade with

8
7

15. In the column 6, the result of adding 8 and 7, 15, is
added to 6. The first form, 15 and 4, does not involve
'bridging' to the next decade. The latter form, 15 and 6,
does involve 'bridging.'

43

In the multiplication, 8, for example, one first secures
the product, 8 × 3. He next secures the product, 8 × 4,
and adds the 2, which is 'carried' from the former product.
The answer, 34, is in the same decade with 32. In the mul-

85

tiplication 6, the second product, 48, is added to the 3,
which is 'carried' from the first. The answer, 51, is in the
next higher decade. In the former case, no 'bridging' is
involved; in the latter case, 'bridging' is needed.

Higher-decade addition without bridging must be distinguished from higher-decade addition with bridging. In the
present chapter, the exercises will be confined to examples
of the former type, with one exception. The pupils have

9   8   3   4

learned such combinations as, 1,   2,   7,   6, etc. They
                               10   10   10   10

should be given opportunity to extend such combinations

19 29 39   18 28 38   13 23 33

to 1, 1, 1, etc., and 2, 2, 2, etc., 7, 7, 7, etc., and

14 24 34

6, 6, 6, etc.

a. *The Extent of Higher-Decade Addition.*   There are, all
told, 765 separate higher-decade addition facts from 10 plus 1
up to sums of 99.   To give specific and intensive drills upon
each of these facts would make the task of *fixing* the idea a
well-nigh insurmountable one. However, as preceding topics
have indicated, there are certain of these 765 combinations
that pupils will have special need for in column addition and
in multiplication. These, it will be seen, are few enough in

number to give the necessary intensive drills and plentiful
enough to prevent a narrowing of the pupils' ideas of the
use of the simple facts of addition in additions of the higher
decades.

In column addition one seldom adds to sums higher than
40. Indeed, sums between 30 and 40 are very infrequent,
when compared with sums between 20 and 30. Infrequently
does the sum in a column of all but the last figure to be
added exceed the 20's. Because of the infrequency of the
occurrence of additions in the decade of the 30's, only those
combinations in the higher decades of 10's and 20's need to
be included in the special drills. That is to say, the drills
should be upon the combinations $\frac{10}{1}$, $\frac{10}{2}$, etc., to $\frac{29}{1}$, $\frac{29}{2}$, etc.,
to $\frac{29}{9}$. There are 180 such combinations, 90 without bridg-
ing, and 90 with bridging.

There are 175 higher-decade additions that are used in
multiplication. Of these 175, 115 involve bridging and 60
do not. Of the 175 additions, 69 are included in the list of
180 combinations that are of frequent occurrence in column
addition, while 106 are not so included. The following
table summarizes our classification of the higher-decade
additions.

HIGHER–DECADE ADDITIONS

	Without Bridging	With Bridging	Total
a. Combinations in the decades of 10's and 20's..........................	90	90	180
b. Additional combinations used in multiplication...................	71	35	106
Total Combinations of common occurrence...........................	161	125	286
Total of infrequent occurrence.......	244	235	479
Total...........................	405	360	765

The additions of common occurrence, which total 161 without bridging and 125 with bridging are the ones that need to be included in the special drills. In the present chapter the 161 additions that do not involve bridging are considered, and attention is given to the higher-decade additions relating to the idea ten, such as $\underline{2}$, $\underline{1}$, $\underline{4}$, $\underline{6}$, $\underline{7}$, etc.
$$18 \quad 29 \quad 36 \quad 54 \quad 63$$
Exercises including these additions should be given special attention.

b. Extending the Children's Ideas. Higher-decade addition is not simple addition combined with "bring down the next figure." It is an *extension* of simple addition — an exercise that involves the development of a general notion of the *application* of simple addition to a situation that is different. For example, in adding 25 and 4, $\underline{4}$, the pupil is not
$$25$$
to add $5 + 4$, 9, and then 'bring down' the 2 to its proper place in the total result. He must learn to add in a single operation, thus, "25 and 4 are 29." In both column addition and multiplication there is no chance in effective work to add 25 and 4 in two separate operations; 4 must be added to the 25 in one operation.

It is commonly believed that, once the pupils learn the simple combinations, they are able to apply them in the higher decades without any special training. It is true that many pupils do learn to generalize and to apply their experiences without guidance or outside direction, and that in the course of time most pupils will learn to generalize and apply by haphazard methods. On the other hand, it is well proved that pupils learn to generalize and apply their knowledge earlier and more effectively when they are trained to generalize.

c. Understanding, Not Mere Skill, as the Goal. Specifically, the purpose of the present section is to suggest means of helping the pupils to build up a single general idea, and not merely to suggest practice exercises on the 161 useful higher-decade additions that do not involve bridging. The general idea to be developed is the idea that any higher-decade addition, such as, "twenty-two and three," "eighty-two and three," etc., is carried through *just like* the corresponding simple addition, "two and three." It is the notion of similarity that is to be emphasized by the teacher, and developed by the pupils.

Our discussion has suggested the possibility of reducing the total of 765 higher-decade additions to 161 for the activities of the present chapter and 125 for the activities of a later chapter and has proposed 161 such additions for the present practice of the pupils. The number of additions for the practice exercises has thus been greatly reduced. Practice upon 286 additions is a much simpler task than practice upon 765 would be. On the other hand, if the task of the pupils is that of 'mastering,' or 'learning,' or 'becoming skilful with' 286 different higher-addition facts — 161 for the present and 125 later — the task is a well-nigh hopeless one.

In appearance, in results, and in uses to which they may be put, no two higher-decade additions are alike. The additions, $\frac{54}{3}$, and $\frac{24}{3}$, are separate and distinct. No two rose bushes are alike. Each bush differs from every other one in many, many details. It is not necessary, however, for one to see and to become familiar with thousands of different rose bushes in order to be able to recognize a rose bush whenever and wherever he sees one. In the recognition of rose bushes, one needs merely to observe enough different rose bushes (and not very many at that) in enough of detail to become familiar with the *common characteristics* of all rose bushes. So, in the learning of the additions in the higher decades, it will not be necessary to give attention to each of the 765 such additions or to give attention even to all the 286 most useful ones — 161 now and 125 later — in order to gain an understanding of how each one of them may be used. They all are different, to be sure; but they all are very much alike, and that is the important thing to consider. Attention must be given to enough of the additions in the higher decades to become familiar with their *common characteristics*, their relations to the simple additions; when these are discovered and observed by the pupils, they will be able to deal with higher-decade additions whenever and wherever they find them.

When the pupils have developed the idea of similarity or of relationship, they need practice in using the idea so that it will be ready for use when needed. Abundant practice, when it is delayed until the pupils understand, is always valuable. The inclusion of the 161 'useful' additions in the practice exercises provides such abundant practice. In the practice of the idea, a less useful addition is just about as valuable for practice as a more useful one; if any choice is to be made, however, the more useful ones should be favored. Concession must always be made to the fact that practice upon the more useful is better than practice upon the less useful, if other things are equal. The purpose of practice, however, should not be lost from sight. In the present case, the purpose is to practice using an idea *after it has been gained.*

Let us turn now to a consideration of how the idea in question may be developed.

d. Illustrating the Processes. For the sake of illustration the teacher may resort to the use of toothpicks bound together in bunches, or groups, of ten, supplemented with a few loose picks. The process might then be developed like this:

Recall a few of the familiar addition arrangements, such as,

2 6 4 2
3, 3, 3, 6, etc., by mentioning, writing, and illustrating them with
5 9 7 8

the grouping together of the loose picks.

Next, place before the pupils a bunch of ten and two. Let the

pupils name the number, "twelve," and express it in writing, "12."
Inquire as to what 12 shows: "one ten and two."

Now, ask the question, "How many are twelve and six?" Write
the question, $\dfrac{12}{6}$. Illustrate the grouping of twelve and six, whether
the pupils can give the answer or not. Let the pupils note a group
of six picks that are added to the twelve (ten and two). Let them
count all the picks. (Bear in mind that the group of ten has already been counted and is known as ten or one ten). The pupils
count the two and six together and determine eight picks with
the group of ten. Let the answer now be given and written, $\dfrac{\begin{array}{c}12\\6\end{array}}{18}$.

Let the arrangement, $\dfrac{\begin{array}{c}12\\6\end{array}}{18}$, be written beside the simple arrangement, thus: $\dfrac{\begin{array}{c}2\\6\end{array}}{8}$, $\dfrac{\begin{array}{c}12\\6\end{array}}{18}$.

Ask the pupils if one looks something like the other. Let them
tell how the actual arrangement, $\dfrac{\begin{array}{c}12\\6\end{array}}{18}$, (one ten and two and six)
compares with the actual arrangement, $\dfrac{\begin{array}{c}2\\6\end{array}}{8}$ (two and six).

Next, illustrate the relation of $\dfrac{22}{6}$, $\dfrac{32}{6}$, $\dfrac{72}{6}$, $\dfrac{92}{6}$, and so on, to $\dfrac{2}{6}$,
in the same way. Call on the pupils in turn to do the illustrating.

Illustrate, and let the pupils illustrate, two or three more
such relations in the same way, for example:

$\dfrac{\begin{array}{c}4\\3\end{array}}{7}$, $\dfrac{\begin{array}{c}14\\3\end{array}}{17}$ $\dfrac{\begin{array}{c}24\\3\end{array}}{27}$, etc., $\dfrac{\begin{array}{c}6\\3\end{array}}{9}$ $\dfrac{\begin{array}{c}16\\3\end{array}}{19}$ $\dfrac{\begin{array}{c}26\\3\end{array}}{29}$, etc., etc.

When the pupils have learned to give attention to the idea of
relationship between the simple arrangement and the higher-decade
arrangements by means of the illustrations, let the relations be
pointed out and attended to by means of the written expressions
of the arrangements only. Place such questions on the board as

3   13   23   93   4   14   24   94
5,   5,   5, and so on to   5,   2,   2,   2, and so on to   2.

Let the pupils in turn give the answer orally.

Let the pupils in turn write the answers to a related set, and give them orally.

Let the pupils in turn explain the extent to which all in a given set are related.

To carry the illustration further, recall and repeat two or three of the additions that the pupils have learned in relation to the
                    3   6   5
group of ten: 7, 4, 5, etc. Let the fact be repeated and re-emphasized that ten objects are *thought together* as a *group of ten*.

Next, place before the pupils a bunch of ten and six. Let the name of the number be given, "sixteen," and expressed in writing, "16." Inquire as to what 16 shows: "one ten and six."

Now ask the question, "How many are sixteen and four?"
                    16
Write the question,   4. Illustrate the grouping. Let the pupils note a group of four added to the sixteen (ten and six). Let them count all the picks. (Bear in mind that the one group of ten has already been counted and is known as ten or one ten). The pupils count the six and the four together and determine another group of ten. For the sake of illustrating the fact that six and four are *thought together* as one ten, place them together into another bunch of ten. "How many tens are there?" Let the answer now be
                    16
given and written, "two tens," or "twenty,"   4. Let the arrange-
                    20

                    6   16
ment be written beside the earlier one: 4,   4. Ask the pupils if
                    10 20
one looks something like the other. Let them tell how the actual
                    16
arrangement,   4, (one ten and six and four) compares with the ac-
                    20

                    6
tual arrangement,   4, (six and four).
                    10

26 36 86 96   6

Next, illustrate the relation of $\underline{4}$, $\underline{4}$, $\underline{4}$, $\underline{4}$, to $\underline{4}$, in the same way. Call on the pupils in turn to do the illustrating.

Let the pupils illustrate two or three other sets of arrangements in the same way, for example:

2   12   22   7   17   27

$\dfrac{8}{10}$, $\dfrac{8}{20}$, $\dfrac{8}{30}$, etc.; $\dfrac{3}{10}$, $\dfrac{3}{20}$, $\dfrac{3}{30}$, etc.

Let the rest of the sets of arrangements that relate to the simple ones belonging to the idea of ten be illustrated by reference to their written expressions.

Let the pupils in turn give the answers orally.

Let the pupils in turn write the answers to a related set, and give them orally.

Let the pupils in turn explain the extent to which all in a given set are related.

e. Practice Exercises. The practice in the beginning should be largely oral. Let the pupils in turn 'tell the whole story' of the simple arrangements. Give each pupil a different arrangement. The pupils start with the oral description of a simple arrangement and proceed to a description of each of the related higher-decade arrangements: "three and two are five," "thirteen and two are fifteen," and so on.

After the pupil has told the 'whole story,' let him write the 'whole story': $\dfrac{3}{5}$, $\dfrac{13}{15}$, $\dfrac{23}{25}$, up to $\dfrac{93}{95}$.

It is intended that the exercises that follow should be practiced orally at first. After the pupils have become fairly familiar with them, they may be organized in written exercises. The final use to be made of the higher-decade additions will not be written; yet, some writing is very desirable for the sake of emphasizing their relation with corresponding simple additions through observation of their similar appearance.

Oral practice may be conducted as follows: Let a pupil take the set of exercises which the teacher has prepared and, standing before the class, read a row of the combinations with their appropriate answers. For example, let him read the first row of exercises, thus: "ten and two are twelve," "twenty and one are twenty-one," "eleven and three are fourteen," etc. The rest of the class will listen attentively and correct any error that may be made. When the pupil has finished the first row, let another pupil take the set of exercises, and read the combinations with appropriate answers from the second row, and so on.

4. Higher-Decade Subtractions

The purposes of teaching the higher-decade subtractions do not parallel those that obtain for the higher-decade additions. In the first place, there is no process of cumulative subtractions that correspond to the process of cumulative additions when a column is added. In the second place, short division, with its successive subtractions is comparable with the multiplication of a two-place (or larger) multiplicand, but in the program that this book is outlining, short division is not recommended as the predecessor of long division. As a consequence, there is no need for any such analysis of the higher-decade subtractions as was made of the higher-decade additions. The only purpose of teaching the subtractions is to give the pupils a larger view of the process of subtraction than they otherwise could have and also to provide for them an opportunity for the practice of the simple subtractions on a different level; in short, to extend their knowledge and understanding of subtraction.

a. Illustrating the Processes. For the sake of illustration let the teacher resort to the use of toothpicks bound together, as before, in bunches, or groups, of ten, supplemented with some loose picks.

Recall a few of the subtraction arrangements, such as

$$\frac{7}{-4} \quad \frac{9}{-3}, \quad \frac{5}{-2}, \quad \frac{6}{-4}, \text{ etc.,}$$
$$\overline{3} \quad \overline{6} \quad \quad \overline{3} \quad \overline{2}$$

by mentioning, writing, and illustrating them with the loose picks.

Next, place before the pupils a bunch of ten and seven. Let the pupils name the number, "seventeen," and express it in writing, "17." Inquire what 17 shows: "one ten and seven."

Now, ask the question, "Fourteen from seventeen is how many?"

Write the question, $\dfrac{17}{-14}$. Illustrate the withdrawal of ten and four from ten and seven. Let the pupils note the ten and four as they are removed, leaving three. Let the answer be given, and written beside the corresponding statement of the simple arrangement, $\dfrac{7}{-4}$, $\dfrac{17}{-14}$. Point out the similarity.

$$\dfrac{7}{-4}_{\,3} \quad \dfrac{17}{-14}_{\,3}$$

Next, illustrate, and have the pupils illustrate, other similar arrangements, writing the result of each beside the original, thus:

$$\dfrac{7}{-4}_{\,3}, \quad \dfrac{17}{-14}_{\,3}, \quad \dfrac{27}{-24}_{\,3}, \quad \dfrac{37}{-34}_{\,3}, \text{ etc.}$$

Encourage the pupils to point out the similarity between the various written arrangements.

In similar manner, let the pupils illustrate other higher-decade subtractions, for example:

$$\dfrac{9}{-3}_{\,6}, \quad \dfrac{19}{-13}_{\,6}, \quad \dfrac{29}{-23}_{\,6}, \quad \dfrac{39}{-33}_{\,6}, \text{ etc.} \qquad \dfrac{5}{-2}_{\,3}, \quad \dfrac{15}{-12}_{\,3}, \quad \dfrac{25}{-22}_{\,3}, \quad \dfrac{35}{-32}_{\,3}, \text{ etc.}$$

Place such questions on the board:

$$\dfrac{6}{-4}, \quad \dfrac{16}{-14}, \quad \dfrac{26}{-24}, \quad \dfrac{36}{-34} \text{ up to } \dfrac{96}{-94}$$

$$\dfrac{8}{-3}, \quad \dfrac{18}{-13}, \quad \dfrac{28}{-23}, \quad \dfrac{38}{-33} \text{ up to } \dfrac{98}{-93}$$

Let the pupils in turn give the answers orally.

Let the pupils in turn write the answers to a related set and give them orally.

Let the pupils in turn explain the extent to which all in a given set are related.

For further development recall and repeat the illustration of two or three of the subtractions that the pupils have learned in relation to the group of ten: $\dfrac{10}{-6}$, $\dfrac{10}{-4}$, $\dfrac{10}{-7}$, etc.

Next, place before the pupils two bunches of ten. Let the name of the combined groups be given, "twenty," and expressed in writing, "20." Illustrate the withdrawal of one ten and six from the two tens. Show the withdrawal of six from one of the tens, and of ten from the other, leaving four remaining: $\begin{array}{r} 20 \\ -16 \\ \hline 4 \end{array}$. In similar manner, illustrate the withdrawal of twenty-six from thirty, thirty-six from forty, etc. Write the results in a set, showing relations, thus:

$$\begin{array}{ccccc} 10 & 20 & 30 & 40 & 100 \\ -6, & -16, & -26, & -36 \text{ up to} & -96. \\ \hline 4 & 4 & 4 & 4 & 4 \end{array}$$

Let the pupils illustrate two or three other sets of arrangements in a similar way, for example:

$$\begin{array}{cccc} 10 & 20 & 30 & 100 \\ -4, & -14, & -24 \text{ up to} & -94 \\ \hline 6 & 6 & 6 & 6 \end{array} \text{ and } \begin{array}{cccc} 10 & 20 & 30 & 100 \\ -7, & -17, & -27 \text{ up to} & -97. \\ \hline 3 & 3 & 3 & 3 \end{array}$$

Let the rest of the sets of arrangements that relate to the simple ones belonging to the idea of ten be illustrated by reference to the written expressions. Let the pupils in turn give the answers orally, write the answers in a related set, and explain relations.

5. Summary

The activities of the present section teach the pupils to extend their knowledge of the simple additions and subtractions they have learned to the corresponding higher-decade additions and subtractions. The pupils thus receive not merely more practice upon what they have learned, but also practice upon a higher level.

IV. Column Addition

1. Results of Previous Activities

The previous activities have led to the development of fairly definite and usable ideas of the groups to ten, and have introduced the pupils to the special meaning and use

1 3

separate additions, such as 2, 4. There is always a breathing space between two separate additions; there can be no breathing space between the additions that are required in a column. The requirement of a longer span of attention is the real distinction between the two types of addition.

5. How Column Addition is Like Simple Addition

Aside from the necessity of a longer span of attention, column addition is actually no different from simple addition, except in the manner of its written expression. In the two forms of addition, one puts together or thinks together in exactly the same way. He writes what he has done differently. Or, to state the matter in another way, both forms of written expression ask exactly the same questions, but ask

1

1 3   2

them in different ways. In the 'questions,' 2, 4, and 4, exactly the same questions are asked, and the answers are determined in exactly the same way. The column is no more than an abbreviated form of asking two or more questions or of giving two or more directions to add.

The difference in the forms of the written expressions of the two types of addition is apparent. The similarity is not so apparent. That which is not so readily seen by the beginner ought to be pointed out to him with much more emphasis than is used in pointing out that which is the more readily seen. The major task of the teacher, then, is to emphasize similarity; the minor task is to make the difference clear.

6. The New Form of Expression

The new form of writing additions in a column may be introduced in connection with a further study of groups of objects up to ten. By means of the further study of groups, which the teacher directs, the pupils may introduce themselves to the meaning of the written column of addends. As the pupils discover by means of their study the meaning of the column, the teacher introduces the written form.

The purpose of the further study of groups to ten is not primarily to gain further ideas of the groups, although such may be a part of the valuable results. It is not for the purpose of encouraging the children to carry in mind the facts of arrangement they may work out and discover. The purpose is merely to impress the point that a larger group, like nine, for example, is composed of smaller groups, like two, three, and four, for example; the purpose is to develop the idea of the column.

7. The Analysis of Groups

The preliminary exercises ought to include three of the usual steps in the study of arrangement:

1. Attention to arrangement by the pupils, when the teacher makes the arrangements.

2. Attention to arrangement by the pupils, when they make the arrangements.

3. Attention to arrangement by the pupils, when they think the arrangements.

Throughout, the oral and written language of arrangement should be used to describe the arrangements, and to direct the attention while they are being made.

Let the teacher at the outset present to the pupils a group of nine objects, let us say. First, let the objects be counted. Now show the children how a group of nine objects may be divided into three smaller groups, groups of two, three, and four:

$$//\qquad///\qquad////$$

Point out that nine is the same as two and three and four, and that two and three and four are the same as nine. As the group of nine is separated into the smaller groups, let the sign for each

2
3
be written, 4. Finally, ask, "Two and three and four are how

many?" Let the three groups be *thought together* by counting. When the answer, "nine," is given, write the nine at the foot of

the column,

$$\begin{array}{c} 2 \\ 3 \\ 4 \\ \hline 9 \end{array}$$

Inquire if the group of nine could be divided into three different groups. Let first one child, then another, attempt the division, until the significance of the question is gained. If the children are slow in comprehending, help them. Finally, the group of nine will be divided, as:

/ /// /////, or as */// // ////,* or as *// ///// //,* etc.

Let each arrangement be written, and each set of groups be counted together, and the answer written, thus:

$$\begin{array}{ccc} 1 & 3 & 2 \\ 3 & 2 & 5 \\ 5 & 4 & 2 \\ \hline 9 & 9 & 9 \end{array} \text{ etc.}$$

As the next step, let each pupil take a group of nine, or ten, or seven, objects. Ask the question, "What three groups make ten?" Let each pupil actually make his own arrangement, and write it on the board. Several arrangements of the ten objects will be made, and written.

As a final step, when the pupils have had ample practice in actually making the arrangements required, let them answer the questions by thinking the arrangements in these ways: (*a*) by looking at ten objects and thinking them separated into groups of two, four, four; or three, five, two; etc., and writing the arrangements; (*b*) by thinking the larger group into the smaller groups when no objects are used.

As the pupils make and think the various arrangements, let each write his own arrangement on the board. A large number of arrangements will thus be written. The basis for the next step will thus be provided.

8. Thinking the Additions

The "next step" just mentioned will be evident if the answers to the written expressions of the arrangements be erased. Before the pupils now will appear written questions that will suggest and require an attack upon the problem of arranging slightly different from the one they have been pursuing. Questions like these will appear: <u>3</u>, <u>2</u>, etc.

$$\begin{array}{cc} 2 & 1 \\ 4 & 4 \end{array}$$

Let the pupils now try to answer the questions. Have them do their thinking aloud, so that it will be known just what method each is using. *Do not let any pupil use the method of trying to remember the answer that was once written below the columns.* If any pupil attempts to use such a method, halt him and let him take the objects called for in the column and count them together to get his answer. Let the pupils try for a while to determine the answers by visualizing the objects, by using actual objects, by counting, but not by remembering. Many pupils will be able to secure the correct answers by roundabout methods. The purpose of such trials is to make clear to the pupils just what will be demanded of them in adding a column three digits high, to prepare them for the direct method of adding that will be shown them presently, and to require them to think the additions.

9. Demonstrating the Method

When the purposes of the preliminary exercises have been accomplished, and the pupils are ready, because of their own attempts, to give attention to the direct method of adding a column, illustrate the procedure to be followed. The addition may be illustrated as follows:

$$\begin{array}{l} 2 \quad \bullet\ \bullet \\ 3 \quad \bullet\ \bullet\ \bullet \\ \underline{4} \quad \bullet\ \bullet\ \bullet\ \bullet \end{array}$$

Point out again that such a column as the one here shown asks that two and three and four be added. Suggest that in counting the three groups of dots, one first counts two of the groups together, and next the third group. Suggest that the column asks that two and three be added and, finally, that four is to be added.

In counting the dots one may count in three ways: (*a*) one, *two;* three, four, *five;* six, seven, eight, *nine;* or (*b*) *two* and *three* are *five; five* and *four* are *nine;* or (*c*) *two* and *three* are *five* — and *four* are *nine.* Point out the saving in words and time of the third method.

Let the points be gone over again and again that such a

2
3

column as 4 means (1) that two and three be added to get five, and (2) that five and four be added to get nine.

Let the pupils now attack the remainder of the 'arrangement questions' that are on the board, doing their work slowly and carefully, and thinking, not *remembering*, as they go each step of the way in adding the column. As the practice proceeds, speed will come; indeed, if the work starts thoughtfully, and proceeds thoughtfully, speed will take care of itself, because the thinking, which is necessarily slow at first, will become more and more rapid thinking.

10. Downward Addition

In the practice exercises the pupils should be expected to add down the column rather than up. The combinations illustrated have been built up with the idea that they will be added downward. Only by adding downward instead of upward can the pupil secure the systematic practice on the simple combinations that has been provided in the selection of the numbers for the columns. It is important to select one or the other method of adding and to use it consistently during the earlier years of the pupil's training. If the pupil is permitted to skip about, using first one method, then the next, his practice cannot be rendered systematic. Let us illustrate.

1
2

In the combination, 5, which will probably appear in one of the practice exercises, it is intended that the pupil will get practice on two simple combinations; namely:

> One and two are three.
> Three and five are eight.

Now, should the pupil be allowed to add up the column, he will miss the practice on the two combinations mentioned, which had been selected through systematic methods, and will get practice on the two following; namely:

> Five and two are seven.
> Seven and one are eight.

One or the other — downward or upward addition — must be selected, if systematic practice is to be expected.

In this discussion downward addition has been given the preference. The reasons follow:

1. The figures are written from top downward. This method of writing the figures gives a slight advantage to downward addition when the combinations are the simple ones.

2. In adding from the top down, one can set his answer down as soon as his eye and his pencil reach the bottom of the column.

3. In adding two or more columns when carrying is necessary, the figure to be carried can be written conveniently at the top of the next column, and the adding can proceed downward at once. There is no room at the bottom of the column to set down the figure that is carried.

4. Salesmen usually add the sales slip from top to bottom, and downward addition seems to be preferred by business schools in general.

5. Downward addition is slightly more accurate than upward addition.[1]   However the evidence upon this point is meager and not very convincing.

---

[1] L. E. Cole. "Adding upward and downward," *Journal of Educational Psychology*, 3: February, 1912, pp. 83–94.

11. Summary

By means of the training that is given in the addition of a column, the pupils not merely learn a new and different process of addition that is useful; they receive practice upon the simple additions they have learned on a new and higher level of endeavor. They receive training in extending their knowledge to new processes and to new uses.

CHAPTER XIV

GROUPING INTO TENS

ARGUMENT

1. The chapter deals with the new method of grouping that pupils should learn; namely, the method that relates to the idea of ten.

2. The 36 additions whose sums extend from 11 to 18 may be learned through the application of a single method of attack.

3. Likewise, the corresponding 36 subtractions may be learned through the application of a single method of attack.

4. In each case the single method of attack relates to the idea of ten. The method in each case should be presented objectively and then practiced by the pupil.

5. Drills should follow, so that eventually the method will not be needed. The method in each case is a method of learning, not a method for later mature usage.

6. The method in each case is important as a means of preventing guesses and as an aid to understanding.

7. The new combinations, when learned, should be drilled upon as were earlier ones.

8. In the study of equal groups, at the outset a given division precedes its corresponding multiplication; later, the procedure is reversed.

9. Multiplications whose products are greater than ten do not involve in each case a piling up of smaller equal groups into a single large group, but a grouping into tens.

10. The new type of grouping is required by the system of decimal notation.

11. The method of grouping into tens should be demonstrated objectively and practiced by the pupils.

12. The method is a method of learning, not one for mature use. It is intended to aid the pupil's understanding.

13. As a given multiplication is learned, its corresponding division may be derived.

14. Systematic practice exercises should follow the learning.

I. RESULTS OF PREVIOUS ACTIVITIES

The activities described in the foregoing chapters are the activities of studying groups by counting them, by comparing them with each other, and by taking them apart and putting the parts together. By means of such studies children develop, enlarge, and clarify their ideas of groups to ten, and develop for the group of ten a special significance; they develop an understanding of the 45 addition, 45 subtraction, 8 multiplication, and 8 division arrangements that relate to the ideas to ten, inclusive; and they have opportunity to extend their knowledge of these simple arrangements as they apply in the adding and subtracting of tens, in the higher-decade additions and subtractions, and in column addition. Thus, without taking up a study of the so-called 'combinations' as a special task, they have developed in their natural, proper relations most of the addition and subtraction combinations and have made a start toward the development of those in multiplication and division. They now will need to learn the remaining ones of the 81 combinations in each of the four processes.

II. A NEW STUDY OF GROUPING

Having developed ideas of groups to nine, and having been introduced to the special significance of the group of ten, the pupils are ready to undertake a new method of studying the arrangements of groups. The new method is the method of studying arrangements as they relate to the group of ten. It involves the rearrangement of groups in terms of the standard. A comparison of the kind of combining arrangements that the pupils have already learned with the kind that remains to be learned will indicate the general character of the new method of study.

In previous exercises, the pupils dealt with combinations in addition whose sums were ten or less than ten, such as $\underline{4}$, $\underline{2}$, etc. In dealing with such combinations, the pupils either brought together (or thought together) into a single group the two groups that were being dealt with in the addition. Thus, to add six and four, for example, the requirement was to discover how large a single group the two groups would make when brought together. In the exercises that will be discussed in the present chapter, the pupils deal with combinations whose sums are greater than ten, such as $\underline{5}$, $\underline{7}$, etc. In dealing with such combinations, the pupils will not be required to bring together or to think together into a single group the two groups being dealt with in the addition; they will be required to rearrange the objects in the two groups into a group of ten and so many more. Thus, to add seven and five, the requirement is to bring or to think the two groups together into a group of ten and a group of two. They will be required to write the result of the regrouping as ten and two, thus: $\frac{\begin{array}{c}7\\ 5\end{array}}{12}$. Though they may designate the answer with a single word, 'twelve,' they must write it and deal with it in all other respects as 'one ten and two.'

Similarly, in previous exercises, the pupils dealt with combinations in multiplication whose products were ten or less than ten, such as $\underline{5}$, $\underline{3}$, etc. In dealing with such combinations, the object in each case was to combine the equal groups as indicated into a single group. In the exercises of the present chapter, the pupils deal with combinations whose products are greater than ten, such as $\underline{3}$, $\underline{4}$, etc. In dealing with such combinations, the object in each case is to recombine the equal groups, not into a single large group, but into a group, or groups, of ten and so many more. Thus, in the combinations, $\underset{\underline{3}}{5}$ and $\underset{\underline{4}}{9}$, the groups are brought together as one ten and five, and as three tens and six, respectively. The answers are so written, 15 and 36, and must be so dealt with.

Accordingly, the purpose of the exercises to be described is as much to teach the pupils *a new method* of rearranging the objects of the groups with which they will deal as to teach certain specific combinations of addition, subtraction, multiplication, and division. If the pupils learn only the combinations, they will be no more independent in their future use of the combinations than their memories will permit; if, however, they learn a method of attack while they are learning the combinations, they will become freed from the vagaries of memory.

III. ADDITION AND SUBTRACTION

1. The Addition Combinations

The addition combinations that remain to be learned follow:

9	9	9	9	9	9	9	9		8	8	8	8	8	8	8
9	8	7	6	5	4	3	2		9	8	7	6	5	4	3
	7	7	7	7	7	7				6	6	6	6	6	
	9	8	7	6	5	4				9	8	7	6	5	
5	5	5	5			4	4	4		3	3				2	
9	8	7	6			9	8	7		9	8				9	

In their previous activities of studying groups, an arrangement of subtraction was first derived by taking the group apart, and this was followed by the study of the corresponding arrangement of addition. Thus, in the study of a group of nine, for example, the group was divided by taking four away, leaving five, $\underset{5}{\underset{-4}{9}}$; next, the two groups of four and five were brought together to make the original group of nine, $\begin{array}{r}4\\5\\\hline 9\end{array}$. In the present activities the object is, first, to bring together two of the groups to nine, inclusive, so as to discover ten and so many more, $\begin{array}{r}7\\5\\\hline 12\end{array}$; next, from the addition arrangement, the corresponding arrangement of subtraction will be derived, $\begin{array}{r}12\\-7\\\hline 5\end{array}$.

The work may well begin with a review of the 45 arrangements of addition that the pupils have learned. These may be set down in order as they are being reviewed. Beside these or under these the 36 combinations yet to be learned may be set down. The order in which the 36 new combinations are set down may be the order shown above. Thus, the first task may be to study the arrangements that must be learned with the groups of the nines.

2. Ten and How Many?

From the outset the pupils must be made aware of what they are undertaking to discover in the case of each arrangement to be studied. To accomplish this the exercises that have been described in Chapter XII may be quickly reviewed. The effort should be to make the pupils conscious of the special significance of the group of ten from the beginning. As an introduction to the work to be undertaken the pupils should be informed that they are to put two groups together to find out how many more than ten the two groups make; that is, to find out "ten and how many?"

Let us suppose the work begins with a study of the rearrangement of a group of nine and a group of nine. (A group of nine and a group of two would serve the purpose quite as well.) Two groups of nine are presented, thus:

● ● ● ● ● ● ● ● ●   ● ● ● ● ● ● ● ●

or the groups may be presented thus:

● ● ●   ● ● ●
● ● ●   ● ● ●
● ● ●   ● ● ●

"How many are in this group?"

"How many are in this group?"

The pupils discover the answer in each case by counting.

"We wish now to find out how many more than ten nine and nine are." Or, "we wish now to add nine and nine to find out ten and how many."

The question should be reduced to writing, thus $\underset{9}{9}$, and explained as before.

If the objects are loose on the desk, the teacher may demonstrate by counting the nine objects in one group and bringing one from the other to make a group of ten.

"How many are there in this group?" (Ten)

"How many are in this group?" (Eight)

"How many altogether?" (Eighteen, 18)

Or, if the objects are dots on the board, they may be brought together in the groups desired, as follows:

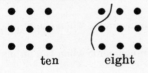

ten   eight

"How many are nine and nine?" $\underset{9}{9}$. (Ten and eight, or eighteen)

The answer *ten* and *eight* should now be written in the appropriate place, $\dfrac{9}{\underline{9}}$.

$$\frac{\begin{array}{r}9\\9\end{array}}{18}$$

When the demonstration has been repeated and discussed sufficiently for the pupils to understand what has been done, the corresponding subtraction arrangement can be presented: "Nine from

18
eighteen is how many?" -9. Though the pupils may be sufficiently familiar with the groups with which the work began so as
18
to be ready with the appropriate answer, -9, they will profit from a
9
complete demonstration of the meaning of the arrangement.

18
The subtraction, -9, is to be represented by a withdrawal of
nine from *ten* and *eight*. Since nine cannot be withdrawn from
eight, nine are withdrawn from the group of ten, and may be represented thus:

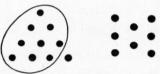

Withdrawing nine, indicated by encircling nine dots, as shown,
leaves *one* and *eight*.

The steps in the study of arrangement followed in previous exercises need to be followed here also:

1. Attention to arrangement, when the teacher makes the arrangement.

2. Attention to arrangement, when the pupils make the arrangement.

3. Attention to arrangement, when the pupils think the arrangement.

4. Attention to arrangement, when the objects are present only
in imagination ('problem-solving,' so-called).

5. Attention to arrangement, when no objects are present.

Each step should be repeated a sufficient number of times
to make the pupils ready for the succeeding one. When the
teacher has demonstrated the grouping of two groups into
ten and so many more, the grouping may be left to the
pupils to undertake in accordance with the directions given
in the questions the teacher asks. Thus, when the pupils

have learned the method, they may be asked, for example, "Seven and six are how many?" They may discover the answer by proceeding according to Step 2. Later, when they are more familiar with what is required, they may discover the answer by proceeding according to Step 3. Finally, they will be able to proceed according to Step 5, and give the answer immediately without having to resort to the use of objects.

As in previous exercises, when it happens that the pupils are moved too rapidly from one step to a succeeding one to undertake it with confidence and independence, they should be moved back to the preceding step for further practice until they are able to move ahead. Likewise, as in previous exercises, the pupils' understanding should be cultivated without regard to their ability to memorize. If the work proceeds slowly enough for the pupils to understand each step of the progress as it is taken, memory will take care of itself and come in due time. The final steps of practice, numbered 4 and 5, provide practice for mastery. Practice exercises, such as were described in Chapter XI, should be provided as the final steps.

3. Thinking the Arrangement

When the pupils have moved to the later steps in the study of arrangement, as just indicated, they frequently have to return to the preceding one of thinking the arrangement of certain combinations that for the moment have slipped from memory. It is important that the pupils be in possession of a method of thinking an arrangement, so that they can resort to its use, whenever necessary, until memorization and habituation can substitute for thinking. The following lesson materials will illustrate the method of thinking, or method of attack, that pupils may be taught to bring to bear upon their difficulties and will indicate anew the teaching procedure that may be followed from the outset.

Teaching Pupils to Think the Answer

1

8
Jane had a question like this, 6, and was not sure that she
knew the answer. She did not guess. She *thought the answer.*
This is the way she did it.

8   She knew that she had to make eight and six into ten and how
6   many, so she thought, "Eight and *two* are ten," and wrote 1
―   8
1   *in ten's place* at the left of the 6 column.

Jane now remembered that she took two from six to go with the
eight, so she thought, "Two from six is four," and wrote 4 *in one's
place* to the right of the 1 *in ten's place* in the answer.

Now, she had the answer, "Eight and six are fourteen." Jane
said the answer, "Eight and six are fourteen," again and again, so
that she would not forget it.

Just suppose you are not sure of the answers to these questions.
Show how to *think the answers.*

9	6	5	7	6	6	9	8
8	5	9	8	7	9	9	8

2

15
Tom had a question like this, −7, and was not sure that he
knew the answer. He did not guess. He *thought the answer.* This
is the way he did it.

15   Tom knew that he had ten and five, and that he had to take
−7   seven away. He was not sure about taking seven from fif-
―   teen all at once; so he took seven from the ten, "Seven from
8   ten is three." He knew now that he had three left from the
ten, and also five left, so he thought, "Three and five are eight,"
and he wrote 8 in the answer. Tom thought it all at once, something like this: "Seven from ten is *three* and five are eight."

Tom now knew the answer, "Seven from fifteen is eight," so he
said the answer, "Seven from fifteen is eight," again and again, so
that he would not forget it.

Just suppose you are not sure of the answers to these questions.
(See following page.) Show how to *think the answers.*

17	11	14	15	13	15	18	14
−8	−5	−9	−7	−6	−6	−9	−7

4. Extending the Ideas

As the pupils acquire, through the activities of Steps 4 and 5, a sufficient mastery of the addition and subtraction combinations to move ahead to practice exercises on a higher level, they should have opportunity to extend what they learn to the addition and subtraction of tens, to the additions and subtractions in the higher decades, and to column addition. The methods of instruction and the procedures of practice have been discussed in the chapter immediately preceding.

In the exercises of adding and subtracting tens, care needs to be taken to have the new combinations that have just been learned appear only in the ten's column. The reason is that the pupils have not yet received instruction in 'carrying.' The exercises will need to be arranged so that carrying will not be necessary, thus:

63	45	178	146
72,	84,	−83,	−65, etc.

In the exercises in the additions and subtractions in the higher decades, the effort should be made to get the pupils to derive the higher-decade combinations from the related simple ones. If the exercises of the preceding chapter have been sufficiently full and clear for the pupils to observe relations, they may be expected here to derive the higher-decade combinations without extended objective demonstration. Enough demonstration, such as was indicated in the preceding chapter, and enough study of relationship by comparisons under the teacher's guidance will need to be undertaken for the pupils to note in the case of each of the higher-decade additions that the answer is in the next decade. For example, the combination, $\frac{7}{5}$, gives an answer that is ten

                                  17
and more; thus, the combination, _5, will give an answer
in 'the next tens' and more; and so on. It should be
borne in mind that the exercises of instruction and practice are not intended to produce a faultless mastery of the
higher-decade combinations at this point. Mastery will
come slowly and only as use is made of the combinations
in later exercises. The purpose of the exercises is to carry
the practice on the combinations to a higher level, and to
help the pupils to develop an idea of relation between the
simple combinations and the corresponding ones in the higher
decades. It is the idea of relation that the teacher should
have in mind to aid the pupils to develop.

In the exercises of column addition it is possible to organize the various possible columns of three into groups that
provide a progression in difficulty from one to the other.
For example, four types of columns may be provided:

A	B	C	D
2	2	6	6
3	3	8	8
4	6	5	9

These four columns may be described as follows:

Type A has an easy seen and an easy unseen combination.

Type B has an easy seen and a hard unseen combination.

Type C has a hard seen and a higher-decade combination without 'bridging' for the unseen combination.

Type D is similar to C except that bridging is involved in the
unseen combination.

Such an organization may well be kept in mind for later
exercises of practice. On the other hand, it may be well to
                                  8
remember that the combination 9 may be no more difficult,
when it is understood and mastered, than the combination
5
4, and that a higher-decade combination involving bridging

may be no more difficult, when such combinations are understood, than a higher-decade combination that does not involve bridging. It should be the teacher's purpose, not merely to provide practice exercises, but to provide exercises by means of which the pupils may develop also an understanding of what they are doing. To this end, it is suggested that the work with column additions begin, as was suggested in the preceding chapter, by directing and permitting the pupils to develop their own columns for practice. For example, when the pupils have completed the study of the simple addition and subtraction combinations that require the use of seventeen objects, let the question be given, "How many groups of three will make seventeen?" The pupils may proceed to the dividing of seventeen into three groups, and such columns as the following may result:

9	5	4	2	1	3	4
4	8	7	8	8	9	5
4,	4,	6,	7,	8,	5,	8, etc.

When such a series of columns has been set down on the board, the pupils may in turn or in concert proceed to the adding of the columns. When other series have been developed with different groups of objects, the columns may be mixed for the succeeding practice exercises, and so on. When the pupils derive their own columns, they will understand the better what is required of them in the addition of a column.

IV. MULTIPLICATION AND DIVISION

1. Purpose of This Section

This section will describe a method of deriving the multiplication and division combinations that is different from the one described in Chapter X as being useful in connection with the study of groups. Inasmuch, however, as there are a good many things to be learned about addition and subtraction before the pupils can properly proceed to the

completion of the 81 combinations in multiplication and of
the 81 combinations in division, it will be suggested that the
method of study described in Chapter X be continued in
connection with the exercises described in the preceding section of this chapter, reserving for a later grade (Grade III)
the development and use of the new method.

2. Division Before Multiplication

As was indicated in the section on the study of equal
groups in Chapter X, when the *fact of multiplication* is
derived from the study of a group, it comes as the answer
to a *question of division*. The object of the study at the
time is a given group of objects. In order to call further
attention to the group, the teacher inquires about the number of equal groups of a given size in the group being studied.
The children discover the answer by dividing the group into
the equal groups indicated in the question.

In the study of groups to ten, inclusive, the following
division questions were asked and answered:

$2\overline{)4}$, $2\overline{)6}$, $3\overline{)6}$, $2\overline{)8}$, $4\overline{)8}$, $3\overline{)9}$, $2\overline{)10}$, $5\overline{)10}$.

In the studies of arrangement outlined in the preceding
section of this chapter, certain divisions and corresponding
multiplications are more or less obvious. For example, in
answering the addition question, "How many are nine and
nine?" the two groups of nine are before the eyes of the
pupils for study:

● ● ●   ● ● ●
● ● ●   ● ● ●
● ● ●   ● ● ●

When the two groups have been combined into ten and
eight — eighteen — the question, "How many nines are in
eighteen?" $9\overline{)18}$, is not difficult to answer; indeed, the answer is before the children's eyes from the beginning, and
they need only to have the answer called to their attention
by the proper question.

Following the question just indicated and the giving of its appropriate answer, the children may just as well answer the remaining questions about equal groups that relate to the quantity eighteen: "How many twos are in eighteen?" $2\overline{)18}$; "How many threes are in eighteen?" $3\overline{)18}$; and "How many sixes are in eighteen?" $6\overline{)18}$.

As a preliminary to the study of equal groups that may be undertaken in connection with the activities of arrangement of the preceding section, the method of finding the answer to questions about equal groups that was used in the study of the groups to ten may be reviewed. Or, if the teacher is not sure that the pupils are familiar with the method, she may demonstrate the method in connection with the review. When the method is clear, the teacher proceeds to the asking of the division questions. Let us suppose that the question is, "How many threes are in eighteen?" The question may be stated both orally and in writing, $3\overline{)18}$.

Having eighteen objects before them, and knowing that they have eighteen, because the preliminary activities, such as were described in the preceding section, have impressed the fact upon their minds, the children determine the answer by arranging the eighteen objects in groups of threes, thus:

● ● ●   ● ● ●   ● ● ●   ● ● ●   ● ● ●   ● ● ●

They count, or note, the number of groups of threes and give their answer orally, "Six threes are eighteen," and in writing, $3\overline{)18}^{6}$. In similar manner they find answers to all the division questions that relate to the ideas twelve to eighteen. The division questions thus considered are these:

$$2\overline{)12} \quad 6\overline{)12} \quad 3\overline{)12} \quad 4\overline{)12} \quad 2\overline{)14} \quad 7\overline{)14}$$

$$3\overline{)15} \quad 5\overline{)15} \quad 2\overline{)16} \quad 8\overline{)16} \quad 4\overline{)16}$$

$$2\overline{)18} \quad 9\overline{)18} \quad 3\overline{)18} \quad 6\overline{)18}$$

The answers that are thus discovered to the division questions are the answers needed for the corresponding questions when put in the form of multiplications. Thus, the question and answer, $3\overline{)18}$, provide the answer to the question, "Six threes are how many?" $\times 6$.

$$\begin{array}{r} 6 \\ 3\overline{)18} \\ \underline{18} \\ 3 \end{array}$$

The five steps in the study of arrangement will need to be taken one by one in connection with the 15 new division and the 15 new multiplication combinations.

V. A New Study of Grouping

In the exercises with equal groups that have been referred to up to this point, division has preceded multiplication. In the new study of grouping, which is begun after a considerable time has elapsed, the pupils undertake to put together the groups to nine, inclusive, to discover in each case "how many tens?"

1. Making a Table of Combinations

The work may be begun with a review of the combinations already learned. These may be set down with the ones yet to be learned in 'tables.' The tables will provide a useful means, at first of setting down the answer to each combination as it is discovered, and finally of conducting reviews and drills. When the tables are first presented, the answers to the combinations yet to be learned may be omitted:

1	1	1	1	1	1	1	1	1
1	2	3	4	5	6	7	8	9
1	2	3	4	5	6	7	8	9

2	2	2	2	2	2	2	2	2
1	2	3	4	5	6	7	8	9
2	4	6	8	10	12	14	16	18

3	3	3	3	3	3	3	3	3
1	2	3	4	5	6	7	8	9
3	6	9	12	15	18			

4	4	4	4	4	4	4	4	4
1	2	3	4	5	6	7	8	9
4	8	12	16					

5	5	5	5	5	5	5	5	5
1	2	3	4	5	6	7	8	9
5	10	15						

6	6	6	6	6	6	6	6	6
1	2	3	4	5	6	7	8	9
6	12	18						

7	7	7	7	7	7	7	7	7
1	2	3	4	5	6	7	8	9
7	14							

8	8	8	8	8	8	8	8	8
1	2	3	4	5	6	7	8	9
8	16							

9	9	9	9	9	9	9	9	9
1	2	3	4	5	6	7	8	9
9	18							

2. Introducing the New Method of Grouping

The new method of grouping may be introduced as indicated below. There should be enough preliminary discussion by the teacher, and enough of objective demonstration for the pupils to become thoroughly familiar with what is required of them and with the method they need to pursue in answering the multiplication questions which will be asked. Many pupils will not need as much objective demonstration as is here indicated to learn the method of attack. A few may need more. Third-grade pupils as a rule quickly learn what is required in the method when it is presented clearly and systematically.

Teaching to Find How Many Tens

Multiplication is a way of finding out *exactly*. Really, most of multiplication is a way of finding out *exactly how many tens*, since every number that is more than 9 and up to 100 is written by putting a figure in *ten's* place. There is no separate figure for eleven; we write it 1 *ten* and 1, thus, 11. There is no separate figure for twenty-five, or forty-seven, or ninety-nine; we just use certain figures from 1 to 9 in different places, thus, 25, 47, 99.

Of course, combinations like $\underset{4}{2}$, $\underset{8}{4}$, $\underset{9}{3}$, which have answers less than ten, do not mean finding out *how many tens*. But combinations like $\underset{5}{2}$, $\underset{2}{5}$, $\underset{4}{3}$, $\underset{8}{2}$, $\underset{2}{9}$, which have answers larger than 9, mean finding out *how many tens*. Suppose we want to find out how many are four fours, or five threes. We try to find out *how many tens*, thus, $\underset{16}{\underset{4}{4}}$, $\underset{15}{\underset{3}{5}}$, and we learn that four fours are 1 *ten* and six (we say *sixteen*), and that five threes are 1 *ten* and five (we say *fifteen*).

All the combinations you will now have to learn are combinations which ask you to find out *how many tens*. Thus, $\underset{7}{3}$ means "seven threes are *how many tens?*" $\underset{4}{6}$ means "four sixes are *how many tens?*" $\underset{7}{9}$ means "seven nines are *how many tens?*" The rest of the combinations ask the same kind of question: *How many tens?*

Let us see if you can find out *how many tens* there are in some of the combinations which you do not already know. Let us start with the 5's. Perhaps you can work most of them out for yourself.

The work is begun using groups of five for the obvious reason that they group readily into *tens*. Note the reason for following with groups of nine, page 308.

The 5's in Multiplication and Division

We may show *one five*, thus: • • • By looking at the group of

dots, or by counting them, we can tell that *one five is five*, $\dfrac{5}{1}$.

We may show *two fives*, thus: • • • • How many are *two*

fives, that is, *how many tens?* By counting we can tell that *two fives*

are 1 ten. We say "Two fives are ten," and write it, $\dfrac{5}{2}$.

We may show *three fives*, thus: • • • • • Three fives

are *how many tens?* We can see that two of the fives are ten, and
that there are five more; so we know that *three fives are 1 ten and*

five. We say, "Three fives are fifteen," and write it, $\dfrac{5}{3}$.

Now, let us work the fives you do not already know. $\underline{4}$ asks
how many tens. Let us show *four fives:*

The first two fives go together to make 1 *ten*, and the next two
fives go together to make 1 *ten*. It is easy to count the tens. This
is the way we find out that *four fives are 2 tens*. We say, "Four

fives are twenty," and write it $\dfrac{5}{4}$.

You should now turn back to the *table of 5's* and write the
answer to the $\underline{4}$ combination. Also write the answer to the $\underline{5}$ combination in the *table of 4's*. If *four fives* are twenty, how many
are *five fours?*

Do you remember the kind of question a sign like this $5\overline{)20}$
asks? It asks, "How many fives in twenty?" Give the answer.
$4\overline{)20}$? Give the answer.

5

5 asks, *how many tens?* Let us show *five fives*, and then count the *tens.*

Five fives are ——? 5? Write the answer to the 5 combination in the *table of 5's.*

5)25 ? Give the answer.

How many are *six fives;* that is, *how many tens?* Let us show *six fives,* and count the *tens.*

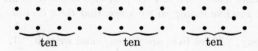

Six fives are ——? 6? Write the answer to the 6 combination in the *table of 5's.* See whether you can now write the answer to

6

the 5 combination in the *table of 6's.*

5)30 ? Give the answer.

6)30 ? Give the answer.

Seven fives are how many tens? Count them.

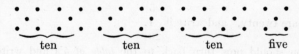

5

Seven fives are ——? 7? Write the answer in the *table of 5's.*

7

Five sevens are ——? 5? Write the answer in the *table of 7's.*

5)35 ? Give the answer.

7)35 ? Give the answer.

Eight fives are *how many tens?* Count them.

ten   ten   ten   ten

Eight fives are ——? $\underset{8}{\underline{5}}$? Write the answer in the *table of 5's.*

Five eights are ——? $\underline{5}$? Write the answer in the *table of 8's.*

$5\overline{)40}$? Give the answer.

$8\overline{)40}$? Give the answer.

Nine fives are *how many tens?* Count them.

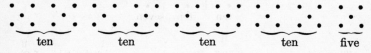

ten   ten   ten   ten   five

Nine fives are ——? $\underset{9}{\underline{9}}$? Write the answer in the *table of 5's.*

Five nines are ——? $\underline{5}$? Write the answer in the *table of 9's.*

$5\overline{)45}$? Give the answer.

$9\overline{)45}$? Give the answer.

Examples with the 5's

Say the answers to these examples across the rows, then down the columns, then up the columns.

5	5	5	5	5	5	5	5	5
1	2	3	4	5	6	7	8	9

1	2	3	4	5	6	7	8	9
5	5	5	5	5	5	5	5	5

$5\overline{)5}$	$5\overline{)10}$	$5\overline{)15}$	$5\overline{)20}$	$5\overline{)25}$	$5\overline{)30}$	$5\overline{)35}$	$5\overline{)40}$	$5\overline{)45}$
$1\overline{)5}$	$2\overline{)10}$	$3\overline{)15}$	$4\overline{)20}$	$5\overline{)25}$	$6\overline{)30}$	$7\overline{)35}$	$8\overline{)40}$	$9\overline{)45}$

Say the answers over and over until you are sure you will not forget them.

Teaching the 9's in Multiplication and Division

You have just found out that it is not hard to work the answers
to the combinations in the *table of 5's;* that is, to find out *how
many tens.* We will now work out the answers to the combinations
in the *table of 9's,* and you will see that they are not very hard
either, since the number *nine* is right next to the number *ten.*

Since you already know these two combinations, $\underline{1}^{\,9}$, and $\underline{2}^{\,9}_{\,18}$, we will
start with *three nines,* $\underline{3}^{\,9}$.

Three nines are *how many tens?* Count the *tens.*

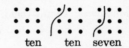

ten   ten   seven

Three nines are ———? $\underline{3}^{\,9}$? Write the answer in the *table of 9's.*

Nine threes are ———? $\underline{9}^{\,3}$? Write the answer in the *table of 3's.*

9)$\overline{27}$? Give the answer.

3)$\overline{27}$? Give the answer.

Four nines are *how many tens?* Count the *tens.*

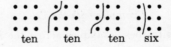

ten   ten   ten   six

Four nines are ———? $\underline{4}^{\,9}$? Write the answer in the *table of 9's.*

Nine fours are ———? $\underline{9}^{\,4}$? Write the answer in the *table of 4's.*

9)$\overline{36}$? Give the answer.

4)$\overline{36}$? Give the answer.

Five nines are *how many tens?* Look at your *table of 9's.* Do
you remember how you found out $\underline{5}^{\,9}$?

See if you get the same answer by counting the *tens*.

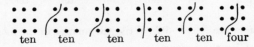

9)45 ? Give the answer.

5)45 ? Give the answer.

Six nines are *how many tens?* Count the *tens*.

Six nines are ——? $\underline{6}$?   Write the answer in the *table of 9's*.

Nine sixes are ——? $\underline{9}$?   Write the answer in the *table of 6's*.

9)54 ? Give the answer.

6)54 ? Give the answer.

Seven nines are *how many tens?* Count the *tens*.

Seven nines are ——? $\underline{7}$?   Write the answer in the *table of 9's*.

Nine sevens are ——? $\underline{9}$?   Write the answer in the *table of 7's*.

9)63 ? Give the answer.

7)63 ? Give the answer.

Eight nines are *how many tens?* Count the *tens*.

Eight nines are ——? $\underline{8}$?   Write the answer in the *table of 9's*.

8
Nine eights are ——? <u>9</u>? Write the answer in the *table of 8's.*

9)72 ? Give the answer.

8)72 ? Give the answer.

Nine nines are *how many tens?* Count the *tens.*

ten   ten   ten   ten   ten   ten   ten   ten   one

9
Nine nines are ——? <u>9</u>? Write the answer in the *table of 9's.*

9)81 ? Give the answer.

Examples with the 9's

Say the answers to these examples: across the rows, then down the columns, then up the columns.

9	9	9	9	9	9	9	9	9
<u>1</u>	2	<u>3</u>	4	<u>5</u>	6	<u>7</u>	8	<u>9</u>
1	2	3	4	5	6	7	8	9
<u>9</u>	<u>9</u>	<u>9</u>	<u>9</u>	<u>9</u>	<u>9</u>	<u>9</u>	<u>9</u>	<u>9</u>

9)9   9)18   9)27   9)36   9)45   9)54   9)63   9)72   9)81

1)9   2)18   3)27   4)36   5)45   6)54   7)63   8)72   9)81

Say the answers over and over until you are sure you will not forget them. Turn back to page 307 and say the answers to those examples.

Exercises similar to the ones just indicated should be developed around the following topics:

Teaching the 8's in Multiplication and Division
Teaching the 6's in Multiplication and Division
Teaching the 7's in Multiplication and Division

3. The Multiplication and Division Table

A useful device for reviews, drills, and for the solution of examples in multiplication and division that immediately follow the learning of the simple combinations is the multiplication and division table shown on the next page.

THE MULTIPLICATION AND DIVISION TABLE

	1	2	3	4	5	6	7	8	9
1	1	2	3	4	5	6	7	8	9
2	2	4	6	8	10	12	14	16	18
3	3	6	9	12	15	18	21	24	27
4	4	8	12	16	20	24	28	32	36
5	5	10	15	20	25	30	35	40	45
6	6	12	18	24	30	36	42	48	54
7	7	14	21	28	35	42	49	56	63
8	8	16	24	32	40	48	56	64	72
9	9	18	27	36	45	54	63	72	81

How to Use the Table

Suppose you want to multiply any two numbers, 6 and 8, let us say. Move your pencil down the column at the left to *6*. Next, move your pencil out the *6* row to the right until you come to the *8* column. Where your pencil stops is the answer, which is 48.

Suppose you want to divide, 7)63, let us say. Move your pencil down the column at the left to *7*. Next, move your pencil out the *7* row to the right until you come to 63. Now, look up at the top of the table to see what column it is. The number of the column, *9*, is the answer, which tells you there are 9 sevens in 63.

Copy this table and use it as much as you need to. Of course, if you already know an answer, you would not need to use the table. Use the table only when you need to make sure.

4. Useful Products

A useful means of review of the new combinations is to consider them in connection with the various possible products in the decades of the 20's to 80's, inclusive. When these are set down, they give the appearance of few combinations, instead of many, to be kept in mind. This is especially true with respect to those combinations the products of which are in the higher decades and that pupils

are inclined to consider as the difficult ones. The products
that come in the several decades from the 20's on are these:

20,	21,	24,	25,	27,	28
30,	32,	35,	36		
40,	42,	45,	48,	49	
54,	56				
63,	64				
72					
81					

In using these products in review, a product can be given,
and the pupils can give the combination, or combinations,
that produce it.   Thus, when 63 is given, the pupils can
give the combinations, "Seven nines are sixty-three," and

$$\begin{array}{ccc} & 9 & 7 \\ \text{"Nine sevens are sixty-three," or write them,} & \dfrac{7}{63} & \text{and} & \dfrac{9}{63}. \end{array}$$

CHAPTER XV

USING THE IDEA OF TEN

ARGUMENT

1. The idea of ten, which began to develop through earlier activities, may develop still further through later use. Moreover, it may serve to clarify the more complex processes of number operation.

2. The pupil should have learned that tens (hundreds, etc.) are added and subtracted just as units are added and subtracted.

3. Using the same idea and giving attention to the positional value of the numerals when written in ten's place, he may learn that:

(a) Tens are multiplied just as units are multiplied;

(b) Tens may be carried in addition and in multiplication;

(c) Tens may be used in subtraction;

(d) Tens are divided just as units are divided;

(e) Tens may be used as multipliers and divisors.

4. Each application of the idea is illustrated by appropriate lesson materials.

5. The decomposition method of subtraction seems to fit the pupil's developing idea of the use of ten better than the method of equal additions.

6. The long-division form is recommended from the outset of division. The short-division form is described as a 'shortcut,' to be learned, if at all, later when the pupil thoroughly understands the process of division.

I. PURPOSE OF CHAPTER

The purpose of the present chapter is to illustrate the means by which the pupil may enlarge and extend his idea of ten and use this growing idea of ten, with the idea of

313

position which goes with it, in developing an understanding of the complex processes of the four fundamental operations.

The pupil sooner or later must move ahead from the simpler processes to the complex processes. He may learn the latter in either of the following ways. (1) He may learn them merely as operations to be performed without understanding what he is attempting to do in each case or why he should do it. (2) He may learn them as operations to be performed, developing in connection with each such understanding as may come from the teacher's explanations. (3) He may learn them as operations that are held together by the common bond of an idea that is his own personal possession and that he may explain for himself each in terms of this central idea. When the pupil learns the complex processes by this last method, he may learn as he proceeds to rely more and more upon his own ability to explain. Since the idea develops in clarity and strength as he proceeds, he is in position to discover that each apparently new process to be learned is in reality not so new, and to learn as he attempts each apparently more difficult process that in reality it is less difficult than preceding ones, because he is more able to provide his own explanation for it than he was for those that preceded.

II. What the Pupil Has Learned about Tens

If the pupil has been through such exercises as have been described in the three chapters immediately preceding, he has learned to pay particular attention to the idea of ten and to give it a special significance. He has learned, in some degree at least, to deal with tens just as he deals with units, and to translate chance groups into tens. Having been required to use the idea of ten more than any other number idea, he has developed for it a special acquaintance. If the teacher now will so direct, he can with ease continue to attach to the idea of ten a special significance, and to look to this idea to suggest the clue to the answers to ques-

tions that now will confront him. The pupil is ready to give
his attention to the learning of the complex processes that
may be classified under the following heads: (1) multiplying tens, (2) carrying tens, (3) dividing tens, (4) multiplying
by tens, and (5) dividing by tens.

III. MULTIPLYING TENS

The pupils have learned that tens are added and subtracted "just like units," and they no doubt have had some
training and practice in adding and subtracting hundreds
and thousands also "just like units." They need but to
review these processes to have a fitting introduction to the
new process of multiplying tens. The review should be intended as a means of raising again to the level of consciousness the fact that tens are added and subtracted as units
are. How are tens added? How are tens subtracted? The
fact that the same answer — "just like units" — answers
both questions should be clear.

The new process to be learned may now be introduced.
This new process is *multiplying tens*. The pupils know how

$$2 \quad 4 \quad 7 \quad 8$$

to multiply units: $\underline{3}, \underline{2}, \underline{6}, \underline{9}$, etc. How are tens multiplied?
Many pupils can readily suggest the answer — "just like
units," and those to whom the answer does not occur will
grasp it quickly when they hear it suggested.

$$\begin{array}{c} 20 \\ \underline{3} \end{array}$$

Suppose the task is to multiply three twenties, $\underline{3}$. The
pupils need first to have clearly in mind the fact that one
multiplies tens "just like units." They may give their attention to the similarity of procedure and results when objects are grouped first as two and two and two, which
amount to six, and when they are grouped as two (bunches
of ten), two (bunches of ten) and two (bunches of ten),
which amount to six (bunches of ten). The procedure in
the one case is thought of as "three twos are six," and in
the other as "three twos are six" (bunches).

In the written form, $\frac{20}{\;\;3}$, the pupil is to realize that he is to multiply tens, but is to proceed just as he does in multiplying units. He thinks, when he multiplies, "Three twos are six," but realizes that his answer, "six," means six tens, and must be written in ten's position. In order to place the 6 in its proper position, one writes a zero at the outset of the proceeding, so that, when the 6 is written, it will show six tens: $\frac{\;\;20\;\;}{\;\;3}$. Note that in this case, as in every
$\overline{60}$
other when the zero is involved, the zero is used to hold position; one does not multiply the zero; he merely uses a zero because he knows, ahead of time, that his answer will be tens, and he wants to write the answer in ten's position.

In multiplying two thirty-fours, $\frac{34}{\;\;2}$, one thinks, "Two fours are eight," and writes 8 in unit's place. Next, he thinks, "Two threes are six" and writes the 6 under the 3 in ten's place: $\frac{\;\;34\;\;}{\;\;2}$.
$\overline{68}$

In similar manner, the pupils may learn how to multiply hundreds and thousands 'just like units.' When they take care to write each part of their answer in its proper position, position keeps the answers clear and relieves them from any thinking other than to proceed in each case to multiply 'just like units.'

IV. CARRYING TENS IN ADDITION AND MULTIPLICATION

The following paragraphs are included to illustrate both the procedure that may be followed in introducing pupils to the idea of carrying tens and the emphasis that may be placed upon the idea of ten that the pupils may now have partly formed in their minds. It is to be understood that each presentation should be followed with enough practice to fix the procedure in mind. It is to be understood further that the notion of carrying, or the meaning of carrying, needs to be developed in the minds of the pupils before they are directed to begin the necessary exercises of practice.

Teaching the Carrying of Tens in Addition

You have already learned a good many things about *tens*. You know how to write them and read them, and how to add, subtract, and multiply them. There is something new for you to learn about *tens*, and that is how to *carry* them. Let us see how *tens* are *carried* in addition.

Suppose we wish to add 25 and 48. We first add the *units*, "five and eight are thirteen." Now 13, as you remember, is 1 *ten* and 3. Since we cannot write all of the 1 *ten* and 3 in *unit's* place in the answer, we write as much of it as we can; that is, we write the 3. But we still have the 1 *ten*. The place to put the 1 *ten* is in the next column with the 2 *tens* and the 4 *tens*. We do not have to write it there, but can just *think* it there with the 2 *tens* and the 4 *tens*. That makes 1 *ten*, and 2 *tens* and 4 *tens* to be added. We think, "One and two are three, and four are seven," and write 7, (which is 7 *tens*), in its proper place. This is the way we think as we add: "Five and eight are thirteen." (Write 3.) "One and two are three and four are seven." (Write 7.)

$$\begin{array}{r} 25 \\ 48 \\ \hline 73 \end{array}$$

Sometimes in order to help us to remember about the "1 (ten) to carry," we write a little 1 (which we later erase) just above the figure at the top of the next column. But we never do that unless we have to. You can do that, if you wish. But see if you are not good enough at remembering without having to write the number you have to carry.

$$\begin{array}{r} 1 \\ 25 \\ 48 \\ \hline 73 \end{array}$$

Teaching the Carrying of Tens in Multiplication

Tens are carried in multiplication just as they are carried in addition. Suppose we wish to multiply 36 by 2. We first multiply the *units*, and then we multiply the *tens*. We think, "Two sixes are twelve." Now 12, as you remember, is 1 *ten* and 2. Since we cannot write all the 1 *ten* and 2 in *unit's* place in the answer, we write as much of it as we can; that is, we write the 2, and remember that we have 1 (ten) to carry to the *ten's* place in the next part of our answer. We now multiply the 3 *tens*, "Two

$$\begin{array}{r} 36 \\ 2 \\ \hline 72 \end{array}$$

threes are six." We know that this is 6 *tens*, and we remember that we have 1 *ten* to take care of which we did not write. So we think like this, "Two threes are six, and one are seven," and we write 7 in its proper place.

Carrying Tens in Addition and Multiplication

We carry from *tens* to *hundreds* just as we carry from *units* to *tens*. You already know how to carry *tens* in an example like this one. We think, "Six and eight are fourteen," write 4, and carry 1 (ten); "One and two are three and four are seven," and write 7. The answer is 74.

$$\begin{array}{r} 26 \\ 48 \\ \hline 74 \end{array}$$

See how easy it is to carry in an example like this, and how much it is like the carrying in the example just above.

$$\begin{array}{r} 260 \\ 480 \\ \hline 740 \end{array}$$

We have no *units* to add, so we write 0 in order to be able to write the answer we get in its proper place. Next we add the *tens* just as if they were *units:* "Six and eight are fourteen." The answer is, of course, 14 tens; that is, 10 tens and 4 *tens*, and it belongs in *ten's* place, but since we cannot write all of it in *ten's* place, we write the 4 in *ten's* place, and carry the 10 *tens* (which is the same as 1 *hundred*), to the next column. We now have 1 *hundred*, and 2 *hundred*, and 4 *hundred* to add. We add, "One and two are three and four are seven," and write 7 in *hundred's* place. The answer is 740. We think, "Nothing," and write 0, in order to put the answer we get in its proper place. We think, "Six and eight are fourteen," and write 4, and carry 1. We think, "One and two are three, and four are seven," and

$$\begin{array}{r} 260 \\ 480 \\ \hline 740 \end{array}$$

write 7. We think, "Three and two are five," and write 5. We think, "Six and eight are fourteen," and write 4, and carry 1. We think, "One and two are three, and four are seven," and write 7. The answer is 745.

$$\begin{array}{r} 263 \\ 482 \\ \hline 745 \end{array}$$

You remember how to carry from *units* to *tens* in multiplication. If the example in multiplication is like this, we think as we multiply: "Two sixes are twelve," and we write 2 and remember that we have 1 *ten* to carry. Now we think, "Two threes are six, and one are seven," and we write 7. The answer is 72.

$$\begin{array}{r} 36 \\ 2 \\ \hline \end{array}$$

See if you can tell how to carry in multiplication in an example like this one,

$$\begin{array}{r} 360 \\ 2 \\ \hline \end{array}$$

There are no *units* to multiply, so we write 0 in *unit's* place. Next we multiply the *tens:* "Two sixes are twelve." (Since it is 12 *tens*, that is, 10 and 2 *tens*, we write the 2 in *ten's* place, and remember to carry the 10 *tens*, which is 1 *hundred*.) Next, we multiply the *hundreds:* "Two threes are six, and one are seven." We write 7 in its proper place. The answer is 720.

$$\begin{array}{r} 360 \\ 2 \\ \hline 720 \end{array}$$

When we multiply, we do not need to be thinking about *units*, *tens*, and *hundreds* any more than just enough to remember to write each answer in its *proper place*, and to carry when we need to.

We notice the 0, think "Nothing," and write 0.

We think, "Two sixes are twelve," write 2, and remember to carry 1.

We think, "Two threes are six, and one are seven," and write 7.

In this last example, we think:

$$\begin{array}{r} 364 \\ 2 \\ \hline 728 \end{array}$$

"Two fours are eight." (Write 8.)

"Two sixes are twelve." (Write 2.) (1 to carry)

"Two threes are six, and one are seven." (Write 7.) The answer is 728.

V. USING TENS IN SUBTRACTION

The following paragraphs are included to illustrate both the procedure that may be followed in introducing pupils to the idea of using tens in subtraction and the emphasis that may be placed upon the idea of ten that the pupils may now have partly formed in their minds. To the pupil who has never had his attention called to the special meaning of the group of ten and who has not already learned to rely upon the idea in his work up to this point, the introduction will appear obscure and not so helpful. To the pupil who has been developing his idea of ten and making use of his idea in thinking about the process he has had to learn to this point, the introduction will be easy to interpret. Indeed, the latter pupil will be able to meet the explanations illustrated halfway, and to contribute a good deal from his previous experiences toward making part of the explanations himself.

1. Illustrative Examples

Teaching the Use of Ten in Subtraction

In subtracting, we sometimes have to take away more ones than we have ones to start with. When we do, we just 'carry back' and use *one of the tens* we have, and then take away ones from the *ten and more.*

Notice how we subtract 27 from 46.

46
27
―

To start with, we have 46, that is, *four tens and six.* Let us show four tens and six dots, and then pretend to take away *two tens and seven* by putting circles around that many dots.

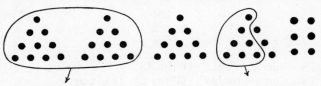

We take away two tens.　　We take away seven.
One ten and *nine* are left.

Since we do not have enough ones to take away seven, we carry back and use *one of the four tens* with the six; then we take away seven from the ten and six.

46
27
――
19

We think, "Seven from sixteen is nine," and write 9.

Next, we take away *two tens.* We remember that we have used one of the four tens already and that we must take two tens from three tens.

We think, "Two from three is one," and write 1 *in ten's place.*

In subtracting, we sometimes have to take away ones when we have no ones to start with. When we do, we just carry back and use *one of the tens we have;* then take away ones from the *ten.*

Notice now how we subtract 26 from 40.

40
26
―

To start with, we have 40, that is *four tens.* Let us show *four tens* dots, and then pretend to take away *two tens and six* by putting circles around that many dots.

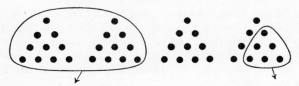

We take away two tens.   We take away six.
One ten and *four* are left.

Since we have no ones to take away six, we carry back and use *one of the four tens;* then we take away six from the *ten* that we carry back.

$$\begin{array}{r} 40 \\ 26 \\ \hline 14 \end{array}$$

We think, "Six from ten is four," and write 4.

Next, we take away *two tens.* We remember that we have carried back and used one of the four tens, and that we must subtract two tens from three tens.

We think, "Two from three is one," and write 1 *in ten's place.*

Giving Practice with Zeros

In subtracting, we sometimes carry back and use one of our tens, or hundreds, or thousands, when we have no ten, or no hundred, or no thousand to take away. It is always easy to write down what we have when we have nothing to take away.

$$\begin{array}{r} 853 \\ 407 \\ \hline 446 \end{array}$$

We think, "Seven from thirteen." We used one of the five tens, so we have only four tens, and we do not take anything away from the four tens, so we still have four tens. We write 4. We now think, "Four from eight."

$$\begin{array}{r} 8534 \\ 4071 \\ \hline 4463 \end{array}$$

We think, "One from four"; "Seven from thirteen"; "Four"; and "Four from eight."

In subtracting, we sometimes have to notice how many tens, or how many hundreds we have at the start. If we do, subtracting is easy.

$$\begin{array}{r} 9603 \\ 2476 \\ \hline 7127 \end{array}$$

We think, "Six from thirteen." We had to use one of our tens. Did we have a ten to use? Yes. Notice that we had 60 tens at the start, and since we carry back and use one of them, we now have 59 tens. It is easy to take 47 from 59. Just think, "Seven from nine"; "Four from five"; "Two from nine."

We think, "Four from ten." We had to use one of our tens.
Did we have a ten to use? Yes. Notice that we had 600
tens at the start, and since we carry back and use one of
them, we now have 599 tens. It is easy to take 465 from
599. Just think, "Five from nine"; "Six from nine"; and
"Four from five."

$$\begin{array}{r} 6000 \\ 4654 \\ \hline 1346 \end{array}$$

The 'carrying back' and 'using' of hundreds, thousands,
etc., is presented in a manner similar to the presentation of
the carrying back and using of tens. Since the pupil has
learned that tens, hundreds, etc., are subtracted *just like ones*,
concrete demonstration of the carrying back and using of
hundreds and thousands is unnecessary.

2. Decomposition versus Equal Additions

In the illustrative exercises that have been included it
will be seen that the method of decreasing in the minuend,
known as the 'method of decomposition,' has been emphasized in preference to the method of increasing in the subtrahend, known as the 'method of equal additions.' Although
certain experimental evidence [1] appears to indicate a slight
superiority in accuracy and speed of the latter method over
the former, the former method has been chosen for emphasis, because it is consistent with the ideas and methods of
thinking relative to the decimal notation and the place
value of the numerals that the pupils up to this point have
been acquiring. Slighter ease in operation in later work in
arithmetic does not justify a choice. Neither is a choice
justified by personal preference or by adult rationalization,

[1] P. B. Ballard. "Norms of performance in the fundamental
processes of arithmetic, with suggestions for their improvement."
Journal of Experimental Pedagogy, 3 : March 5, 1915, pp. 9–20, esp. p. 9.
  W. W. McClelland. "An experimental study of the different methods
of subtraction." *Journal of Experimental Pedagogy*, 4 : December 5,
1918, 293–299, esp. p. 298.
  W. H. Winch. "'Equal additions' versus 'decomposition' in teaching subtraction: An experimental research." Pp. 220, 270. *Journal of
Experimental Pedagogy*, 5 : June 5 and December 6, 1920, pp. 207–220,
261–270.

as commonly illustrated by the labored attempts to explain 'borrowing' through the substitution of the relation between dimes and cents for the relation between tens and ones, hundreds and tens, and so on, and by the explanation of equal additions in the following quoted paragraph:

> The method of equal additions is far more practical, and, though not so obviously 'natural,' is simple enough to explain ... It rests, of course, on the axiom that if equals are added to unequals their difference is unaltered; if the difference between my height and Tony's is marked upon the wall, and Tony and I then increase our heights by standing together on a form, the difference between us is still the same; and if I am 50 and Tony is 11 the difference between our ages will still be 39 when each of us is another year or another twenty years older.[2]

The method of decomposition is the method of 'using tens'; that is, of making use of one of the tens expressed in the minuend. This the pupil has learned in his simple subtractions. In the subtraction, $\frac{15}{-8}$, a ten is present to be used, and when the minuend, 15, is considered as expressing a *ten* and a *five*, the original subtraction of eight is made directly from the ten. No ten has to be 'borrowed' (suggesting the idea of 'paying back') and no ten has to be brought in from the outside (involving a new and usually labored explanation) to be added to both minuend and subtrahend. At the outset, as indicated in the chapter immediately preceding, the child uses the ten in making the subtraction. It is not a difficult step from that to using a ten in the method of decomposition. As suggested at the beginning of this section, the child comes to the learning of the method of decomposition with all the necessary ideas of how the subtraction is to be made already in his mind. The

---

[2] E. A. Greening Lamborn. *Reason in Arithmetic.* (Oxford University Press, London, 1930). Pp. 31–32.

only new thing to be learned is a new application in a closely related, though slightly different, situation.

Moreover, since the pupil has learned to subtract tens, hundreds, etc., just like ones, he can quickly make the step to 'carrying back' and 'using' a hundred, or a thousand, when necessary, just as he carries back and uses a ten.

Our discussions offer no objection to the procedure of teaching the pupil the other method after he has learned the one — provided in each case the learning is raised to the level of understanding. Understanding a second method and its contrasts with the first may, indeed, aid in furthering the pupil's understanding of the first; but care must then be exercised that the pupil is led to make distinctions and to see them clearly; otherwise, the teaching of a second method may lead to confusion.

VI. Dividing Tens

The following paragraphs are included to illustrate both the procedure that may be followed in introducing pupils to the idea of dividing tens and the emphasis that may be placed upon the idea, already considerably developed, that tens are dealt with in all operations 'just like units.' As in the illustrative exercises that have preceded, it is to be understood that each step of the presentation should be followed with sufficient practice to fix it in mind before proceeding to the next step.

1. Illustrative Examples

Teaching the Dividing of Tens

How do you think *tens* are divided?

Do you remember that *tens* are added, subtracted, and multiplied just the way *units* are added, subtracted, and multiplied; that *tens* are carried just the way *units* are carried; — in fact, that you can do everything with *tens* that you can do with *units* so long as you remember that they are *tens?* How are *tens* divided? You can guess the answer, it is so easy. *Tens* are divided exactly the

way *units* are divided. All you need to do is remember that they
are *tens*, and to write the ten's answer, *in ten's place*.

Suppose we want to find out how many threes there are in 69.

$$3\overline{)69}$$

We can see that 69 is 6 *tens* and 9; so we first find out how
many threes there are in six *tens*. We think, "Threes in six, two."
(Of course, we remember that it really is, "threes in six *tens*, two
tens," though we do not have to say "tens" at all.) We write the
2 above the 6, because we want the 2 (tens) to have the same position as the 6 (tens). We now think, "Two threes are six," and
write 6 under 6, and draw a line. Since we still have the 9 to divide, we write 9 under the line, and think, "Threes in nine, three."
We write the 3 above the 9, because the 3 is 3 *units*, and we want
it to have the same position as the 9 *units*. We now think, "Three
threes are nine," and write 9 under 9, and draw a line. Our
answer is 23, which tells us that there are 23 threes in 69. This
is the way our example looks when we have it worked.

$$
\begin{array}{r}
23 \\
3\overline{)69} \\
6 \\
\hline
9 \\
9 \\
\hline
\end{array}
$$

$$
\begin{array}{r}
81 \\
7\overline{)567} \\
56 \\
\hline
7 \\
7 \\
\hline
\end{array}
$$

Suppose we want to find how many sevens there are in
567. We see that the first number to be divided is 5 (hundred), and we know that there are no sevens in five; so
we look at the 56 (tens) and start by finding out how many
sevens there are in 56 (tens). We think, "Sevens in fifty-
six, eight," and because we know that the 8 means 8 *tens*, we write
the 8 just over the 6 so it will be in *ten's* place. We think, "Eight
sevens are fifty-six," and write 56 under 56, and draw a line. We
can see that we still have 7 to divide, so we write 7 underneath.
We think, "Sevens in seven, one," and write 1 beside the 8 in the
answer. We think, "One seven is seven," and write 7 under the 7.
Our answer is 81, which says that there are 81 sevens in 567.

In each case we can prove our answers by multiplying:

$$
\begin{array}{r}
23 \\
3 \\
\hline
69
\end{array}
\qquad
\begin{array}{r}
81 \\
7 \\
\hline
567
\end{array}
$$

Teaching Trial Division

In 'trial division' we 'try' the answer we think is correct to see whether it is correct. If the answer is not correct, we try another one. Notice how we try answers to see whether they are correct.

$$\begin{array}{r} 4 \\ 2\overline{)9} \\ 8 \\ \hline 1 \end{array}$$

Suppose we are trying to find how many twos in nine. We think, "Twos in nine, four," and write 4. We think, "Four twos are eight," and write 8 under 9; subtract, and write 1. Since the 1 we have is *less than 2*, we know that 4 is the right trial answer.

$$\begin{array}{r} 4 \\ 3\overline{)14} \\ 12 \\ \hline 2 \end{array}$$

Since the 2 we get after subtracting is *less than the 3*, we know that 4 is the right trial answer.

$$\begin{array}{r} 5 \\ 2\overline{)9} \\ 10 \\ \hline \end{array}$$

Suppose we are not careful, and happen to try 5 as an answer in this example. We think, "Twos in nine, five," and write 5. We think, "Five twos are ten," and write 10. But we can see that 10 is more than 9; so we know that 5 is not the right trial answer, and we must erase and try again.

$$\begin{array}{r} 3 \\ 2\overline{)9} \\ 6 \\ \hline 3 \end{array}$$

Suppose we are not careful, and happen to try 3 as an answer in this example. We think, "Twos in nine, three," and write 3. We think, "Three twos are six," write 6, and subtract. The 3 we get by subtracting is *more than 2*, so we know that the trial answer is not the correct one. Then we must erase, and try again.

$$\begin{array}{r} 4 \\ 3\overline{)16} \\ 12 \\ \hline 4 \end{array}$$

Suppose we had made the mistake in this example of trying 4 as an answer. We multiply, and subtract. Since the 4 we get by subtracting is *more than the 3*, we know that our trial answer is not the correct one.

Of course, the thing to do is to think carefully, so as not to make such mistakes; then our first trial answer will be the correct trial answer.

Teaching the Use of Trial Division in Dividing Tens

$$\begin{array}{r} 48 \\ 2\overline{)96} \\ 8 \\ \hline 16 \\ 16 \\ \hline \end{array}$$

Suppose we want to find how many twos in 96. We see that we first have 9 *tens* to divide, and we know that *tens* are divided just like *units;* so we think, "Twos in nine, four," and we write 4 in our answer over the 9. We know that since the 9 is 9 *tens* the 4 in our answer must be 4 *tens;* so we write it in the same place that the 9 has. Next we multiply, "Four twos are eight," and write 8 under 9; subtract, and write 1. (We look to be sure that 4 is the right trial answer.)

We had 9 *tens* to divide at the start, but we have divided only 8 of them, and still have 1 *ten* left to divide, and also 6 *units*. We now write the 6 beside the 1, which shows 1 *ten* and 6. We now have 16 to divide. We think, "Twos in sixteen, eight," and write 8 beside the 4 in our answer. We think, "Eight twos are sixteen," and write 16 under 16. Our answer is 48, which shows that there are 48 twos in 96.

To prove that our answer is correct, we multiply 48 by 2.

$$\begin{array}{r} 48 \\ 2 \\ \hline 96 \end{array}$$

$$\begin{array}{r} 68 \\ 3\overline{)204} \\ 18 \\ \hline 24 \\ 24 \\ \hline \end{array}$$

Here we see that the 2 (hundreds) is less than 3, so we think of 20 *tens*. We first divide the *tens*. We think, "Threes in twenty, six," and write 6 in what will be *ten's* place in the answer. We think, "Six threes are eighteen," and write 18 under 20; subtract, and write 2. This is, of course, 2 *tens*, and we still have it and 4 *units* to divide. We write 4 next to the 2, and think, "Threes in twenty-four, eight." We write 8 next to the 6 in our answer, and think, "Eight threes are twenty-four." We write 24 under 24. Our answer is 68, which shows that there are 68 threes in 204. The multiplication then proves that our answer is correct:

$$\begin{array}{r} 68 \\ 3 \\ \hline 204 \end{array}$$

Teaching the Use of Zeros in Division

You have already learned that in looking at a number with a zero you do not have to pay any attention to the zero except to notice the *place it holds*. That is about all the attention you need to give the zero when you see it in division. Let us see how the zero is to be used in division.

$$\begin{array}{r} 30 \\ 2\overline{)60} \\ 6 \\ \hline 0 \end{array}$$

Suppose we want to find how many twos there are in 60. We first pay attention to the 6 (tens). We think, "Twos in six, three," and because we know that the 3 is really 3 *tens*, we write it in our answer above the 6, so that it will show 3 *tens*. We think, "Three twos are six," and write 6 under 6. Since 6 is the same as 6, we know that we have all of our *tens* divided, and we have no *units* to be divided, so we write 0. Since we have 0, or nothing, to be divided, we do not think about dividing, but just write a 0 in our answer beside the 3, so that it will show 3 *tens*. Our answer is 30, which tells us that there are 30 twos in 60.

$$\begin{array}{r} 15 \\ 4\overline{)60} \\ 4 \\ \overline{20} \\ 20 \\ \overline{} \end{array}$$

Suppose we want to find how many fours there are in 60. We first pay attention to the 6 (tens). We think, "Fours in six, one," and write 1 over the 6 so it will be in *ten's* place. We multiply, "One four is four," and write 4 under 6; subtract, and write 2. The 2 shows that we still have 2 *tens* yet to be divided, and as we have no *units* to be divided, we write 0 beside the 2, which now shows 20. We think, "Fours in twenty, five," write 5 above 0 in the answer, and multiply. We think, "Five fours are twenty," and write 20 under 20. Our answer is 15, which tells us that there are 15 fours in 60.

Teaching the Dividing of Hundreds and Tens

How would you think *hundreds* are divided? Perhaps you remember that *hundreds* are added, subtracted, and multiplied just as *tens* and *units* are added, subtracted, and multiplied: that *hundreds* are carried just as *tens* are carried; in fact, that you can do everything with *hundreds* that you can do with *tens* and *units*, so long as you remember that they are *hundreds*. How are *hundreds* divided? The answer is easy. *Hundreds* are divided just as *tens* and *units* are divided. All you need to do is remember that they are *hundreds*.

$$\begin{array}{r} 230 \\ 3\overline{)690} \\ 6 \\ \overline{9} \\ 9 \\ \overline{0} \end{array}$$

Suppose we want to find how many threes there are in 690. First we notice the 6 (hundreds). We think, "Threes in six, two," and we write 2 in the answer just over the 6, because we know that the 2 is really 2 (hundreds). We multiply, "Two threes are six," and write 6 under 6. Since 6 is the same as 6, we know that we have divided all of our *hundreds*. We now have 9 *tens* to divide. We think, "Threes in nine, three," and we write 3 in our answer over the 9, because we know that the 3 is really 3 (tens). We multiply, "Three threes are nine," and we write 9 under 9. We can see that we have divided all our *tens*, and we have 0 *units* to divide; so we write 0. Since there is 0, or nothing, to divide, we just write 0 in our answer, to show that the 3 is 3 *tens* and the 2 is 2 *hundreds*. Our answer is 230, which tells us that there are 230 threes in 690.

Let us see how we divide *hundreds* and *tens* when we have to use trial division.

Suppose we want to find how many fives there are in 2650. We
notice the 2, and can tell that there are no fives in 2, so we look
at 26, which we can see is really 26 *hundred*. We first find

$$5\overline{)2650} \quad \begin{array}{r} 530 \\ \hline \end{array}$$

how many fives there are in 26 (hundreds). We think,
"Fives in twenty-six, five," and because we know that the
five really means five *hundred*, we write 5 in our answer
just over the 6 in order to make it show 5 *hundred*. We
now multiply, "Five fives are twenty-five," and we write
25 under 26; subtract, and write 1. The 1 shows that
we still have 1 *hundred* yet to divide, and we can see that we have
5 *tens* yet to divide; so we write 5 beside the 1. We now have
15 (tens) to divide. We think, "Fives in fifteen, three," and we
write 3 in our answer over the 5, because the 3 is really 3 *tens*.
We multiply, "Three fives are fifteen," and we write 15 under 15.
We can see that we have divided all our *tens*, and we have 0, or
no, *units* yet to divide. Since we have nothing to divide, we do
not think about dividing, but write a 0 in our answer over the 0
to hold the *unit's* place, and to make the 3 show 3 *tens* and the 5
show 5 *hundred*. Our answer is 530, which tells us that there are
530 fives in 2650.

2. The Forms of Division

With the presentation of the procedure of dividing tens
the teacher is required to reach a decision upon certain matters that may be grouped together roughly as the 'forms' of
division. Consideration must be given to such matters as
(*a*) 'short' and 'long' division, (*b*) partition and division,
and (*c*) remainders in division.

a. Short and Long Division. With respect to short and long
division, our suggestions are that the pupil learn the so-
called 'long form' from the beginning and that no distinction between the two forms be called to the attention of
pupils in the early grades. At the outset, when the pupil is
asked, "How many twos are in eight?" orally as indicated,
and in writing thus, $2\overline{)8}$, he should learn to give the complete answer, "Four twos are eight," and he should learn to
write the complete answer as completely as our method of
writing divisions will permit. Thus, as our preceding dis-

cussions have recommended, when the pupil writes the an-

swer to the question, 2)8, he writes it as indicated: 2)8.

Learning to write the 'complete' answer from the beginning, the pupil, by giving a multiplication answer to his division question, learns to multiply as part of his procedure in division, without thinking of the multiplying as something extra to do. Having multiplied in the giving of answers to such questions as 2)8, 7)63, 6)24, etc., without thinking of the multiplications other than as the answers that the division questions have required of him, he is ready to take up his dividing of tens and hundreds in each of which two or more division questions are asked that require two or more multiplication answers. In other words, the need to multiply when dividing does not then suddenly arise as something new to be done in a new kind of division; multiplying is part of the total procedure from the outset, and since it is, such extra attention as is required in the more complex processes may be given to the procedure of subtraction. To put the matter in another way, when the so-called 'long form' is learned from the beginning, attention, not being required for the learning of a 'new' form in the later processes, can be given almost exclusively to the new ideas of procedure that must be developed in connection with them.

Moreover, 'short' division is in reality a 'short-cut' process, which, because of its difficulty, should be learned only when the 'long,' step-by-step process has become thoroughly understood. It may be employed with one-digit divisors only and has, therefore, only a limited use. Such facts as these help to explain the mistaken psychology of the teacher who presents short division first, thinking it is the easier. Short division may be used only in the easier divisions (those with one-digit divisors); long division *must* be used in the more difficult divisions (those with two-or-more-digit divisors). Therefore, reasons many a teacher, short division is easy, and long division is difficult. What the teacher should consider is that short-cuts are always very difficult for beginners and that the more complete the work can be shown from the outset, the easier it is for the beginner to grasp. The long division form is really the easier one, because it shows more and requires the computer to carry less in his mind while he is working; it is the easier one because it is the only form that can be used with the difficult divisions. Therefore, let the teacher decide to introduce the easy form of procedure, first, with the easier processes, and later, with the more difficult processes; and let her introduce the harder form, if at all, still later, with the easier processes. The teacher who reasons that short division is the easier is making no distinction between divisions to be learned and procedure to be learned. The teacher ought to stop long enough to inquire why, if short division is the easier, it cannot be used with the more difficult divisions? If it is so easy, why does its use have to be confined to the easier divisions? If it is so easy, why must it be abandoned when the pupil moves ahead to his later work in division?

b. Partition and Division. With respect to partition and division, it is suggested that no distinction be attempted at the outset. The pupil will have enough to learn if he learns to divide. When he has learned division as the process of discovering the number of smaller equal groups in a larger group, he will pass on to the idea of the fraction as involving the procedure of dividing into equal parts. In the latter connection, he will learn that one-half of a thing is obtained by dividing it by two. Now, if he has learned division, he can engage in partition — finding one-half, one-third, etc. — of a number by means of division. Practice in using division in partition will eventually lead the pupil to make his own generalization respecting the distinction between the two ideas.

c. Remainders in Division. With respect to remainders in division, it is suggested that the pupil be guarded against the necessity of having to deal with remainders until he has a chance, in the study of fractions, to learn what to do with one when he gets it. If the suggestion is followed, the pupil will neither be disturbed by the necessity of dealing with remainders while he is learning to divide nor be misled by having to learn a false method of thinking about them. In the first place, the pupil will have enough to do to learn to divide without being troubled by remainders. In the second place, he is inclined to dissociate the remainder and divisor, when in reality the former may be interpreted only in terms of the latter.

To illustrate, when the pupil is required to deal with remainders from the outset, he is inclined to consider the answers in such divisions as the following to be the same: $2\overline{)7}$, $3\overline{)10}$, $4\overline{)13}$. In

$$\begin{array}{ccc} 3 & 3 & 3 \\ 6 & 9 & 12 \\ \hline 1R & 1R & 1R \end{array}$$

each, he secures the answer, 3 and 1 Remainder. In each case, the 1 Remainder is meaningless, because it is kept out of relation with the divisor. Instead of the three divisions producing the same answer, they obviously produce different answers: $3\frac{1}{2}$, $3\frac{1}{3}$, and $3\frac{1}{4}$.

VII. Multiplying by Tens

The following paragraphs are included to illustrate both the procedure that may be followed in introducing pupils to the idea of multiplying by tens and the emphasis that may be placed upon the idea that tens are multiplied "just like units." Each step of the presentation suggests its own type of practice, which should be provided before the succeeding step is attempted.

The Teaching of Multiplying by Tens

Last year you learned that you can do a number of interesting things with *tens*. Whatever they were, you learned that you can do the same with *tens* that you can do with *units*, so long as you remember that they are *tens* or keep the answers you get in their proper places. One of the things you learned was that you multiply *tens* exactly as you multiply *units*.

The thing to be learned now is how to multiply *by tens*. How do you suppose that is done? The answer is easy. You multiply by *tens* exactly as you multiply by *units*. The only thing to remember when you are multiplying by *tens* is to keep the answer in *ten's* place. If you just remember to put the answers in their proper places, you can go right ahead and multiply without even thinking of *tens*. Let us see.

$$\begin{array}{r} 4193 \\ 20 \\ \hline 83860 \end{array}$$

We multiply by 2 *tens* exactly the way we would multiply by 2. We think, "Two threes are six," "Two nines are eighteen," and so on. But look where we write our answer. When we think, "Two threes are six," we write 6 just under the 2, which is in *ten's* place. (We remember that we are multiplying by 2 *tens*.) In order to put our answer in *ten's* place, we must write 0 to the right to put it there. Actually, we write the 0 right at the beginning, so that we shall not have to think about our answer being *tens*. So we do our multiplying like this:

$$\begin{array}{r} 4193 \\ 20 \\ \hline 83860 \end{array}$$

We notice in the beginning that there are no *units* to multiply by, and that we will start multiplying by the 2 *tens;* so we write 0 under 0, and think, "Two threes are six," write 6 under 2, think, "Two nines are eighteen," write 8 and remember 1 to carry, and so on.

The Teaching of Multiplying by Units and Tens

You have just learned how to multiply by *tens*. Let us see how to multiply by *units* and *tens*. Suppose we want to multiply 523 by 42.

$$\begin{array}{r} 523 \\ 42 \\ \hline 1046 \\ 2092 \\ \hline 21966 \end{array}$$

Our multiplier is 42, which is, as you know, 4 *tens* and 2. First, we multiply by the 2 (*units*), and start the writing of our answer just under the 2. The product is 1046, which is only part of the whole product that we have to find. We have yet to multiply by the 4 *tens*. We now multiply by the 4 *tens* just as though it were 4 *units*, and start the writing of our answer just under the 4. The product is 20,920. (Notice that this part of the product is written, 2092, which really is 2092 *tens*.) There is no need to write the zero in this case, as the rest of the answer keeps this part in its proper place.

We now have two parts of the whole product that we have to

find, 1046 and 20,920. In order to find the whole product we add
the two parts, which gives the answer.

First, multiply by *units*.

Second, multiply by *tens*.

Third, add the two part products.

Throughout, keep each part of the answer in its proper place.

The Teaching of Multiplying by Hundreds

You already know that you can add, subtract, multiply, and divide *hundreds* exactly the way you add, subtract, multiply, and
divide *tens* and *units*. How do you suppose you should multiply
by hundreds? The answer is easy, isn't it? You multiply by *hundreds* in exactly the same way that you multiply by *tens* and *units*.
The only thing to be careful to do is to begin writing the answer
you get in the proper place, which is *directly underneath* the multiplier.

$$\begin{array}{r} 734 \\ 200 \\ \hline 146800 \end{array}$$

We see at the start that there are no *units* and no *tens* in
the multiplier, and that when we multiply, we must multiply by 2 (*hundred*). Thus we know that our answer
must show *hundreds*. Just as when we multiply by *tens*,
we now must start writing our answer *directly underneath* the 2, so
that our answer will show *hundreds*. Not having any *units* or *tens*
in our multiplier, we will get no *units* or *tens* in our answer to hold
those places for us, so we start right at the beginning to write a 0
under 0 in *unit's* place, and a 0 under 0 in *ten's* place, and then
start our multiplying by the 2 (*hundred*). "Two fours are eight,"
"Two threes are six," "Two sevens are fourteen." The two zeros
we write at the start place our answer in the places it belongs.

The Teaching of Multiplying by Units, Tens, and Hundreds

You have just learned how to multiply by *hundreds*. Let us see

$$\begin{array}{r} 658 \\ 425 \\ \hline 3290 \\ 1316 \\ 2632 \\ \hline 279650 \end{array}$$

how to multiply by *units*, *tens*, and *hundreds*. Suppose
we want to multiply 658 by 425.

Our multiplier is 425, which is, as you know, 4 *hundred*,
2 *tens*, and 5. First we multiply by the 5 (*units*), and
start writing our answer just under the 5. The product
is 3290, which is only part of the whole product we have
to find. We have yet to multiply by the 2 *tens* and the
4 *hundred*. We now multiply by the 2 *tens* just as though it were 2
units, and start writing our answer just under the 2 in order that

this part of our answer will show *tens*. The product is 13,160. (Notice that this part of the whole product is written, 1316, which really is 1316 *tens*.) There is no need to write the zero in this case, as the rest of the answer keeps this part in its proper place. We now have two parts of the whole product, the product of multiplying by the 5 *units*, and the product of multiplying by the 2 *tens*. We have yet to multiply by the 4 *hundred*.

We now multiply by the 4 *hundred* just as though it were 4 *units*, and start writing our answer just under the 4 in order that this part of our answer will show *hundreds*. The product is 263,200. (Notice that it is written, 2632, which really is 2632 *hundreds*.) There is no need to write two zeros to show *hundreds*, since the rest of our answer keeps this part in its proper place.

We now have three parts of the whole product that we have to find, 3290; 13,160; and 263,200. In order to find the whole product, we add the three parts, which gives the answer.

First, multiply by *units*.

Second, multiply by *tens*.

Third, multiply by *hundreds*.

Last, add the three part products.

Throughout, keep each part of the answer in its proper place. Do this by starting to write each part of the answer *directly underneath* the multiplier.

Teaching What To Do with Zeros in the Multiplier

Zeros in the multiplier make the multiplication easier, because they give you less to do. Suppose the multiplier is 504. You need to multiply only by *units* and *hundreds*. Suppose the multiplier is 540. You need to multiply only by *tens* and *hundreds*. Suppose the multiplier is 500. You already know that in this case you have to multiply only by *hundreds*, as there are no *units* and no *tens*.

$$\begin{array}{r} 863 \\ 504 \\ \hline 3452 \\ 4315 \\ \hline 434952 \end{array}$$

First, we multiply by the 4 *units*, and start writing our answer under the 4. This gives us the product, 3452, which is only part of the whole product we have to find. We have yet to multiply by the 5 *hundred*.

We notice that there are no *tens* in the multiplier; so we proceed to multiply by the 5 *hundred;* and in order to make that part of our answer show *hundreds*, we start writing it *directly underneath* the 5. This gives us the product, 431,500. (Notice that this part of the whole product is written, 4315, which really is 4315 *hundreds*.) There is no need to write the zeros, as the rest of our work keeps this part of our answer in its proper place.

We now have two parts of our whole product that we have to find, 3452 and 431,500. In order to find the whole product, we add the two parts.

Let us now multiply when we have zero in *unit's* place in the multiplier and need to multiply by *tens* and *hundreds* only.

$$\begin{array}{r} 863 \\ 540 \\ \hline 34520 \\ 4315 \\ \hline 466020 \end{array}$$

First, we write 0 under 0, so that when we multiply by the 4 *tens* the product will show *tens*. We multiply by the 4 *tens* just as though it were 4 *units*, and start writing the answer just under the 4. The product is 34,520, which is only part of the whole product we have to find. We have yet to multiply by the 5 *hundred*.

We now multiply by the 5 *hundred* just as though it were 5 *units*, and since that part of our answer must show *hundreds*, we start writing it just under the 5. There is no need to write any zeros, as the rest of the work keeps that part of the whole answer in its proper place. The product is 431,500. (Notice that this part of the whole product is written, 4315, which really is 4315 *hundreds*.)

We now have two parts of our whole product that we have to find, 34,520 and 431,500. In order to find the whole product, we add the two parts.

VIII. DIVIDING BY TENS

The following paragraphs are included to illustrate both the procedure that may be followed in introducing pupils to the idea of dividing by tens and the emphasis that may be placed upon the idea that tens may be employed in thinking and in computation "just like units." As in the illustrative exercises that have been included under former topics, it is to be understood that each step of the presentation should be followed with sufficient practice to fix it in mind before the work proceeds to the next step.

The Teaching of Dividing by Tens

Last year you learned that you can add, subtract, multiply, and divide *tens* just the way you add, subtract, multiply, and divide *units*. (Of course, you know that you have to be careful in each case to write the numbers in their proper places, and to put the answers in their proper places.) You have just been dividing *tens* and *units*, and *hundreds*, *tens* and *units*, and you remember that you have divided them all just like *units*.

This year you have already learned one new thing, and that is that you can *multiply by tens* exactly the way you *multiply by units*. The thing to be learned now is how to *divide by tens*. How do you suppose that is done? You can guess the answer. You *divide by tens* exactly as you *divide by units*. Let us see. Suppose we want to divide 83,860 by 20; that is, to find out how many twenties there are in 83,860.

$$\begin{array}{r} 4 \\ \hline 20)\overline{83860} \end{array}$$

The first question is, how many 20's in 83? (Of course, you know that 20 is 2 *tens* and 83 is 8 *tens* and a little more.) Why not think of 20 as 2 (*tens*, of course), and of 83 as 8 (*tens*, of course)? Now the question is, how many twos in eight? The answer is 4. (Notice where 4 is written.) The next thing to do is to multiply and subtract. Then bring down the next figure, which is 8, and the example looks like this:

$$\begin{array}{r} 4 \\ \hline 20)\overline{83860} \\ 80 \\ \hline 38 \end{array}$$

The next question is, how many 20's in 38? (Look at the 2 (*tens*) and at the 3 (*tens*), which tells you, "Twos in three, one.") Write 1 in the answer, multiply, subtract, and bring down the next figure. The example now looks like this:

$$\begin{array}{r} 41 \\ \hline 20)\overline{83860} \\ 80 \\ \hline 38 \\ 20 \\ \hline 186 \end{array}$$

The question now is, how many 20's in 186? (Look at the 2 (*tens*) and at the 18 (*tens*), which tells you, "Twos in eighteen, nine.") Write 9 in the answer, multiply, subtract, and bring down the next figure. The example now looks like this:

$$\begin{array}{r} 419 \\ \hline 20)\overline{83860} \\ 80 \\ \hline 38 \\ 20 \\ \hline 186 \\ 180 \\ \hline 60 \end{array}$$

The question now is, how many 20's in 60? (Look at the 2 (*tens*) and at the 6 (*tens*), which tells you, "Twos in six, three.") Write 3 in the answer, and multiply. The example is now worked, and looks like this:

(The complete example appears on the next page.)

```
     4193
20)83860
     80
     ──
     38
     20
     ──
     186
     180
     ───
      60
      60
     ──
```

You think and work like this:

"Twos in eight, four." Multiply, subtract, bring down.

"Twos in three, one." Multiply, subtract, bring down.

"Twos in eighteen, nine." Multiply, subtract, bring down.

"Twos in six, three." Multiply.

```
      537
60)32220
   300
   ───
   222
   180
   ───
    420
    420
    ───
```

Look at the 6 (*tens*) in the divisor, and since the first figure, 3, in the dividend is less than 6, look at the 32. Think, "Sixes in thirty-two, five." (Notice where 5 is written.) Multiply, subtract, and bring down the next figure. Look at 6 and at 22. Think, "Sixes in twenty-two, three." Write 3 in the answer, multiply, subtract, and bring down the next figure. Look at the 6 and at the 42. Think, "Sixes in forty-two, seven." Write 7 in the answer, and multiply.

In dividing by *tens, keep your eye on the number in ten's place in the divisor.* This is the important number. You know that it is *tens,* but you can think of it in dividing the same as you think of *units* in dividing. Be sure to write the answer in its proper place in the quotient.

Teaching What To Do with Zeros in Division

You know that zero is used just to hold a place when there is no number to write in it. In dividing, the zero will often help you to *put each part of the answer in its proper place.*

```
     3 6
70)21420
   210
   ───
   420
   420
   ───
```

What is wrong with the answer? The 3 is in its proper place above 4, and the 6 is in its proper place above 0.

This is the right way to work the example:

```
     306
70)21420
   210
   ───
   420
   420
   ───
```

70's in 214? Look at the 7 and at the 21, which tells you, "Sevens in twenty-one, three." Write 3 in its proper place, multiply, subtract, and bring down the next number.

70's in 42? You can see that there are no 70's in 42; so you write 0 in the answer to keep the 3 (*hundreds*) in its proper place, and bring down the next figure. Now you can divide.

70's in 420? Look at the 7 and at the 42. Think, "Sevens in forty-two, six," write 6, and multiply.

The Teaching of Dividing by Tens and Units

You have just learned how to divide by *tens* — that you divide by *tens* just as you divide by *units;* and that in dividing you think of the *tens* as *units*. The main thing is to *keep your eye on the number in ten's place in the divisor*.

The thing to be learned now is how to divide by *tens* and *units*. You divide by *tens* and *units* just the way you divide by *tens*. All you need to do is think of the *tens* as *units*, keep your eye on the *number in ten's place in the divisor*, and be sure to put each answer in its proper place. Exactly the same steps are taken in dividing by *tens* and *units* as are taken in dividing by *units*. The only thing extra to do is to be more careful each time to make the right division. Let us see.

$$\begin{array}{r} 2 \\ 21\overline{)483} \\ 42 \\ \hline 6 \end{array}$$

21's in 48? Look at the 2 (*tens*) in 21, and at the 4 (*tens*) in 48. Think, "Twos in four, two." Write 2 in its proper place, and multiply. (Notice that the product, 42, is less than 48. *This product must be either the same as the number above it or less.*) Subtract. (Notice that the remainder, 6, is less than 21. *This remainder, when there is one, must always be less than the divisor.*) Bring down the next figure, and the example looks like this:

$$\begin{array}{r} 2 \\ 21\overline{)483} \\ 42 \\ \hline 63 \end{array}$$

21's in 63? Look at the 2 (*tens*) in 21, and at the 6 (*tens*) in 63. Think, "Twos in six, three." Write 3 in the answer, and multiply. Notice that the product is the same as the number above it, and since there is nothing more to bring down, the example is finished. It now looks like this:

$$\begin{array}{r} 23 \\ 21\overline{)483} \\ 42 \\ \hline 63 \\ 63 \\ \hline \end{array}$$

$$\begin{array}{r} 7 \\ 74\overline{)53576} \\ 518 \\ \hline 17 \end{array}$$

Since 53 is less than 74, the first question will be, 74's in 535. Look at the 7, and at the 53. Think, "Sevens in fifty-three, seven." Write 7 in its proper place, and multiply. (Notice the product.) Subtract. (Notice the remainder.) Bring down the next figure, and the example looks like this:

$$\begin{array}{r} 7 \\ 74\overline{)53576} \\ 518 \\ \hline 177 \end{array}$$

74's in 177? Look at the 7, and at the 17. Think, "Sevens in seventeen, two." Write 2 in the answer, and multiply. (Notice the product.) Subtract. (Notice the remainder.) Bring down the next figure. The example now looks like this:

$$\begin{array}{r} 72 \\ 74\overline{)53576} \\ 518 \\ \hline 177 \\ 148 \\ \hline 296 \end{array}$$

74's in 296? Look at the 7, and at the 29. Think, "Sevens in twenty-nine, four." Write 4 in the answer, and multiply. (Notice the product.) Since the product is the same as the number above it and there is nothing more to bring down, the example is worked. The completed example looks like this:

$$\begin{array}{r} 724 \\ 74\overline{)53576} \\ 518 \\ \hline 177 \\ 148 \\ \hline 296 \\ 296 \\ \hline \end{array}$$

Teaching True Quotient Answers

In the examples of division by *tens* and *units* that you have just been working, the quotient answer you found in each case by thinking of the *tens* in the divisor as *units* has been the 'true' quotient answer. Let us illustrate.

$$\begin{array}{r} 6 \\ 76\overline{)4788} \\ 456 \\ \hline 22 \end{array}$$

In this example we wish to find how many 76's there are in 4788. To divide, we think of the 7 (*tens*) as 7, and think, "Sevens in forty-seven, six." We write 6 in its proper place and multiply. We notice the product, 456, and see that it is less than 478; so we subtract. We now notice the remainder, 22, and see that it is less than 76. (The product, if it is not the same as the number above it, must be less;

the remainder, if there is one, must be less than the divisor.) So
we bring down the next figure, and our example looks like this:

$$\begin{array}{r} 6 \\ 76)\overline{4788} \\ 456 \\ \hline 228 \end{array}$$

Again, we think of the 7 (*tens*) as 7, and think, "Sevens
in twenty-two, three." We write 3 in the answer and
multiply. We notice the product, 228, and see that it
is just the same as the number above it. As there is no
remainder, and nothing else to bring down, we have
finished the example.

$$\begin{array}{r} 63 \\ 76)\overline{4788} \\ 456 \\ \hline 228 \\ 228 \end{array}$$

Let us review. When we think, at the beginning of the example,
"Sevens in forty-seven, six," we *try* 6 as a quotient answer. That
is, we use 6 as a 'trial' answer. *We try it by multiplying and noticing that the product is less than the number above it.* We are now
almost sure that 6 is also the 'true' quotient answer, *but not quite
sure.* We now subtract, and *notice that the remainder is less than the
divisor.* We are now sure that 6 is the true quotient answer. We
now bring down the next figure, and *try* for an answer here.

We think, "Sevens in twenty-two, three," and we *try* 3 as a
quotient answer. That is, we use 3 as a trial answer. *We try it
by multiplying and noticing that the product is the same as the number
above it.* This makes us sure that the trial answer is also the true
answer.

Teaching Trial Quotient Answers

It often happens, when one is dividing by *tens* and *units*, that
the trial quotient answer does not turn out to be the true quotient
answer. When this happens, one has to *try* another answer, and
to keep on *trying* until he does get the true answer. Let us see.

$$\begin{array}{r} 7 \\ 76)\overline{4940} \\ 532 \end{array}$$

In this example we wish to find how many 76's there are
in 4940. To divide, we think of the 7 (*tens*) as 7, and
think, "Sevens in forty-nine, seven." We write 7 in its
proper place and multiply. When we multiply, *we notice
that the product, 532, is greater than the number above it.* This makes
us certain that our trial answer is not the true answer. We erase,
and *try* the next smaller number, 6, as a quotient answer.

$$\begin{array}{r} 6 \\ 76\overline{)4940} \\ 456 \\ \hline 38 \end{array}$$

We try 6 *by multiplying and noticing that the product is less than the number above it.* We are now *almost* sure that 6 is also the true quotient answer, *but not quite sure.* We now subtract, and *notice that the remainder is less than the divisor.* We are now quite sure that 6 is the true quotient answer. We now bring down the next figure.

$$\begin{array}{r} 65 \\ 76\overline{)4940} \\ 456 \\ \hline 380 \\ 380 \\ \hline \end{array}$$

We again think of the 7 (*tens*) as 7, and think, "Sevens in thirty-eight, five." We *try* 5 *by multiplying and noticing now that the product is the same as the number above it.* This makes us sure that 5 is the true quotient answer. If we wish, we can prove our answer by multiplying 76 by 65, or 65 by 76.

Let us try another example. Suppose we wish to find out how many 48's there are in 2736. We divide.

$$\begin{array}{r} 6 \\ 48\overline{)2736} \\ 288 \end{array}$$

We think of the 4 (*tens*) as 4, and think, "Fours in twenty-seven, six." We *try* 6 as a quotient answer *by multiplying noticing that the product, 288, is greater than the number above it.* This makes us certain that 6 is not the true answer. We erase and *try* the next smaller number, 5, as a quotient answer.

$$\begin{array}{r} 5 \\ 48\overline{)2736} \\ 240 \\ \hline 33 \end{array}$$

We *try* 5 *by multiplying and noticing that the product is less than the number above it.* But yet we cannot be entirely sure of 5 until we subtract, and *notice that the remainder is less than the divisor.* When we do that, we are sure that 5 is the true quotient answer. We bring down the next figure.

$$\begin{array}{r} 58 \\ 48\overline{)2736} \\ 240 \\ \hline 336 \\ 384 \end{array}$$

We think of the 4 (*tens*) as 4, and think, "Fours in thirty-three, eight." We *try* 8 as a quotient answer *by multiplying and noticing that the product is greater than the number above it.* This makes us certain that 8 is not the true answer. We erase and *try* the next smaller number, 7, as a quotient answer.

$$\begin{array}{r} 57 \\ 48\overline{)2736} \\ 240 \\ \hline 336 \\ 336 \\ \hline \end{array}$$

We *try* 7 *by multiplying and noticing that the product is the same as the number above it.* This makes us sure that 7 is the true quotient answer. Since there is no remainder, and nothing to bring down, our example is finished. If we wish, we can prove our answer by multiplying 48 by 57, or 57 by 48.

In the exercises you have been taking to find out if the trial quotient answers are the true ones, you have been making your *trials* by actually working them out on your papers. This causes you much extra work erasing. Let us see how such *trials* can be made *mentally* and without so much pencil work and erasing.

$$\begin{array}{r} 6 \\ 76\overline{)4788} \end{array} \quad 456$$

We think of the 7 (*tens*) as 7, and think, "Sevens in forty-seven, six." Suppose before writing 6 we multiply mentally; "Six sixes are thirty-six." (Remember 3 to carry.) "Six sevens are forty-two and three are forty-five." Our last part product, 45, we note is less than 47; so we can be reasonably sure that 6 is the true quotient answer. Or, if we cannot do all this multiplying *mentally* and at the same time remember what we have done, we can write the trial answer and the product at the side of our example or on a separate piece of paper,

as shown above: 456.

$$\begin{array}{r} 6 \end{array}$$

We can now write 6 in its proper place, multiply, *notice the product*, subtract, *notice the remainder*, and bring down the next figure.

$$\begin{array}{r} 7 \quad 6 \\ 76\overline{)4940} \quad 532 \quad 456 \end{array}$$

In this example we think of the 7 (*tens*) as 7, and think, "Sevens in forty-nine, seven." At the side of our example, or on another piece of paper, or *in our heads* (if we can), we write the trial quotient

$$7$$

answer and the product, 532. Since 532 is more than 494, we try

$$6$$

6, 456. We can now write 6 in the answer, multiply, *notice the product*, subtract, *notice the remainder*, and bring down the next figure.

Let us work another example to show how much we gain if we can do our "trying" *in our heads*:

$$\begin{array}{r} 57 \quad\quad 6 \quad\quad 5 \\ 48\overline{)2736} \quad 288 \quad 240 \\ \underline{240} \\ 336 \quad\quad 8 \quad\quad 7 \\ 336 \quad 384 \quad 336 \end{array}$$

This is the way an example might look with the trial work at the side.

$$\begin{array}{r} 57 \\ 48\overline{)2736} \\ \underline{240} \\ 336 \\ 336 \end{array}$$

This is the way the same example might look with the trial work on another piece of paper, or *in our heads*.

More About Trial Quotient Answers

Sometimes we have to *try* more than one trial quotient answer before we can find the true one.

$$
\begin{array}{r}
4 \\
27\overline{)1242} \\
108 \\
\hline
16
\end{array}
\qquad
\begin{array}{ccc}
6 & 5 & 4 \\
162 & 135 & 108
\end{array}
$$

We think of the 2 (*tens*) as 2, and think, "Twos in twelve, six." We *try* 6 by multiplying, and *noticing the product.* Next, we *try* 5 in the same way. Next, we *try* 4 in the same way. We write 4 in the answer, multiply, *notice the product,* subtract, *notice the remainder,* and bring down the next figure.

$$
\begin{array}{r}
46 \\
27\overline{)1242} \\
108 \\
\hline
162 \\
162
\end{array}
\qquad
\begin{array}{ccc}
8 & 7 & 6 \\
216 & 189 & 162
\end{array}
$$

We think of the 2 (*tens*) as 2, and think, "Twos in sixteen, eight." We *try* 8 by multiplying, and *noticing the product.* Next, we *try* 7 in the same way. Next, we *try* 6 in the same way. We write 6 in the answer, multiply, and *notice the product.*

In dividing by *tens* and *units,* think of the *tens* as *units* and divide. *Try* the quotient answer *by multiplying.* If the product is larger than the number above it, *try* the next smaller number as a quotient answer. Keep on *trying* the next smaller number until you get the true quotient answer. A quotient answer is the *true* one if, when you multiply the divisor by it, the product is less than the number above it, or the same as the number above it, and if, when you subtract, the remainder, if there is any, is less than the divisor.

$$
\begin{array}{r}
9 \\
28\overline{)2436} \quad 252
\end{array}
$$

Notice, first, there are no 28's in 24, and the first question is, 28's in 243. Think of the 2 (*tens*) as 2, and think, "Twos in twenty-four; of course, the answer is 12." But since 9 is the largest quotient answer one can use at any one time, *do not try 12, then 11, then 10;* but use 9 as the first trial answer. In this case, 9 is not the true answer, but 8 is.

$$
\begin{array}{r}
9 \\
17\overline{)1581} \quad 153
\end{array}
$$

Notice, first, there are no 17's in 15, and the first question is, 17's in 158. Think of the 1 (*ten*) as 1, and think, "Ones in fifteen." Since that answer is larger than 9, use 9 as the first trial answer. In this case, 9 proves to be the true answer.

Remember: *Never use a number larger than 9 as the first trial quotient answer.*

Pointing Out a Mistake to Avoid

Sometimes in *trying* quotient answers a person makes a mistake in multiplying by a trial answer, and so fails to recognize the true answer, and passes it for a lower trial answer. One can always tell when he has made such a mistake if he keeps his eyes open. Let us see.

$$\begin{array}{c} 7 \\ 34\overline{)2788} \\ 238 \end{array} \quad \begin{array}{c} 9 \\ 306 \end{array} \quad \begin{array}{c} 8 \\ (282) \\ ? \end{array} \quad \begin{array}{c} 7 \\ 238 \end{array}$$

In dividing 2788 by 34, we notice that there are no 34's in 27, and that our first question is, 34's in 278. We think of the 3 (*tens*) as 3, and think, "Threes in twenty-seven, nine." We *try* 9 *by multiplying*, as shown at the side of the example. Since 9 is too large, we *try* 8 *by multiplying*. Suppose we make a mistake in multiplying by 8, or for some other reason, move down to 7, and *try* it by multiplying. Our product is 238. Since 238 is *less than the number above it*, we have *some* reason to think that 7 is the true quotient answer. But our *trial* is not complete until we subtract. Let us subtract, and our example looks like this:

$$\begin{array}{c} 7 \\ 34\overline{)2788} \\ 238 \\ \overline{40} \end{array}$$

$$\begin{array}{c} 8 \\ 34\overline{)2788} \\ 272 \\ \overline{6} \end{array}$$

Look at the remainder. It is *greater* than the divisor, not *less*, as it should be; so we know that 7 is the wrong quotient answer. We must *try* a higher number than 7. We *try* 8, and this time we multiply *carefully and correctly. Our product, 272, is less than the number above it.* We subtract, and *notice that the remainder is less than the divisor.* We now know that 8 is the true quotient answer; so we bring down the next figure, and go ahead.

Teaching the Use of Zeros in Division

You know that zero is used just to hold a place. In dividing, the zero will often help in *putting each part of the answer in its proper place.* Let us see.

$$\begin{array}{c} 507 \\ 65\overline{)32955} \\ 325 \\ \overline{455} \\ 455 \end{array}$$

The first question is, 65's in 329? Look at the 6 and at the 32, and think, "Sixes in thirty-two, five." Write 5, multiply, notice the product, subtract, and notice the remainder. Bring down the next figure. 65's in 45? You can see that there are no 65's in 45; so write 0 in the answer to keep the place. The zero will keep the other parts of the answer in their proper places. **Bring down the next figure, and complete the division.**

65's in 455? Look at the 6 and at the 45, and think, "Sixes in forty-five, seven." Write 7, and multiply.

$$
\begin{array}{r}
570 \\
65\overline{)37050} \\
325 \\
\hline
455 \\
455 \\
\hline
0
\end{array}
$$

In this next example the first question is, 65's in 370? Look at the 6 and at the 37, and think, "Sixes in thirty-seven, six." *Try* 6. Since that is too much, *try* 5. Multiply, notice the product, subtract, and notice the remainder. Bring down the next figure.

65's in 455? Look at the 6 and at the 45, and think, "Sixes in forty-five, seven." Write 7, and multiply. Notice the product. Since there is no remainder, bring down the next figure, which is zero. This means that there are no *units* to be divided, and that the answer so far is *tens*, and that there are no *units* in the answer. Write 0 in the answer to keep the rest of the answer in its proper place.

Teaching Dividing by Hundreds

You have been learning how to divide by *tens*, and you have found out that you divide by *tens* in exactly the same way that you divide by *units*. And you have learned that you need to be careful to put each part of the answer *in its proper place*, and to *try* each quotient answer until you find the *true* one.

Let us see how one divides by *hundreds*. How do you suppose that is done? Perhaps you can guess. You remember, of course, that *hundreds* are added, subtracted, multiplied, and divided just like *tens* and *units*, and that you multiply by *hundreds* just as you multiply by *tens* and *units*. The answer is that one divides by *hundreds* just as he divides by *tens*, and just as he divides by *units*. One thinks of the *hundreds* as *units*, and divides by *hundreds* just as he would if they were *units*. He must be careful, though, to put each part of the answer *in its proper place*, and to *try* each quotient answer until he finds the true one.

$$
\begin{array}{r}
73 \\
600\overline{)43800} \\
4200 \\
\hline
1800 \\
1800 \\
\hline
\end{array}
$$

We notice at the beginning that there are no 600's in 4, or in 43, or in 438; so our first question is, 600's in 4380. (Notice where we must write our first quotient answer.) We look at the 6 (*hundreds*) and at the 43 (*hundreds*), and think, "Sixes in forty-three, seven." We *try* 7 by multiplying, noticing the product, subtracting, and noticing the remainder. We bring down the next figure, and complete the division.

600's in 1800? We look at the 6 (*hundreds*) and at the 18 (*hundreds*), and think, "Sixes in eighteen, three." We write 3 in the answer, and multiply. Our answer is 73.

$$\begin{array}{r} 94 \\ 440\overline{)41360} \\ 3960 \\ \hline 1760 \\ 1760 \\ \hline \end{array}$$

We notice in the beginning that there are no 440's in 4, or in 41, or in 413, and that our first question is, 440's in 4136? We look at the 4 (*hundreds*) and at the 41 (*hundreds*), and think, "Fours in forty-one, ten." Since 9 is the largest quotient answer we can use, we *try* 9 by multiplying, noticing the product, subtracting, and noticing the remainder. We bring down the next figure.

440's in 1760? We look at the 4 and at the 17, and think, "Fours in seventeen, four." We write 4 in the answer, and multiply. Our answer is 94.

$$\begin{array}{r} 48 \\ 736\overline{)35328} \\ 2944 \\ \hline 5888 \\ 5888 \\ \hline \end{array}$$

We notice in the beginning that there are no 736's in 3, or in 35, or in 353; so our first question is, 736's in 3532? (Notice where we must write our first quotient answer.) We look at the 7 and at the 35, and think, "Sevens in thirty-five, five." But when we *try* 5, we find that it is too large; so we *try* 4, and find that it is the true quotient answer. After multiplying and subtracting, we bring down the next figure.

736's in 5888? We look at the 7 and at the 58, and think, "Sevens in fifty-eight, eight." We *try* 8 by multiplying and find that 8 is the true answer. Our answer is 48.

$$\begin{array}{r} 75 \\ 509\overline{)38175} \\ 3563 \\ \hline 2545 \\ 2545 \\ \hline \end{array}$$

We notice that there are no 509's in 3, or in 38, or in 381; so our first question is, 509's in 3817? We look at the 5 and at the 38, and think, "Fives in thirty-eight, seven." We *try* 7, by multiplying, noticing the product, subtracting, and noticing the remainder. We bring down the next figure.

509's in 2545? We look at the 5 and at the 25, and think, "Fives in twenty-five, five." We *try* 5, by multiplying and noticing our product. Our answer is 75.

CHAPTER XVI

COMPARISON AND CONTRAST OF THE PROCESSES

ARGUMENT

1. To the extent that pupils understand the number system, they are intelligent about the varied number processes they are called upon to learn.

2. The use of the 'problem' to provide either a motive for the learning of a process or an opportunity to apply the process is limited. The real purpose of the problem is to provide practice in the recognition of general ideas, or, later, illustration of situations of which the general ideas are a part.

3. A general idea once developed serves to unite in thought certain practical situations that otherwise are radically different in character and in setting.

4. The general idea that is portrayed in a problem should be the center of attention, not the problem itself. To this end, the pupil's attention should be directed away from the momentarily interesting and attractive features of the problem situation toward the general idea. The procedure is briefly illustrated by appropriate lesson materials.

5. Lesson materials are used to illustrate the similarities and difference between:

   (*a*) Addition and multiplication;
   (*b*) Addition and subtraction;
   (*c*) Subtraction and division;
   (*d*) Multiplication and division.

6. Two-step problems are described as means of providing practice in the recognition of general ideas on a level higher than is provided by one-step problems.

7. The additional, or 'higher level,' practice is provided by the necessity to search for the hidden question.

8. The type of instruction that may be given to introduce the two-step problem is illustrated by a variety of exercises.

I. Attention to Arrangement

The activities suggested in the chapters immediately preceding may be described as activities of giving attention to arrangement. Throughout the activities the pupils are given direction in their studies of arrangement, and their studies become gradually both more progressive and more systematic.

The studies become more progressive in the sense that they depend less and less upon perceptual experience with arrangement and deal more and more with arrangement as a matter of thought. Instead of moving very slowly from the teacher's demonstrations through the various stages of their studies of arrangement, as was necessary in the beginning, the pupils gradually acquire the ability to proceed almost directly, in learning a new process, to a consideration of arrangement when no objects are present.

The studies become more systematic in the sense that they deal less and less with isolated items of experience and more and more with items grouped together in terms of a central idea — an idea that serves not merely as a means of explanation and a standard of evaluation, but also as a common mode of procedure or method of attack. Instead of having to think of each new arrangement in terms of its appearance when actual demonstration is made, as was necessary in the beginning, the pupils gradually acquire the ability to think of each new arrangement in terms of its relation to the idea of ten and to the method of dealing with tens.

The progress of pupils may be explained in another way. They are gradually coming into possession of an understanding of the number system, and this system makes their thinking about large numbers more and more precise. The following quoted paragraphs will help to make the point clear:

Beyond ten, all kinds of objects pass out of the range of direct apprehension. No one can see twenty-five objects and clearly distinguish them from twenty-four or twenty-six. Only gross differences can be recognized when the number of objects exceeds ten. Ten subjects were shown groups of lines drawn in the middle of a page. Twenty-five short lines scattered irregularly over four square inches could always be recognized as less than thirty-two. If the two groups differed by less than seven, the subjects were irregular in their estimates, sometimes deciding that there were more than twenty-six and sometimes exhibiting doubt.

Even twenty-five is a relatively small number. A group of lines which can be distinguished from a group containing 126 lines must contain a number very far removed from 126. Two subjects seemed to be only fairly certain of the contrast between two groups containing 126 and 150 lines, respectively. These facts show clearly that such knowledge as one has of very large numbers is defective and altogether dependent on the use of some kind of a tally system. If a well-arranged tally system, such as the Arabic numeral system, can be used, thinking about large numbers can be made precise in spite of the fact that the group which a particular tally represents is itself too large to be apprehended directly. Within the tally system, 126 and 127 are clearly distinguishable, while the groups to which the two numbers refer are quite indistinguishable. If we wish to deal with large numbers, it is evident that we can be precise only when we use a tally system.[1]

Of necessity, the pupils must rely less and less upon experiences with the concrete and depend more and more upon the system of dealing with tens "just like units." Thus, in the easy subtraction, $\begin{array}{r} 53 \\ -28 \end{array}$, the pupils do not attempt to set before themselves 53 objects, count off 28 and take them away, and count the number remaining. Such a task would be tedious and greatly subject to error. Instead, the pupils take units from units, and, when that task is completed, they take tens from tens in exactly the same manner. In

---

[1] C. H. Judd. *Psychological Analysis of the Fundamentals of Arithmetic* (Department of Education, The University of Chicago, Chicago, 1927), p. 73.

the division, 5)1875, the task of counting out 1875 objects, grouping them into fives, and counting the fives, would be a long and tiresome one. Instead, the pupils divide hundreds, then tens, then units, just as they learned to divide units at the outset of such practice. Thus, hard and tedious tasks are rendered easy and short, because the number system enables one to assemble large numbers into understandable groups and to deal with the groups in a common way.

II. THE USES OF PROBLEMS

'Problems' — exercises that describe and call to mind concrete situations — are sometimes used to introduce the number combinations and processes that the pupils have to learn. When so used, the problems are presented before the combinations are presented, as a means of justifying in the minds of the pupils the learning of the combinations and of supplying an interest in, or a feeling of need for, the combinations before they are learned. Problems are sometimes used after a particular combination or process has been learned as a means of providing opportunity for its application. The theory underlying such a use of problems appears to be that the pupil first learns a process — addition, let us say — as something to do, and next becomes familiar with the various concrete situations of life in which the formula of addition may be applied. In the one case, the problem is used to provide a motive for learning; in the other, it is used to provide an opportunity to apply what has been learned; in both, the problem is a kind of justification for the learning of a process that otherwise would be (so it appears to be considered) a wholly meaningless and useless performance. In both cases, the problem, or the situation it describes, is the center of interest, and the process that is to be learned or that has just been learned is a matter of secondary importance, possessing little, if any, value in its own right.

The foregoing paragraph is not offered in criticism of the

uses named. To the extent that problems can be so used, such uses are without doubt justifiable ones. The paragraph is intended, rather, to indicate the limitations of such uses, and to call attention to the narrowness of any procedure that seeks to hide from the consideration of pupils the meaning and the value of the number system.

While the problems that are appropriate as exercises following the various processes illustrated in the foregoing chapter, for example, will have as one of their purposes the presentation of concrete illustration of the uses that can be made of such processes, they should be intended also as a means of furthering the purpose of problems stated in Chapter XI. The purpose of problems in the early stages of arithmetic has been described as that of giving opportunity for practice in recognizing such general ideas as addition, etc., in familiar situations, in order that these ideas may be clarified and enlarged. Since the pupils who are engaged in the task of learning the processes illustrated in the foregoing chapter are still in the early stages of arithmetic, we may say that the purpose of the problems that accompany such processes is to further the development of the general ideas of addition, subtraction, multiplication, and division.

III. The Importance of General Ideas

The importance of general ideas has already been discussed. What may be said here will, therefore, be in the nature of further illustration of their importance.

To many pupils, addition means merely something to do. They have a word in their vocabulary — 'addition' — that has a very narrow meaning. When told to add, either by their teacher, or by some sign or clue in an exercise, such as +, "how many altogether," "sum," etc., they can respond by adding. 'Addition' then, means for them to perform in a given way. Many pupils can so perform without having any idea of the meaning of the performance or what really has been accomplished by such performance. The writer has encountered pupils in the fifth grade, who, when presented with "problems" involving the simple operations only, have raised their hands to inquire: "Do the problems mean 'add'?" When such pupils are told to add, they can proceed to add, or, if told to subtract or multiply, they can proceed with equal assurance to perform these operations. Such pupils have missed the rich background of experiences[2] that make the term 'addition' meaningful; they can use addition as a means of getting an answer (which also is meaningless) only after someone has made the decision for them. They cannot use addition as an idea that holds in relation a series of concrete experiences that, in all other respects, are separate and unrelated items of experience.

Our discussions of 'problem-solving' have pointed out that the pupil needs practice in recognizing the general ideas of the processes in a variety of familiar situations. We need to bear in mind that such varied situations, though familiar, may, because of their variety, become confusing rather than helpful unless the pupil is already in partial possession of the general ideas mentioned and is consciously seeking an expression of them in the situations presented. The general idea, which may be illustrated by many situations, serves as a means of bringing the many situations together in a common bond of relationship. To illustrate:

Before one groups together cases in which money is earned and cases in which money is otherwise acquired, one should clearly recognize the fact that a mature abstract idea of positive accumulation is implied as existing in the mind of the reader of the problems. The word 'earned' and the phrase 'received as a gift' are not identical and do not belong together except in the thinking of an individual who has converted the two distinct concrete ideas into abstract arithmetical ideas. When pupils begin to study number relations, they do not have the general idea of addition, and they cannot bring

[2] See G. T. Buswell and Lenore John. *The Vocabulary of Arithmetic.* Chap. VI. (Department of Education, The University of Chicago, Chicago, 1931.)

together in their thinking 'earning' and 'receiving as a gift' except as they cultivate the more general notion of accumulation.[3]

In the cases mentioned in the foregoing quotation, if the pupil is resorting to the problems that involve 'earning' and 'receiving as a gift' for opportunity to 'apply' the process of addition, which to him is but a process to perform, his interest will center in the two quite different situations and their very differences may obscure the opportunity to apply addition. If, on the other hand, he resorts to them with the various general ideas in mind for the purpose of discovering one or the other of the ideas illustrated by the situations, his interest will center in the particular general idea that appears in the two situations in question and that brings them together in thought.

In a study of the "effect of unfamiliar settings on problem-solving," Brownell and Stretch have discovered some data that "suggest that problems may be so difficult for children that the addition of an unfamiliar situation does not materially alter children's procedures in dealing with them ... Likewise, these data suggest that problems may be so easy for children that the presence of an unfamiliar setting fails to obscure from them the arithmetical relationships involved."[4] Perhaps this is only another way of stating that when the general idea — in this case, the idea of 'on the average' — is somewhat obscure, it is about equally obscure in the situations involving the number of words spelled in a test and "brets of graks"; and that when the general idea — in the latter instance, the ideas of addition and subtraction — is fairly familiar, it may be recognized with equal ease in a situation dealing with a "Russian serf," "pushnas," and "chukets," and in one dealing with "school children," "Health Week," and "making posters."

[3] Judd. *Op. cit.*, p. 94.

[4] W. A. Brownell and L. B. Stretch. *The Effect of Unfamiliar Settings on Problem-Solving* (Duke University Press, Durham, 1931), p. 45.

The fact that it may be the number system, including its general ideas of combination, that should occupy the center of the stage in problems and problem-solving is suggested in the following paragraph:

> The question which is here proposed is, What are the comparative merits of unfamiliar and of familiar settings in problems for developing free number ideas and abstract principles of operation? Is there any danger that, by supplying to children only problem-settings which are vividly within their experience, the freeing of number concepts from personalized imagery may be undesirably delayed? On the other hand, may it not be preferable, from the point of view of ultimate outcomes, to begin rather early the use of unfamiliar settings in problems? Is it not possible that the use of such unfamiliar settings might have the effect of impressing on children the notion that numbers are essentially impersonal and that their relations are determined by the nature of the number system rather than by the character of the objects which they designate? Admittedly no answer is to be found for these questions in the data of the present investigation, but the absence of an answer does not make the questions any the less important. The rôle played by familiar as opposed to unfamiliar problem-settings will not be adequately understood until the ultimate outcomes of arithmetic instruction receive at least as much consideration as is now accorded the immediate outcomes of children's interest and of the difficulty of problems. [5]

IV. Emphasizing the General Ideas

The activities already suggested by the discussions in this book are such as to call the various general ideas to the attention of pupils from the beginning of their work. It has been understood that the general idea of addition, for example, appears as a part of many otherwise diverse situations, and that, if the pupil is to be expected to develop the idea so that he can look for it and recognize it under many circumstances, he will have to cultivate a power of

[5] Brownell and Stretch. *Op. cit.*, pp. 85–86.

abstraction that he does not possess when he first comes to school. It has been recognized that if the pupil is to be expected to give his attention to a given idea of procedure, or arrangement, or grouping, such as is designated, for instance, by the name 'addition,' he will need to have someone direct his attention away from other interesting features of situations and to help him to notice the procedure, or arrangement, or grouping, whenever things are 'put together' or 'thought together.' The process of abstraction is one of analysis, of neglect of certain features of the situation, and especially of concentration upon other features. From the outset, the teacher has made analyses for the pupil and has assisted him in making analyses by emphasizing and holding up for special study and discussion the arrangements of 'putting together,' 'thinking things away,' 'equal groups,' etc. In the beginning, the idea of taking away, for example, was demonstrated, discussed, described, and, later, given the name 'subtraction.' Later, the pupils engaged in taking away and thinking away, following the teacher's directions and questions. Still later, the pupils were presented with a number of situations (problems) that served to illustrate the idea of taking away, and, in dealing with these situations, the pupils were instructed and guided in looking for and discovering the idea of taking away. Moreover, by frequent reviews of what had been learned, the idea of taking away was given renewed emphasis. The following exercises illustrate the means of emphasizing the idea of taking away in contrast with the idea of putting together in the reviews. By means of such contrasts the pupil learns how to look for distinctions and how to make distinctions.

Illustrative Exercises Teaching Pupils to Know Things Exactly

1. Susan had 4 books at school and 5 books at home. How many books did Susan have?

Of course, we could say that Susan had 4 books and 5 books. But we have learned that it is better to say that she had 9 books, because then we know *exactly* how many books she had.

2. Henry had 8 marbles in his pocket when he started to school. On the way 3 marbles dropped out. How many marbles did he have left?

Of course, we could say that Henry then had 3 from 8 marbles, but that does not sound just right. We have learned that it is better to say that Henry then had 5 marbles, because then we know *exactly* how many marbles he had left.

In the first problem, we have learned to add like this, $\begin{array}{r} 4 \\ 5 \\ \hline 9 \end{array}$, because adding is a way of finding out *exactly* what we want to know.

In the second problem, we have learned to subtract (take away) like this, $\begin{array}{r} 8 \\ -3 \\ \hline 5 \end{array}$, because subtracting is another way of finding out *exactly* what we want to know.

Addition is a way of finding out *exactly*, and subtraction is a way of finding out *exactly*. Addition and subtraction are exactly alike. That is not quite true, is it? What we mean is that addition and subtraction are the same *in one way*. But in another way they are *different*. The next two topics will tell you in what way they are different.

Teaching Putting Things Together

Nancy has 6 crayons in her pencil box and 3 crayons on her desk. How many crayons does she have?

How do we find out *exactly* how many she has? Of course, you know that we find out by *adding*, like this, $\begin{array}{r} 6 \\ 3 \\ \hline 9 \end{array}$. We find out by putting 6 crayons and 3 crayons together. Actually we do not put them together by piling the 6 crayons and the 3 crayons together in one pile. We just make believe that we do; we just pretend we put them together. In order to find out how many crayons Nancy had, we put them together by adding, which is the same as *thinking* them together.

What is addition? Addition is a way of finding out *exactly* by putting things together or thinking things together. Addition answers the question, "How many altogether?"

Teaching Taking Things Away

George has 7 cents. How many cents would he have left if he should spend 3 cents for candy?

How do we find out *exactly* how many cents George would have left? Of course, you know that we find out by subtracting, like this, $\begin{array}{r} 7 \\ -3 \\ \hline 4 \end{array}$. We find out by taking 3 cents from 7 cents. Actually we would not have to make George spend 3 cents in order to find out, would we? We just imagine that 3 cents are taken away; we just pretend. We just *think* 3 cents from 7 cents. That is what is meant by 'subtraction.' Subtraction is a way of finding out *exactly* by taking things away or by thinking things away.

Taking away is subtraction. *Putting together* is addition. That is the way they are different. Do you remember how they are alike?

V. SIMILARITIES AND DIFFERENCES

Enough has been said in our previous discussions, and the available literature [6] is sufficiently complete and explicit, to remind the reader of the essential relations and contrasts between the general ideas of addition, subtraction, multiplication, and division. The reader's interest is not in how he may remind himself of such relations and contrasts, but in how he may call them to the attention of pupils. The following paragraphs are included in order to suggest a means by which the pupil may be repeatedly reminded of relations and contrasts. The point emphasized is that the pupil will need not merely to review a thing when he has learned it, but also to review it in its relations and contrasts with other things he has learned.

Comparing Addition, Subtraction, Multiplication, Division

The following pages, which compare and tell the difference between Addition and Multiplication, Addition and Subtraction,

[6] See G. T. Buswell and C. H. Judd. *Summary of Educational Investigations Relating to Arithmetic.* Chap. V. (Department of Education, The University of Chicago, Chicago, 1925); also Judd. *Op. cit.*, Chap. V.

Subtraction and Division, and Multiplication and Division, do not tell you anything you do not already know something about. They are written to help you to review the things you already know. You do not need to try to memorize anything that is written on these pages. You do not need to be able to explain to anyone else what these pages tell. All you will need to do is to read them carefully, and *understand* what they tell. Anything you do not understand your teacher will explain.

You do not need to study about your friends and playmates, (Mary Jones, Henry Smith, and the others), until you can describe them to someone else. You are *acquainted* with them and can *recognize* them wherever you meet them. So it is with your old friends, Addition, Subtraction, Multiplication, and Division. You do not need to describe them to someone else. All you need to be able to do is to *understand* them, that is, be *acquainted* with them, well enough to be able to *recognize* them wherever you meet them.

There will be some problems. Problems are intended to introduce your friends to you. In the problems, see how quickly and surely you can *recognize* your friends, Addition, Subtraction, Multiplication, and Division.

How Addition and Multiplication Differ

You have already learned that addition and multiplication both mean to *put things together* or to *think things together*. In this way, addition and multiplication are alike. You have also learned that addition and multiplication are different. Let us review the ways they are different.

1. The Good Citizens Club of the fourth grade made candy to take to the Children's Hospital. The first week they made 24 pieces, the second week they made 32 pieces, the third week they made 26 pieces, and the fourth week they made 30 pieces. How many pieces of candy did the Club make?

2. The Good Citizens Club of the fourth grade made candy to take to the Children's Hospital. They made 28 pieces each week for 4 weeks. How many pieces of candy did the Club make?

Problems 1 and 2 are both *put-together* or *think-together* problems. The questions at the end tell you that. Notice that the questions are exactly alike. Of course, the questions at the end do not tell you by themselves which is addition and which is multiplication. You have to look carefully at the first part of the problem to learn what particular kind of problem it is.

The first part of Problem 1 tells *separately* how many pieces of candy were made the first week, how many the second week, how many the third, and how many the fourth. Because the number for each of the four weeks is told *separately*, you know that Problem 1 is an addition problem. Whenever *how many* or *how much* for more than one case or more than one thing is told *separately* for each, and the problem is a *put-together* or *think-together* problem, it is an *addition* problem.

The first part of Problem 2 does not tell separately for each week how many pieces of candy were made, but gives the number that is *the same for all*. (Notice: it says "28 pieces *each* week for 4 weeks.") Because the number for each of the four weeks is not told separately, but is *the same for all*, you know that Problem 2 is a multiplication problem. Whenever *how many* or *how much* for more than one case or more than one thing is *not told separately*, but is the same for all, and the number of cases or things is told, the problem is a *multiplication* problem.

Notice how Problem 3 tells how much *separately*, and how the last part tells you that it is a *think-together* problem. By "how much separately" you can tell that it is an addition problem.

3. For lunch Susan bought a salad for 10 cents, a bowl of soup for 5 cents, some vegetables for 8 cents, bread and butter for 4 cents, and milk for 5 cents. How much did her lunch cost?

Notice how Problem 4 tells how much *not separately*, but *the same for all*, and gives the number of cases or things. By "how much *the same for all*" you can tell that it is a multiplication problem.

4. For lunch Susan spent 32 cents each day for 5 days. How much did her lunches cost?

How Addition and Subtraction Differ

You have learned that addition and subtraction do not mean the same. Addition means *put things together* or *think things together*, and subtraction means *take things away* or *think things away*. Addition is used to find the total, or sum, or how much or how many altogether, and subtraction is used to find the difference, or how much or how many left, and also to find out about more or less, greater or smaller, etc.

1. There are 38 children in the fourth grade of the Adams School, and there are 45 children in the fifth grade. How many children are in both of these grades?

2. There are 38 children in the fourth grade of the Adams School, and there are 45 children in the fifth grade. How many more children are there in the fifth grade?

Problems 1 and 2 both tell how many *separately*. By that you know they are not multiplication problems. Notice the questions at the end of the problems, and how they tell you exactly what kind of problem each one is.

3. Henry had $6.75. He made $3.50 by running errands. How much did he then have?

4. Henry had $10.25. He spent $4.00 for a pair of shoes. How much did he have left?

Problem 3 tells how much separately, and asks how much altogether. Problem 4 tells how much altogether, how much was taken away, and asks how much was left.

When a problem tells you to *think things together*, and is not multiplication, it is an addition problem. When a problem tells you to *think things away* to find out how much is left, or when it tells you to find out about *more* or *less*, it is a subtraction problem.

How Subtraction and Division Differ

Subtraction is sometimes something like division, yet they are never exactly the same. They are somewhat alike when they both deal with wholes and parts. In subtraction sometimes the whole is given, and one part is given, and you have to *find the other part* by subtracting. In division sometimes the whole is given, and the number of parts is given, and you have to find how many or how much *in each part* by dividing; or the whole is given, and how much or how many in each part is given, and you have to find the *number of parts* by dividing. (Notice the word "each" in the sentence telling about division.)

1. There are 637 children in the Central School. There are 351 children in the lower grades. How many children are there in the upper grades? (Notice that the whole is given (637), and one part is given (351), and that you are to *find the other part*.)

2. There are 18 teachers in the Central School. Each grade has the same number of teachers. There are 6 grades in the school. How many teachers are there in each grade? (Notice that the whole is given (18), and the number of parts is given (6), and that you are to *find how many in each part.*)

3. There are 18 teachers in the Central School. There are 3 teachers in each of the grades. How many grades are there? (Notice that the whole is given (18), and the number in each part is given (3), and that you are to *find the number of parts.*)

How Multiplication and Division Differ

Multiplication and division are alike in some ways, but, as you remember, each is the opposite of the other. The word 'each' usually tells that a problem is either a multiplication or a division one, and it is easy to tell one from the other.

1. There are 18 classrooms in the Central School. In each classroom there are 6 sections of blackboard. How many sections of blackboard are there in all of the classrooms?

2. Helen bought 12 colored pencils for her drawing kit. Each pencil cost 6 cents. How much did all the pencils cost?

You can tell that Problems 1 and 2 are multiplication problems. Problem 1 tells the *number of parts* and *how many in each part.* Problem 2 tells the *number of parts* and *how much in each part.* In Problem 1 you are to find *how many altogether*, and in Problem 2 you are to find *how much altogether.*

3. There are 108 sections of blackboard in the 18 classrooms of the Central School. In each classroom there are the same number of sections. How many sections of blackboard are there in each classroom?

4. There are 108 sections of blackboard in the Central School. There are 6 sections in each classroom. How many classrooms are there?

5. Helen bought 12 colored pencils for her drawing kit for 72 cents. How much did each pencil cost?

6. Helen bought some colored pencils for her drawing kit for 72 cents. Each pencil cost 6 cents. How many pencils did she buy?

You can tell that Problems 3, 4, 5, and 6 are division problems. Problems 3 and 5 tell the *whole amount*, or how many or how much altogether (108 and 72 cents) and also the *number of parts* (18 and 12). You are to find *how many* or *how much in each part.* Problems 4 and 6 tell the *whole amount,* or how many or how much altogether (108 and 72 cents), and also *how many* (6 sections) or *how much* (6 cents) *in each part.* You are to find in each problem the *number of parts.*

Multiplication and division are alike in this respect, that one must pay attention to the number of parts and to the fact that the parts are *equal* in *size* or *amount* or *cost* or whatever is being talked about. Multiplication and division differ — that is, they are opposites — in this respect, that in multiplication the *whole amount is to be found* while in division the *whole amount is told.* The word 'each' usually lets you know that the problem is not addition or subtraction, but either multiplication or division. *Whole amount to be found* lets you know that the problem is multiplication, and *whole amount told* lets you know that the problem is division.

VI. Two-Step Problems

When the pupil has learned to deal with problems in which a single operation is involved or a single general idea is illustrated, he is introduced to the so-called 'two-step problem' in which two operations are involved or two general ideas are illustrated. In problems of the former type, a single step of recognition is necessary; in those of the latter type, two steps of recognition must be taken.

At first glance the two-step problem gives the appearance of being nothing more than two one-step problems in one and of providing the pupil the same kind of practice he has been having with problems of the easier type. In the one-step problem, he must recognize one idea; in the two-step problem, he must recognize two ideas. Thus it appears that the two-step problem is different only in the respect that it gives a double amount of practice. The only extra difficulty that appears on the surface is the difficulty of deciding upon and performing two operations in a given exercise instead of one. Accordingly, the two-step problem is frequently introduced as a means of providing the pupil with more practice and practice of a more difficult kind on the same level as the practice he has become accustomed to receiving. An additional justification for the two-step problem is the fact that in many a situation in actual life more than a single operation is necessary.

The two-step problem does provide practice in double amounts, and it does provide an introduction to many concrete situations that have a practical importance; but to explain it merely as a double problem is to omit from its description the statement of a very important element. The one-step problem presents in a single situation a single idea; the two-step problem presents in a single situation — not two situations — two ideas.   To state the matter in another way, in the one-step problem, a single question is involved and a single question is asked; in the two-step problem, two questions are involved and a single question is asked, leaving the other question to be discovered by the pupil.   Herein is the fundamental difference between the two types of problems that in some manner or other must be called to the attention of pupils.

VII. Practice on a Higher Level

Because one of the questions that are involved in the two-step problem is not explicitly stated, the pupil is required to examine the situation presented by the problem in order to discover the question for himself. He must, as it were, read between the lines in order to discover the question.   To do this, he will have to come to the task of attacking the two-step problem with certain general ideas already fairly well in mind.   Since the problem does not tell him what ideas are present and leaves one of them unsuggested by a question, the pupil must attack it with the conscious purpose of discovering what is hidden.   In other words, the general ideas that are to be illustrated by the two-step problems not only must be well enough known to be recognized when they have an obvious description, as in the one-step problem, but also must be so familiar as to be readily available both as a means of interpreting the situation and as a means of suggesting the hidden question. The new demands that the two-step problem imposes raises practice to a new level, and makes of the problem a new means of training. To be sure, it is more difficult to recognize addition, for example, when it appears in a situation with another, or a like operation, than it is to recognize addition when it appears alone. But this is not the whole story. The two-step problem not only provides additional practice in recognizing the general ideas of addition, subtraction, multiplication, and division and thus increases their familiarity, but also requires the conscious use of these ideas as means of attack and of interpretation. The two-step problem becomes an aid in instruction; its requirements help to provide an added emphasis to the efforts the teacher may have been making to impress upon the pupil the meaning of the general ideas.

The following exercises are presented to illustrate the type of instruction the teacher may initiate with regard to two-step problems, the kind of training and practice such problems may give, and the essential points of interest in such problems upon which the pupils must be led to center their attention.

Illustrative Teaching of 'Two-in-One' Problems

You have learned to solve the problems that are known as one-step problems; that is, problems in which you have to do *one thing* — either add, subtract, multiply, divide, or use a fraction. The problems you are now to learn to solve are known as 'two-step' problems. Two-step problems are the ones that ask you to do *two things*. You could call them *double* problems, or *two-in-one* problems, because each is really two problems in one. Let us see. Here is a two-step problem:

1. Billy sold 55 papers and James sold 61. How much did they both get for them if they sold the papers at 4¢ each?

This is the way the problem looks, if we make two problems out of it.   (Read 1a and 1b together.)

1a. Billy sold 55 papers and James sold 61. How many papers did they both sell?

1b. Billy and James sold 116 papers at 4¢ each. How much did they get for them?

Of course you know how to solve Problems 1a and 1b. Let us solve them and compare the way they are solved with the way Problem 1 is solved.

$$
\begin{array}{lll}
\text{(1a)}\quad
\begin{array}{r}
55\\
61\\
\hline
116 \text{ papers}
\end{array}
&
\text{(1b)}\quad
\begin{array}{r}
116\\
.04\\
\hline
\$4.64
\end{array}
&
\text{(1)}\quad
\begin{array}{r}
55\\
61\\
\hline
116\\
.04\\
\hline
\$4.64
\end{array}
\end{array}
$$

Problem 1 is an Addition-Multiplication problem, or an **AM** problem.

2. John spent 60 cents for marbles. He paid 2 cents for each marble. He divided them among 6 boys. How many marbles did each boy get?

Let us make Problem 2 into two problems:

2a. John spent 60 cents for marbles. He paid 2 cents for each marble. How many marbles did he buy?

2b. John bought 30 marbles. He divided them among 6 boys. How many did each boy get?

Compare the way Problems 2a and 2b are solved with the way Problem 2 is solved:

$$
\begin{array}{llll}
\text{(2a)}\ 2\overline{)60}\ \dfrac{30 \text{ marbles}}{}
& \text{(2b)}\ 6\overline{)30}\ \dfrac{5 \text{ marbles}}{}
& \text{(2)}\ 2\overline{)60}\ \dfrac{30}{}
& 6\overline{)30}\ \dfrac{5 \text{ marbles}}{}
\end{array}
$$

(2a) 2)60   30 marbles   (2b) 6)30   5 marbles   (2) 2)60 30   6)30 5 marbles
        6   30   6   30
        0   0

Problem 2 is a Division-Division problem, or a **DD** problem.

3. Joe made \$45.80, and spent \$10.80. How much does he need in order to make a payment of \$75.00 on a Ford?

Let us make Problem 3 into two problems:

3a. Joe made \$45.80, and spent \$10.80. How much does he have left?

3b. Joe has \$35.00. How much does he need in order to make a payment of \$75.00 on a Ford?

Compare the way Problems 3a and 3b are solved with the way Problem 3 is solved.

(3a) $45.80	(3b) $75.00	(3) $45.80	$75.00
10.80	35.00	10.80	35.00
$35.00	$40.00	$35.00	$40.00

Problem 3 is a Subtraction-Subtraction problem, or an SS problem.

4. A farmer had 931 bushels of oats. He sold 485 bushels and put the rest into bags, 2 bushels in each bag. How many bags of oats did he have?

Let us make Problem 4 into two problems:

4a. A farmer had 931 bushels of oats. He sold 485 bushels. How many bushels did he have left?

4b. A farmer put 446 bushels of oats into bags, 2 bushels in each bag. How many bags of oats did he have?

Compare the way Problems 4a and 4b are solved with the way Problem 4 is solved:

	223 bags		223
(4a) 931	(4b) 2)446	(4) 931	2)446
485	4	485	4
446 bushels	4	446	4
	4		4
	6		6
	6		6

Problem 4 is a Subtraction-Division problem, or an SD problem.

5. Mr. Brown sold celery at 9 cents a bunch. He found that if he trimmed it nicely he could get 12 cents a bunch. Last week he sold 87 bunches nicely trimmed. How much extra did he make by trimming it?

Let us make Problem 5 into two problems:

5a. Mr. Brown sold celery at 9 cents a bunch. He found that if he trimmed it nicely he could get 12 cents a bunch. How much extra did he make on a bunch of celery by trimming it?

5b. Mr. Brown made 3 cents extra on a bunch of celery by trimming it. Last week he sold 87 bunches nicely trimmed. How much extra did he make?

Compare the way Problems 5a and 5b are solved with the way Problem 5 is solved:

(5a)	12	(5b)	87	(5)	12		87
	9		.03		9		.03
	3¢		$2.61		3¢		$2.61

Problem 5 is a Subtraction-Multiplication problem, or an SM problem.

6. Henry is working to make enough money to buy a tennis racket that costs $5.50 and a ball that costs 75¢. He is paid 25¢ an hour for each hour he works. How many hours will Henry have to work to make enough money to pay for them?

Let us make Problem 6 into two problems:

6a. Henry is working to make enough money to buy a tennis racket that costs $5.50 and a ball that costs 75¢. How much will Henry have to pay for both of them?

6b. Henry is working to make enough money to buy a tennis racket and ball. They both cost $6.25. Henry is paid 25¢ for each hour he works. How many hours will he have to work to make enough money to pay for them?

Compare the way Problems 6a and 6b are solved with the way Problem 6 is solved:

			25 hours			25 hours
(6a)	$5.50	(6b)	.25)6.25	(6)	$5.50	.25)6.25
	.75		5 0		.75	5 0
	$6.25		1 25		$6.25	1 25
			1 25			1 25

Problem 6 is an Addition-Division problem, or an AD problem.

7. Mary wants to buy a hat that costs $3.50 and a dress that costs $5.25. She now has $6.20. How much more money does she need?

Let us make Problem 7 into two problems:

7a. Mary wants to buy a hat that costs $3.50 and a dress that costs $5.25. How much do they both cost?

7b. Mary has $6.20. She wants to buy a hat and a dress that cost $8.75. How much more money does she need?

Compare the way Problems 7a and 7b are solved with the way Problem 7 is solved:

(7a) $3.50	(7b) $8.75	(7) $3.50	$8.75
5.25	6.20	5.25	6.20
$8.75	$2.55	$8.75	$2.55

Problem 7 is an Addition-Subtraction problem, or an AS problem.

8. Sam works 8 hours each day. He makes 40¢ each hour he works. Last month Sam worked 26 days. How much did he make last month?

Let us make Problem 8 into two problems:

8a. Sam works 8 hours each day. He makes 40¢ each hour he works. How much does he make each day?

8b. Sam makes $3.20 each day. Last month he worked 26 days. How much did he make last month?

Compare the way Problems 8a and 8b are solved with the way Problem 8 is solved:

(8a) $ .40	(8b) $3.20	(8) $ .40	$3.20
8	26	8	26
$3.20	19 20	$3.20	19 20
	64 0		64 0
	$83.20		$83.20

Problem 8 is a Multiplication-Multiplication problem, or an MM problem.

9. Jane gave $20 to help buy a radio, Harry gave $35, and John gave as much as Jane and Harry. How much did they all give?

Let us make Problem 9 into two problems:

9a. Jane gave $20 to help buy a radio, and Harry gave $35. How much did they both give?

9b. Jane and Harry gave $55 to help buy a radio. John gave the same as Jane and Harry both gave. How much did they all give?

Compare the way Problems 9a and 9b are solved with the way Problem 9 is solved:

(9a) $20	(9b) $55	(9) $20	$55
35	55	35	55
$55	$110	$55	$110

Problem 9 is an Addition-Addition problem, or an AA problem.

10. Frank sold 45 dozen ears of corn at 30¢ a dozen. With the money he bought young chickens that cost 50¢ each. How many chicks did he buy?

Let us make Problem 10 into two problems:

10a. Frank sold 45 dozen ears of corn at 30¢ a dozen. How much did he get for the corn he sold?

10b. Frank spent $13.50 for young chickens. He paid 50¢ for each chick. How many chicks did he buy?

Compare the way Problems 10a and 10b are solved with the way Problem 10 is solved:

			27			27
(10a)	45	(10b)	.50)$13.50	(10)	45	.50)$13.50
	.30		10 0		.30	10 0
	$13.50		3 50		$13.50	3 50
			3 50			3 50

Problem 10 is a Multiplication-Division problem, or an MD problem.

Teaching How to Work Two-Step Problems

You have noticed that each of these ten two-step problems is in reality a double problem, that each is really two problems in one. Of course, in each only one question is asked, and the one question makes it seem as if there is only one thing to do. But have you noticed in working each problem that you yourself had to ask a question that the problem did not state and answer that one, and then pay attention to the question that the problem did state and answer that one? So, in reality, each two-step problem has two questions to be answered, but *one of these questions is not stated in the problem and you yourself have to ask it.*

In order to work a two-step problem, you yourself must ask one of the questions.

Each two-step problem is two problems in one. The two problems are not stated as two problems, but stated together as one. *You yourself must make it into two problems.* In other words, you must *read between the lines* some words that are not stated, making the problem read like two problems, and then work each one of them. Each part of a two-step problem is very easy to work. The only thing that may be hard to do is to make the problem read like two problems.

In order to work a two-step problem, you yourself must make it into two problems. You yourself must ask the hidden question.

You must read between the lines.

Turn back to the ten problems that have been worked for you and notice how each one was first turned into two problems by reading between the lines. Let us take some of the ten problems, and see how to *read between the lines.*

1. Billy sold 55 papers and James sold 61. How much did they both get for them if they sold the papers at 4 cents each?

We must read the whole problem carefully, so that we will know exactly what it is about. When we understand, we start *reading between the lines*, making the problem into two problems, and working them as we go along. Notice:

Billy sold 55 papers and James sold 61. (How many did they both sell?) How much did they get for them if they sold the (116) papers at 4 cents each?

$$
\begin{array}{r} 55 \\ 61 \\ \hline 116 \end{array}
\qquad
\begin{array}{r} 116 \\ .04 \\ \hline \$4.64 \end{array}
$$

2. John spent 60 cents for marbles and paid 2 cents for each marble. He divided them among 6 boys. How many did each boy get?

We must read the whole problem carefully, so that we will know exactly what it is about. When we understand, we start *reading between the lines*, making the problem into two problems, and working them as we go along. Notice:

John spent 60 cents for marbles and paid 2 cents for each marble. (How many marbles did he buy?) He divided them (the 30 marbles) among 6 boys. How many did each boy get?

$$
\begin{array}{r} 30 \\ 2\overline{)60} \\ 6 \\ \hline 0 \end{array}
\qquad
\begin{array}{r} 5 \\ 6\overline{)30} \\ 30 \\ \hline \end{array}
$$

Read Problems 3 to 10. *Read between the lines*, working each part of each problem as you go along. In each problem, as you read it, *look for the hidden question*. You yourself must find and ask the hidden question.

The Ten Kinds of Two-Step Problems

There are only four things to do in order to work any of the ten two-step problems that have been given — add, subtract, multiply, and divide. In each problem you are asked to do two of them. There are ten different combinations of the two things:

AA	— Addition-Addition	See Problem 9.
AS	— Addition-Subtraction	See Problem 7.
AM	— Addition-Multiplication	See Problem 1.
AD	— Addition-Division	See Problem 6.
SS	— Subtraction-Subtraction	See Problem 3.
SM	— Subtraction-Multiplication	See Problem 5.
SD	— Subtraction-Division	See Problem 4.
MM	— Multiplication-Multiplication	See Problem 8.
MD	— Multiplication-Division	See Problem 10.
DD	— Division-Division	See Problem 2.

Getting Practice with These Problems

There are three ways of getting good practice with these problems:

1. Read each problem carefully, so that you will understand what it is about. Then read it again, *reading between the lines*, making it into two problems.

2. Read each problem carefully, so that you will understand what it is about. Then tell what kind of a problem it is — an AA, AS, AM, AD, SS, SM, SD, MM, MD, or a DD problem.

3. Read each problem carefully, so that you will understand what it is about. Then read it again, *reading between the lines*, making it into two problems, and working the two as you read along.

Practice the way your teacher tells you. Practice upon most of them the third way named.

CHAPTER XVII
THE STUDY OF PARTS

ARGUMENT

1. The idea of the fraction is the idea of the part. It is developed and clarified through a systematic study of parts.

2. Incidental contact with parts leads to familiarity with the names of fractions, but not to an acquaintance with the characteristics of fractions.

3. The fraction is an idea of relation between two amounts.

4. Such type idea is an important element in the full meaning of the fraction.

5. Fractions must also be dealt with in relation to each other. The full meaning is necessary for an intelligent handling of such relations.

6. The relational idea of individual fractions must be very familiar if the relations between fractions are to be studied without distraction and confusion.

7. The equality of sizes in fractional divisions is a fundamental idea. Attention both to size of parts and number of parts is necessary to a complete comprehension of any given fractional part.

8. Lesson materials are used to illustrate the study of a fraction:

    (a) As one or more of the equal parts of a unity or group;

    (b) As composed of, and as related to, smaller equal parts into which it may be divided;

    (c) As related to other parts in respect to size and number.

9. Decimals embody the familiar ideas of size and number of parts represented by the familiar decimal system of notation. The fundamental operations are presented as extensions of such operations with whole numbers.

10. Percentage is a special study and use of hundredths. Lesson materials are used to illustrate how the study of percentage may be introduced.

373

The idea of the fraction is the idea of the part. It is developed and clarified through a systematic study of parts. Just as groups have to be studied in a systematic and orderly way as a means of developing and clarifying the ideas of number, so must parts be studied in a systematic and orderly way as a means of developing and clarifying the ideas of fractions. The methods used in the study of groups suggest the methods to be followed in the study of parts. Parts may be studied (1) by giving attention to first one typical and commonly used part, then another, separately; (2) by separating one part after another into the smaller constituent parts of which each is composed; and (3) by the comparison of parts. Just as the study of groups did not consist of the study of the manipulation of the numerals that stand for them, so the study of parts does not consist of the study of the manipulation of the fractional expressions. As the numerals are used as a language of expressing number ideas and of keeping the thinking about groups systematic, so must the fractional expressions be used as a language of expression and of thinking. It must be kept in mind that it is parts that are to be studied, not primarily the way the fractional expressions may be written and used.

I. Early Introduction to Fractions

From the time the child has entered school he has been learning to use certain fractional expressions in a manner that for all practical purposes has been sufficiently precise. He has learned to speak of half a day, half a pint, half a yard, half a stick of candy, etc., and, insofar as his needs and experiences are concerned, he has come into possession of the ideas for which each expression stands. He has been absent from school, for example, half a day; and he has been sent to the store to buy and bring home half a pint of milk. The girl has bought at the ten-cent store half a yard of ribbon for her doll; and has broken her stick of candy to give her friend half. In school, half of the class has been instructed to go to the board, or report for recitation, and half to remain at their desks, and so on.

Coincident with the pupil's instruction in division, he has been introduced to the fraction as a way of stating a division. A number must be divided into six equal parts; so he learns to speak of finding one-sixth of the number as dividing by six. The directions — find $\frac{1}{4}$ of 24, $\frac{1}{3}$ of 96, $\frac{1}{5}$ of 75, etc. — have come to mean, divide 24 by 4, 96 by 3, 75 by 5, etc. The pupil is not unacquainted with the idea of the fraction when he begins his systematic study of parts. Having become accustomed to using some of the fractions, both in speaking and writing, he is able to approach the systematic study of parts with some degree of familiarity with what is to be called to his attention.

II. The Fraction as an Idea of Relationship

Though the fraction is not unknown to the pupil when he begins its systematic study, the idea of the fraction that he has developed is a very inadequate one. Though he uses the fractional form of expression in speaking of 'half a day,' he does not necessarily think of the half day in its relation to the whole day. The half day is not considered by him as a *division* of a stated unit of time; it is thought of as a unit of time by itself, just as he would think of an hour or of thirty minutes as a unit of time. When he brings a half pint of cream from the store, though he may bring at the same time a pint of milk, he does not think of the half-pint as a division of the pint. The half pint of cream is in one bottle, just as the pint of milk is in one bottle. The only apparent relation between the two is that one is smaller than the other. The half-pint bottle is a whole bottle just the same as the pint bottle or the quart bottle is a whole bottle. When the girl buys a half-yard of ribbon for her doll, she buys a whole piece of ribbon. The piece is a single piece. The piece shows within itself no division; it is a continuous piece of ribbon; it is a unity, not a part of a unity. Though the original stick of candy is broken in two, and each piece is called "a half," the piece given away and the piece that is retained do not necessarily impress their relation with the original stick. Each piece is a unity, and may not be considered as a part of a unity. The child's everyday experiences with parts do not impress him with the characteristic feature and relationship of parts. They afford him a convenient way of expression, not an adequate idea.

Something of the idea of relation of the part to the whole is, however, impressed by the exercises of finding one of the equal parts of a quantity by dividing the quantity by the number of parts desired. The answer secured, which is the quotient of the division, is not an absolute result, but one that must be thought of in its relation to the number that has been divided. The question asked at the outset, and usually repeated as part of the description of the quotient, serves to bring the quotient into proper relation with the original number. For example, the question, "What is one half of 24?" serves to describe the answer, 12, in its relation to 24. The pupil through such exercises is required to give some consideration to the fraction as an expression of relation.

These observations suggest the point that the fraction, or the idea of a part, is not a separate and distinct idea, however much it may be given an isolated use. A given fraction, one half, for example, may be spoken of, written, and used in computation as though its meaning were wrapped up entirely within itself. But 'one half' as an actual idea always refers to the thing that has been divided; and, though it often appears in actual experience as a unity within itself — as half a day, half a yard, etc. — its meaning can never be clear until it has been derived from the two quantities, or amounts, that designate the relation that one half expresses.

On the other hand, the pupil will have to learn to deal with the idea 'half' in a variety of situations that do not permit constant reference to such quantities and amounts as give the relation that is expressed by one half. He will have to deal with one half at the same time he deals with a third, a fourth, and so on. He will have no time or opportunity to be going back in his thinking to get the various relations established. When he deals with the half and the third, for example, he will need to deal with them in relation to each other, and not each in its relation to its particular set of dual quantities or dual amounts. In other words, he must learn to deal with the half as a single abstraction, not as a part of a larger abstraction; he must gain the ability to deal with the half as a separate idea, although in reality it is never a separate idea. Or, to state the matter in another way, he must learn to deal with the fraction as a separate idea, though it is always a related idea.

Since the idea of the fraction is the idea of the part (of something) — which indicates that its true meaning is one of relationship — it can never be used intelligently as an isolated expression or as an expression of an isolated amount if its meaning is neglected or abandoned. One does not need, of course, to be thinking of the meaning of the fraction while he is trying to use it; but he does need to provide that its true meaning be not neglected. Some means must be at hand, therefore, to develop the meaning of the fraction, so that while it is being used as an isolated expression of quantity or amount, its true meaning of relationship will still be retained.

III. Size and Number

If the pupil has been engaged in the kinds of activities that have been suggested in the preceding chapters, he will have gained from his studies of groups certain ideas that will be very useful and necessary ones in his study of parts. In his study of groups he has had to deal, whether intelligently or not, with the idea of size and the idea of number. He will now, in his study of parts, have to deal, whether intelligently or not, with the same ideas. These ideas are given expression in what are called the *terms* of the fraction; namely, the denominator and the numerator. If now the pupil can be led to give his attention to the *size* of the parts, expressed by the denominator, as well as to the *number* of parts, expressed by the numerator, he will have two serviceable ideas to aid him in keeping the meaning of the fraction clear. The amount of the fraction is always expressed in terms of size of parts and number of parts, and attention to these two ideas gives meaning to, and preserves meaning for, the expression of the fraction.

The idea of size is never entirely absolute; it is always in some degree a related idea. Being an idea of relation, it easily adjusts itself as a carrier of the relational meaning of the fraction. What is more to the point, however, is the fact that the individual can develop considerable familiarity with certain standard sizes or certain frequently studied sizes, whether of groups or of parts. If now the pupil can develop familiarity with certain commonly used sizes of parts, he can resort to the expression and use of a given size of part (shown by the denominator) with those of a given number of parts (shown by the numerator) to make meaningful and keep meaningful a given fractional expression that he can think of and deal with as an expression of an isolated amount. Unless the pupil does develop acquaintance with sizes of parts, he will be unable to deal intelligently with the fraction as a single abstraction, either because he has no meaning for it or because he is compelled to interrupt his thinking by the necessity of returning to concrete experiences for meaning. Ideas of size and number are the central ideas in the study of parts, just as they are the central ideas in any systematic study of groups.

IV. Purpose of the Chapter

The purpose of the present chapter is to suggest means of developing the idea of the fraction, so that it may be clear and unmistakable in whatever form it may be expressed; and to present and discuss the three ways of expressing and dealing with the fractional idea. The chapter will seek to emphasize the fact that the fraction retains the same characteristics and uses, whether it is expressed as a common fraction, as a decimal, or as a percent. For the sake of convenience, however, the three forms of expression will be considered in the order (1) common fractions, (2) decimal fractions, and (3) percentage.

V. COMMON FRACTIONS

1. Studying Separate Parts

Before the pupil can undertake the systematic comparison of fractions or begin the use of fractions each in relation to the other, he must be led to develop a fairly definite idea of each fraction as a separate entity. He must have brought to his attention, as objectively and as forcefully as possible, the idea of division, the equality of the parts resulting from the division, the fact that the parts combined make the original whole, how the size of the parts is designated, and how a given number of parts is indicated. The half, the third, the fourth, etc., are studied each by itself — the half as one of the two equal parts of the thing divided, the third as one of the three equal parts, the fourth as one of the four equal parts, and so on. Objective demonstration is necessary in order to impress the essential characteristics of each of the fractions to be studied.

Let us suppose the fourth is being studied. Any object that may be easily divided into fourths will be appropriate to use. Let us say that a circle is chosen. First, the circle is divided into four equal parts. Next, the equality of the parts is again called to attention by questioning, discussion, etc. What each part is called (one-fourth) is emphasized. The number of fourths in the whole circle is impressed. Finally, how the parts are expressed in writing is pointed out.

From the beginning, the figure above the line of the fraction must be emphasized as the one that shows the number of parts: thus, one fourth is written, $\frac{1}{4}$; two fourths, $\frac{2}{4}$, etc. Since the number of parts (fourths) in the whole circle is shown thus, $\frac{4}{4}$, it should be made clear that the 4 above the line shows all the parts (fourths) in the circle; that is, the number of parts into which the circle was divided. Likewise, from the beginning, the figure below the line must be emphasized as the one that shows size. In this case, though written as 4, it does not show four, nor is it read as four, but as *fourths*. Since the idea of size is relative, there should perhaps be some comparison of sizes from the beginning, however inexact the comparison may have to be. Thus, while the pupils are studying fourths, they may be led to notice comparisons with thirds and halves, which have already been studied.

Which is the largest — one half, one third, or one fourth? Which is the smallest? Which is the larger — one third or one fourth? Which is the smaller? The purpose of such questions is to contribute to the developing idea of size and to develop the fact that the larger the figure in the denominator, the smaller is the size of the part.

It is not to be expected that the pupil will gain a complete idea of size at the very beginning. The idea of size, through the comparison of sizes, must, however, be called to attention from the beginning. Further reference to the idea of size of parts will be made presently.

2. Division and Combination of Parts

The work indicated in the foregoing topic proceeds until the pupil has gained fairly distinct ideas of each of the most commonly used common fractions. The next step is to enlarge his idea of each of the fractions by the method of analysis and synthesis. Such a method leads to a comparison of a given fraction with those most closely related to it and prepares for the steps of study that must necessarily follow. The method may be illustrated, as follows:

Illustrative Lesson on Studying Halves

Let us divide a circle into 2 equal parts. Each part is $\frac{1}{2}$ of the circle. There is an upper $\frac{1}{2}$ and a lower $\frac{1}{2}$. Let us remember how much of the whole circle $\frac{1}{2}$ is. Now let us divide the same circle

into 4 equal parts. We can do that by dividing each half into 2 equal parts. We will keep the heavy line to show the circle as it was first divided into halves, and use lighter lines to show it divided into fourths. Our circle will now look like this one:

There are four fourths ($\frac{4}{4}$) in the whole circle.

Count the fourths in $\frac{1}{2}$ of the circle. You can see that in one half ($\frac{1}{2}$) of the circle there are two fourths ($\frac{2}{4}$). We can say it like this, "One half equals two fourths," and we can write it like this, $\frac{1}{2} = \frac{2}{4}$.

Now let us divide the circle into 8 equal parts. We can do this by dividing each fourth into 2 equal parts. We will keep the heavy line to show the circle as it was first divided into halves, and use lighter lines to show it divided into eighths. Our circle will now look like this one:

There are eight eighths ($\frac{8}{8}$) in the whole circle.

Count the eighths in $\frac{1}{2}$ of the circle. You can see that there are four eighths ($\frac{4}{8}$) in one half ($\frac{1}{2}$) of the circle. We can say it like this, "One half equals four eighths," and we can write it like this, $\frac{1}{2} = \frac{4}{8}$.

In the same way we can show other fractions that $\frac{1}{2}$ equals:

1.	2.	3.	4.	5.

Circle 1 shows $\frac{4}{4} = 1$.   How many fourths in $\frac{1}{2}$? $\frac{1}{2} = \frac{}{4}$?

Circle 2 shows $\frac{6}{6} = 1$.   How many sixths in $\frac{1}{2}$? $\frac{1}{2} = \frac{}{6}$?

Circle 3 shows $\frac{8}{8} = 1$.   How many eighths in $\frac{1}{2}$? $\frac{1}{2} = \frac{}{8}$?

Circle 4 shows $\frac{10}{10} = 1$.   How many tenths in $\frac{1}{2}$? $\frac{1}{2} = \frac{}{10}$?

Circle 5 shows $\frac{12}{12} = 1$.   How many twelfths in $\frac{1}{2}$? $\frac{1}{2} = \frac{}{12}$?

In the same way with other circles we could show:

$\frac{14}{14} = 1$. How many fourteenths in $\frac{1}{2}$? $\frac{1}{2} = \frac{}{14}$?

$\frac{16}{16} = 1$. How many sixteenths in $\frac{1}{2}$? $\frac{1}{2} = \frac{}{16}$?

$\frac{18}{18} = 1$. How many eighteenths in $\frac{1}{2}$? $\frac{1}{2} = \frac{}{18}$?

$\frac{20}{20} = 1$. How many twentieths in $\frac{1}{2}$? $\frac{1}{2} = \frac{}{20}$?

In similar manner, the third and the fourth may be studied. When the pupils have learned to work out the relations indicated through actual divisions of the parts being studied, and have summarized their work in a table of equivalents, like the following:

$\frac{1}{2} = \frac{2}{4} = \frac{3}{6} = \frac{4}{8} = \frac{5}{10} = \frac{6}{12} = \frac{7}{14} = \frac{8}{16} = \frac{9}{18} = \frac{10}{20}$, etc.

$\frac{1}{3} = \quad \frac{2}{6} = \quad \frac{3}{9} = \quad \frac{4}{12} = \quad \frac{5}{15} = \quad \frac{6}{18}$, etc.

$\frac{1}{4} = \quad \frac{2}{8} = \quad \frac{3}{12} = \quad \frac{4}{16} = \quad \frac{5}{20}$, etc., they should be shown a shorter method of discovering equivalents. The shorter method may be illustrated, as follows:

Explaining Partial Cancellation

Let us try another way of finding out about fractions. The way we have been using of dividing circles (or anything else for that matter) into parts and counting the parts is a very good way. The only thing the matter with that way is that it is very difficult for us to divide anything into more than eight or ten equal parts and to do it very exactly. The more parts we try to divide a thing into, the more tedious the task becomes. Let us try a shorter, easier way. This way we will call *partial cancellation.*

Cancellation means *striking out* by *dividing.*

In using the method of *partial cancellation* we need to remember that 1 is the same as $\frac{4}{4}$, or $\frac{10}{10}$, or $\frac{15}{15}$, or $\frac{20}{20}$, etc.

Suppose we were asked

(in words)   "One half is how many tenths?" or
(in writing) $\frac{1}{2} = \frac{}{10}$?

We could find the answer by thinking like this,

If 1 equals 10 tenths ($\frac{10}{10}$),
$\frac{1}{2}$ equals $\frac{1}{2}$ of 10 tenths, or five tenths ($\frac{5}{10}$).

We can do our thinking to ourselves and write what we think, like this,

$$\frac{1}{2}\text{ of }\frac{\overset{5}{10}}{10} = \frac{5}{10}.$$

$$\frac{1}{3} = \frac{}{18}? \qquad\qquad \frac{2}{3} = \frac{}{18}?$$

$$\frac{1}{3}\text{ of }\frac{\overset{6}{18}}{18} = \frac{6}{18} \qquad \frac{2}{3}\text{ of }\frac{\overset{6}{18}}{18} = \frac{12}{18}$$

This is a short way to help us in thinking: If 1 equals eighteen eighteenths, one third equals one third of eighteen eighteenths, or six eighteenths, and two thirds equal two times six eighteenths, or twelve eighteenths.

We can turn back to the circles we have been using, or divide other circles or any other objects, and count the tenths in $\frac{1}{2}$, and the eighteenths in $\frac{1}{3}$, and the eighteenths in $\frac{2}{3}$, and we will find that our answers are correct.

Notice how the answers to these questions are found in the shorter, easier way of *partial cancellation:*

1. $\frac{2}{3} = \frac{}{9}$?

2. $\frac{1}{4} = \frac{}{16}$?

1. $\frac{2}{3}$ of $\frac{\overset{3}{\cancel{9}}}{9} = \frac{6}{9}$

2. $\frac{1}{4}$ of $\frac{\overset{4}{\cancel{16}}}{16} = \frac{4}{16}$

3. $\frac{3}{4} = \frac{}{16}$?

4. $\frac{1}{3} = \frac{}{15}$?

3. $\frac{3}{4}$ of $\frac{\overset{4}{\cancel{16}}}{16} = \frac{12}{16}$

4. $\frac{1}{3}$ of $\frac{\overset{5}{\cancel{15}}}{15} = \frac{5}{15}$

3. Comparing Parts

When the pupils have made and studied such comparisons as have been indicated in the method of analysis and synthesis, they should be made conscious of what things are involved in a comparison, in order that they may be able to compare any fraction with any other one. The idea of size of parts and the idea of number of parts must be made as impressive as possible. The following paragraphs indicate the type of lessons that may lead the pupil to give his attention to both size and number of parts when he undertakes comparisons.

Illustrative Lessons on Comparing Parts

A good way to learn about fractions is to *compare* them. When a person compares two things, he is able to find out something new about both of them. He is able to tell whether they are both the same size or one is larger than the other. If they are of different sizes, he can tell which is larger and which is smaller, and how much larger and how much smaller. Last year you learned some things about numbers by comparing them. For example, in comparing 8 and 12, you learned that 8 is 4 less than 12, and that 12 is 4 more than 8. Now you will have a chance to learn some new things about halves, thirds, fourths, fifths, and so on, by comparing them. You will compare one half and one third, for example, and you will find out which is the larger and which is the smaller, and, what is more important, you will learn *exactly* how much larger and how much smaller. When you have learned to make comparisons between a number of fractions, you will not only know a lot more about them than you do now, but you will also be better able to use them.

In making a comparison, a person has to pay attention to *two things*. If he pays attention to either one of them only and forgets the other one, he makes a great mistake. Let us see if you can tell what these two things are. You will have to know them and *always remember them* to compare fractions.

1. Henry and James were comparing the amounts of money they had saved. Henry had several coins and James had several coins. Who had the more money, Henry or James? (Tell why you cannot solve this problem.)

2. Susan had 5 coins and Margaret had 10 coins. Who had the more money, Susan or Margaret? (Tell why you cannot solve this problem.)

3. Mary had some dimes in her dime-saver, and Sara had some dimes in hers. Who had the more money, Mary or Sara? (Tell why you cannot solve this problem.)

4. Robert had 7 nickels and Walter had 4 dimes. Who had the more money, Robert or Walter? (You can solve this problem. Tell why you can.)

Let us study these four problems. Problem 1 does not tell us either the *number* or the *size* of the coins each had. Problem 2 is not much better. It tells us the *number* of coins each had, but it forgets to tell us the *size*. Number without size does not help us very much. Problem 3 is just the opposite. It tells us the *size* of the coins (dimes), but it forgets to tell us the number each had. Size without number does not help us very much. Let us notice Problem 4. It tells us everything we need to know. It tells us both the *number* and the *size* of the coins each had. We can compare the money Robert had with the money Walter had, because we know the *number* and the *size* of the coins.

In order to compare, one must know and pay attention to both *number* and *size*.

Notice how we work Problem 4. We do not compare the 7 nickels with the 4 dimes, and say that Robert had the more money because he had 7 coins and Walter had only 4. The nickels and the dimes *are not of the same size*, so we just think them into *coins of the same size:* 7 nickels = 35¢, and 4 dimes = 40¢. We now compare 35 with 40, because the two amounts are both thought of in coins of the same size; that is, both are in cents.

Helen said to Jane, "Which would you rather have — 3 pieces of candy or 5 pieces of candy?" Jane answered, "It depends on the *size* of the pieces."

Which would you rather have — 1 dish of ice cream or 2 dishes of ice cream?

5. In the first-grade and second-grade rooms at our school they have tables arranged in rows. In the first-grade room there are 6

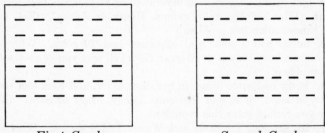

First Grade　　　　　　*Second Grade*

rows with 6 tables in a row. In the second-grade room there are 5 rows with 7 tables in a row? In which room are there the more tables?

This problem is easy to solve, because we are told both the *number* of rows and the *size* of each row in each of the rooms. But notice: we do not try to compare 6 rows in one room with 5 rows in the other or the size of a row (6 tables) in one room with the size of a row (7 tables) in the other. It would be foolish for the first-grade pupils to say, "We have more tables, because we have 6 rows, and you have only 5 rows," and it would be foolish for the second-grade pupils to say, "We have more than you, because we have 7 tables in each of our rows." Instead of trying to make a foolish comparison like that, we just think the number and the size of the rows in the two rooms into *tens;* that is, into something of the same size. We just think, "Six sixes are thirty-six," and "Five sevens are thirty-five," and compare the 36 with the 35.

In order to compare, we must (1) know and pay attention to both *number* and *size*, and (2) think the things that are of different sizes into *things of the same size.*

Now let us try to compare two fractions, $\frac{1}{2}$ and $\frac{2}{3}$. But before we begin, let us review what a fraction shows us or tells us. Every fraction has two terms. The one above the line is the *numerator*, and the one below the line is the *denominator*. The *numerator* in a fraction tells the *number* of parts, and the *denominator* tells the *size* of each part. So, in comparing two fractions, like $\frac{1}{2}$ and $\frac{2}{3}$, we always have given the two things in each that we must pay attention to, *number* and *size*. All we need to do is to think the fractions that are of different sizes into *fractions of the same size*.

It will be foolish in comparing $\frac{1}{2}$ and $\frac{2}{3}$ to try to compare the *numbers* of the parts — the numerators, 1 and 2 — and forget all about the *different sizes*. And, of course, it will be equally foolish to try to compare the *sizes* — the denominators, 2 and 3 — and forget all about the *numbers*. There is only one thing to do, and that is to think the two fractions, $\frac{1}{2}$ and $\frac{2}{3}$, into *fractions of the same size*. When we get them into fractions of the same size, then we can easily compare the *number* of parts in the one with the *number* of parts in the other.

Which would you rather have — 1 stick of candy or 2 sticks of candy? That depends on the *size* of the sticks, doesn't it?

Which is the larger — 1 *half* or 2 *thirds?* That depends on the *size* of the parts.

Let us compare $\frac{1}{2}$ and $\frac{2}{3}$ by using circles to illustrate what we must either actually do or think as we compare them. We divide one circle into 2 equal parts and the other circle into 3 equal parts:

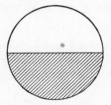 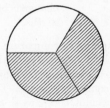

We can tell that one of the halves is not so large as two of the thirds, but we cannot tell exactly how much smaller it is just by looking. In order to compare the one half with the two thirds, we must cut the half and the thirds into parts that will be the *same size*. We can do that by cutting each circle into 6 equal parts, and

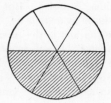 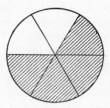

noticing how many sixths there are in $\frac{1}{2}$ and how many sixths there are in $\frac{2}{3}$.

We now can compare the $\frac{1}{2}$ and the $\frac{2}{3}$, because we have each fraction made into sixths, or *parts of the same size*. In $\frac{1}{2}$ there are $\frac{3}{6}$, and in $\frac{2}{3}$ there are $\frac{4}{6}$. We can see that $\frac{1}{2}$ is $\frac{1}{6}$ less than $\frac{2}{3}$, or that the fraction $\frac{2}{3}$ is $\frac{1}{6}$ more than the fraction $\frac{1}{2}$.

Thinking the Comparison

In comparing fractions, like $\frac{1}{2}$ and $\frac{2}{3}$, we can use circles or any other objects, and actually change the $\frac{1}{2}$ to $\frac{3}{6}$ and the $\frac{2}{3}$ to $\frac{4}{6}$ by cutting each into sixths. Instead of using objects to change the fractions actually, we can *think* them into fractions of the same size. This is the shorter, easier way. Let us see.

We decide to change $\frac{1}{2}$ into sixths and $\frac{2}{3}$ into sixths, so that we can compare them. We change both by the method of partial cancellation, remembering in each case that there are $\frac{6}{6}$ in 1.

$\frac{1}{2}$ of $\frac{\overset{3}{\cancel{6}}}{6} = \frac{3}{6}$ We can now compare $\frac{1}{2}$ and $\frac{2}{3}$, because we have

$\frac{2}{3}$ of $\frac{\overset{2}{\cancel{6}}}{6} = \frac{4}{6}$ changed both into *parts of the same size*, into sixths.

Sometimes in comparing two fractions, like $\frac{1}{2}$ and $\frac{2}{3}$, in order to make them into parts of the same size, we have to change both fractions. Sometimes we need to change only one of the fractions. Let us compare $\frac{2}{3}$ and $\frac{5}{6}$.

We cannot compare $\frac{2}{3}$ and $\frac{5}{6}$ as they are, because the parts, thirds and sixths, are *not of the same size*. We know, however, that we can change the $\frac{2}{3}$ to sixths, and the $\frac{5}{6}$ is already in sixths without being changed. So we just change the one fraction to sixths, $\frac{2}{3}$ of $\frac{\overset{2}{\cancel{6}}}{6} = \frac{4}{6}$, and compare it with the $\frac{5}{6}$.

Let us compare $\frac{1}{4}$ and $\frac{3}{8}$. Since we can change fourths to

eighths, we need to change only one of our fractions, $\frac{1}{4}$ of $\frac{\overset{2}{\cancel{8}}}{8}$ = $\frac{2}{8}$.
We now compare $\frac{2}{8}$ and $\frac{3}{8}$.

Let us compare $\frac{1}{3}$ and $\frac{1}{4}$. Since we cannot change thirds to fourths, we must change both fractions to *parts of the same size.*
We can change thirds to twelfths, and fourths to twelfths:

$$\frac{1}{3} \text{ of } \frac{\overset{4}{\cancel{12}}}{12} = \frac{4}{12}$$
$$\frac{1}{4} \text{ of } \frac{\overset{3}{\cancel{12}}}{12} = \frac{3}{12}$$

We can now compare $\frac{4}{12}$ and $\frac{3}{12}$.

4. Common Denominators

When the pupils have developed the idea that parts must be of the same size if they are to be compared, they may be introduced to the term that is used to stand for equal-sized parts; namely, 'common denominator.' The name should not precede the idea; nor should the idea be abandoned when the name is introduced. The name is useful, just like all names, to stand in place of the idea. It facilitates thinking and discussion.

With the introduction of the new term should go the method of finding the common denominator. The following procedure illustrates the method that may be used to introduce the term.

Teaching the Common Denominator

Common means *the same. Denominator* tells *size of parts.*

In comparing two fractions that have different denominators — that is, with *parts of different sizes* — we must change either one or both of them to *parts of the same size.* That is, we must change either one or both of them in such a way that they will have a *common denominator.*

Just what the *common denominator* is to be in comparing two fractions is sometimes puzzling. In comparing $\frac{1}{4}$ and $\frac{1}{6}$, we know we have to change both fractions, since we cannot change fourths to sixths, but we do not like to try sevenths, then eighths, then ninths, and so on, until we just happen to find the common denominator. We would like to have some easy rule to follow to find the common denominator. On the next page is an easy rule to follow:

First try the larger denominator, which is 6 here, and see whether it can be divided *even* (that is, without a remainder), by the other denominator, which is 4. Since 6 cannot be divided even by 4, multiply 6 by 2, which gives 12, and see whether 12 can be divided *even* by 4. Since 12 can be divided *even* by 4, twelfths is the *common denominator*, and we change both $\frac{1}{4}$ and $\frac{1}{6}$ to twelfths by partial cancellation:

$$\frac{1}{4} \text{ of } \frac{\overset{3}{\cancel{12}}}{12} = \frac{3}{12} \qquad\qquad \frac{1}{6} \text{ of } \frac{\overset{2}{\cancel{12}}}{12} = \frac{2}{12}$$

Let us compare $\frac{1}{6}$ and $\frac{1}{8}$. Since 8 cannot be divided *even* by 6, we multiply 8 by 2, which gives 16. But 16 cannot be divided *even* by 6; so we next multiply 8 by 3, which gives 24. Since 24 can be divided *even* by 6, twenty-fourths is the *common denominator*, and we change both $\frac{1}{6}$ and $\frac{1}{8}$ to twenty-fourths by partial cancellation:

$$\frac{1}{6} \text{ of } \frac{\overset{4}{\cancel{24}}}{24} = \frac{4}{24} \qquad\qquad \frac{1}{8} \text{ of } \frac{\overset{3}{\cancel{24}}}{24} = \frac{3}{24}$$

Let us compare $\frac{1}{12}$ and $\frac{1}{15}$. 15 cannot be divided even by 12; so we multiply 15 by 2, which gives 30. 30 cannot be divided *even* by 12; so we multiply 15 by 3, which gives 45. 45 cannot be divided *even* by 12; so we multiply 15 by 4, which gives 60. Since 60 can be divided *even* by 12, we know that sixtieths is the *common denominator*, and we change $\frac{1}{12}$ and $\frac{1}{15}$ to sixtieths by partial cancellation:

$$\frac{1}{12} \text{ of } \frac{\overset{5}{\cancel{60}}}{60} = \frac{5}{60} \qquad\qquad \frac{1}{15} \text{ of } \frac{\overset{4}{\cancel{60}}}{60} = \frac{4}{60}$$

To find the common denominator in comparing two fractions, first see if the larger denominator can be divided even — that is, without remainder — by the smaller. If it cannot, multiply it (the larger denominator) in turn by 2, 3, 4, etc., until you get a number that can be divided even.

When you know what the common denominator is, change the fractions by the method of partial cancellation.

5. Addition and Subtraction

The addition and subtraction of fractions should be delayed until the pupil has enlarged and clarified his ideas of the most frequently used common fractions. The reason for this delay is that he will not be prepared to add or to subtract fractions with intelligence until he is able to view each of the fractions to be dealt with in its relation to the other. Just as previous discussions have pointed out that there is a great gap between counting and the combinations of groups (which ought to be filled with the systematic study of groups through comparison and through analysis and synthesis of groups) so our present discussions are intended to indicate that a somewhat similar gap exists between the viewing of each fraction by itself as one or more of the equal parts of something and the combination of parts by addition and subtraction (which needs to be filled with somewhat similar systematic studies of parts). Paying attention to the size and number of parts when one fraction is viewed in its relation to another prepares for addition and subtraction. Addition and subtraction give further opportunity to study size and number of parts.

The methods by which size and number of parts may be emphasized have been illustrated in connection with preceding topics. Such illustrations need not be repeated here. We should bear in mind, however, that the addition and the subtraction of fractions introduce what appear at first glance to be new operations, but that turn out to be operations that in every case give opportunity for constant reference to previous studies of divisions of parts into equivalents, of comparisons, and of size and number. Let us mention the outstanding ones of these 'new' operations.

Reduction is one of the new operations. Often the answer to an addition or to a subtraction is one that may be 'reduced,' $\frac{6}{8}$, $\frac{10}{12}$, $\frac{2}{6}$, for example. At the outset the reduction should be made through an inspection of equivalents, a table of which has previously been prepared: $\frac{1}{4} = \frac{2}{8} = \frac{3}{12} = \frac{4}{16}$, etc.; $\frac{1}{3} = \frac{2}{6} = \frac{3}{9} = \frac{4}{12}$, etc. Or the reduction may be made through a reinspection of the circles that were originally divided into various equal parts. Thus, by viewing the circle that is divided into eighths, the pupil may remind himself that $\frac{6}{8}$ is the same as $\frac{3}{4}$. A number of fractions that may be reduced should be studied in a similar way and their reduced equivalents noted, written down, and compared with the originals. Finally, the general rule for reduction should be evolved; namely, that both terms of the fraction may be divided by the same number without changing its value.

Other 'new' processes may be introduced as follows:

Teaching More about Addition

1. Frances had a candy bar that was divided into six parts. She ate $\frac{4}{6}$ of the bar at lunch and the other $\frac{2}{6}$ at recess. How much of the bar did she eat?

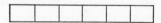

Of course, this problem is too easy. You know at once that Frances ate all of her candy bar. Let us see how to write what we do in working the problem. We add $\frac{4}{6}$ and $\frac{2}{6}$, using either form:

$$\begin{array}{l}\frac{4}{6}\\[2pt]\frac{2}{6}\\[2pt]\frac{6}{6}\end{array} \quad \text{or} \quad \frac{4}{6}+\frac{2}{6}=\frac{6}{6}$$

The answer, $\frac{6}{6}$, tells us that she ate the whole bar, because we know that $\frac{6}{6}=1$. Let us see how we can tell.

Last year you learned that a fraction means *to divide*, and this year you have learned that the denominator tells the *size of the parts*, because it shows into how many parts a thing *is divided*. A fraction, like $\frac{2}{3}$, or $\frac{3}{4}$, or $\frac{6}{6}$, or $\frac{12}{3}$, or $\frac{16}{5}$, means, along with other things, that the number above the line is to be divided by the number below the line. In the case of fractions, like $\frac{2}{3}$, $\frac{3}{4}$, etc., we let them stand as they are, $\frac{2}{3}$, $\frac{3}{4}$, etc., *since we have not yet learned how to divide a smaller number by a larger number*. We shall learn how to do that next year.

In the case of fractions, like $\frac{6}{6}$, $\frac{12}{3}$, and $\frac{16}{5}$, we can divide, like this:

$$\frac{6}{6}=6\overline{)6} \qquad\qquad \frac{12}{3}=3\overline{)12}$$

$1\frac{6}{5} = 5\overline{)16} \quad \begin{array}{r} 3\frac{1}{5} \\ \hline 16 \\ 15 \\ \hline 1 \end{array}$

When we divide 16 by 5, we divide only 15 of the 16 and have 1 left *to be divided*. Since we do not yet know how to divide 1 by 5, we merely show that we would divide if we could by writing $\frac{1}{5}$ beside the 3 in the answer. $3\frac{1}{5}$ is read *three and one fifth*.

Our answers are 1, 4, and $3\frac{1}{5}$.

2. Robert ate $\frac{3}{4}$ of a cantaloupe and John ate $\frac{2}{3}$ of one. How much cantaloupe did they both eat?

We add $\frac{3}{4}$ and $\frac{2}{3}$ just as we add any other fractions. We first change them into fractions, or parts, *of the same size* by finding the *common denominator* and using *partial cancellation:*

$$\frac{3}{4} \text{ of } \frac{\overset{3}{\cancel{12}}}{12} = \frac{9}{12}$$
$$\frac{2}{3} \text{ of } \frac{\overset{4}{\cancel{12}}}{12} = \frac{8}{12}$$
$$\overline{\frac{17}{12}}$$

$$\frac{17}{12} = 12\overline{)17} \quad \begin{array}{r} 1\frac{5}{12} \\ \hline 17 \\ 12 \\ \hline 5 \end{array}$$

When we add $\frac{9}{12}$ and $\frac{8}{12}$ we get $\frac{17}{12}$, which means divide 17 by 12. We do, but have 5 left, which we do not yet know how to divide, so we just show that we mean to divide it by 12 by writing the fraction $\frac{5}{12}$ beside the 1 in the answer. Our answer is $1\frac{5}{12}$.

Teaching More about Subtraction

In subtracting fractions it is often necessary to subtract a fraction from a whole number or from a whole number and a fraction. Neither is hard to do, because all one has to remember before he tries to subtract is to make the *parts of the same size* by finding the *common denominator.*

1. Jane had 1 yard of goods. She used $\frac{3}{8}$ of a yard to make a dress for her doll. How much of the goods had she left?

In order to subtract $\frac{3}{8}$ from 1, we first think 1 into *eighths*, or *parts of the same size* — that is, we think, $1 = \frac{8}{8}$, and then we subtract $\frac{3}{8}$ from $\frac{8}{8}$. The answer is $\frac{5}{8}$ yard.

2. Ellen had $1\frac{5}{8}$ yards of goods. She used $\frac{3}{8}$ of a yard to make a dress for her doll. How much of the goods had she left?

$\begin{array}{c} 1\frac{5}{8} \\ \underline{\frac{3}{8}} \\ 1\frac{2}{8} \text{ or } 1\frac{1}{4} \end{array}$ We subtract $\frac{3}{8}$ from $\frac{5}{8}$, which gives $\frac{2}{8}$. We have nothing to take from 1; so our answer is $1\frac{2}{8}$, or $1\frac{1}{4}$ yards.

3. Susan had $1\frac{3}{8}$ yards of goods. She used $\frac{5}{8}$ of a yard to make a dress for her doll. How much of the goods had she left?

$1\frac{3}{8}$
$\frac{5}{8}$
$\overline{}$
$\frac{6}{8}$ or $\frac{3}{4}$

Since we cannot take $\frac{5}{8}$ from $\frac{3}{8}$, we think the 1 into *eighths* $(1 = \frac{8}{8})$ and count it with the $\frac{3}{8}$, which gives $1\frac{1}{8}$. We now subtract $\frac{5}{8}$ from $1\frac{1}{8}$, which gives $\frac{6}{8}$, or $\frac{3}{4}$ yard.

4. Sam had $1\frac{3}{4}$ yards of tape. He used $\frac{2}{3}$ of a yard to tape the handle of his tennis racket. How much tape had he left?

$1\frac{3}{4}$
$\frac{2}{3}$
$\overline{}$
$1\frac{1}{12}$

We first change the $\frac{3}{4}$ and the $\frac{2}{3}$ to *parts of the same size:* $\frac{3}{4}$ of $\frac{\overset{3}{12}}{12} = \frac{9}{12}$; $\frac{2}{3}$ of $\frac{\overset{4}{12}}{12} = \frac{8}{12}$. Since $\frac{9}{12}$ is larger than $\frac{8}{12}$, we subtract, and get $\frac{1}{12}$, and as we have nothing to take from 1, we have 1 left also. Our answer is $1\frac{1}{12}$ yards.

5. George had $1\frac{2}{3}$ yards of tape. He used $\frac{3}{4}$ of a yard to tape the handle of his tennis racket. How much tape had he left?

$1\frac{2}{3}$
$\frac{3}{4}$
$\overline{}$
$\frac{11}{12}$

We first change the $\frac{2}{3}$ and $\frac{3}{4}$ to *parts of the same size:* $\frac{8}{12}$ and $\frac{9}{12}$. Since $\frac{8}{12}$ is smaller than $\frac{9}{12}$, we change the 1 to *twelfths* $(1 = \frac{12}{12})$, and count it with the $\frac{8}{12}$, which gives $\frac{20}{12}$. We now subtract $\frac{9}{12}$ from $\frac{20}{12}$, which gives $\frac{11}{12}$ yard. Our answer is $\frac{11}{12}$ yard.

Things to remember and do:

1. See that the fractions are in *parts of the same size.*
2. Notice which fraction is the larger.
3. When necessary, change the whole number in the minuend to a fraction, *with parts of the same size*, and count it with the fraction in the minuend.

Teaching Carrying in the Addition of Mixed Numbers

If you remember everything you have learned about fractions, you are now ready to learn how to add whole numbers and fractions to whole numbers and fractions. Sometimes you will have to carry; sometimes you will not. Let us see.

1. Add $3\frac{1}{2}$ and $4\frac{1}{3}$.

$3\frac{1}{2}$ $\quad \frac{1}{2}$ of $\frac{\overset{3}{6}}{6} = \frac{3}{6}$
$4\frac{1}{3}$ $\quad \frac{1}{3}$ of $\frac{\overset{2}{6}}{6} = \frac{2}{6}$
$\overline{7\frac{5}{6}}$ $\qquad\qquad\quad \frac{5}{6}$

First, change the fractions to *parts of the same size*, and add: $\frac{1}{2} + \frac{1}{3} = \frac{5}{6}$, which is less than 1. Write $\frac{5}{6}$ and add the whole numbers. The answer is $7\frac{5}{6}$.

2. Add $3\frac{1}{2}$ and $4\frac{4}{5}$.

$3\frac{1}{2}$ $\frac{1}{2}$ of $\frac{10}{10} = \frac{5}{10}$

$4\frac{4}{5}$ $\frac{4}{5}$ of $\frac{10}{10} = \frac{8}{10}$ $1\frac{3}{10}$

$8\frac{3}{10}$ $\frac{13}{10} = 10\overline{)13}$

                         $\underline{10}$

                         3

First, change the fractions to *parts of the same size*, and add: $\frac{1}{2} + \frac{4}{5} = \frac{13}{10} = 1\frac{3}{10}$. Write $\frac{3}{10}$ and *carry* 1 to the whole numbers and add with them. The answer is $8\frac{3}{10}$.

Teaching Carrying in the Subtraction of Mixed Numbers

If you remember everything you have learned about fractions, you are now ready to learn how to subtract whole numbers and fractions from whole numbers and fractions. Sometimes you will have to carry; sometimes you will not. Let us see.

1. Subtract $2\frac{1}{3}$ from $4\frac{1}{2}$.

$4\frac{1}{2}$ $\frac{1}{2}$ of $\frac{6}{6} = \frac{3}{6}$

$2\frac{1}{3}$ $\frac{1}{3}$ of $\frac{6}{6} = \frac{2}{6}$

$2\frac{1}{6}$ $\frac{1}{6}$

First, change the fractions to *parts of the same size*. When the upper fraction is the larger, subtract: $\frac{3}{6} - \frac{2}{6} = \frac{1}{6}$. Write $\frac{1}{6}$ and subtract the whole numbers. The answer is $2\frac{1}{6}$.

2. Subtract $5\frac{1}{2}$ from $8\frac{1}{3}$.

$8\frac{1}{3}$ $\frac{1}{3}$ of $\frac{6}{6} = \frac{2}{6} + \frac{6}{6} = \frac{8}{6}$

$5\frac{1}{2}$ $\frac{1}{2}$ of $\frac{6}{6} = \frac{3}{6}$

$2\frac{5}{6}$ $\frac{5}{6}$

First, change the fractions to *parts of the same size*. When the upper fraction is the smaller, use 1 (*changed to parts of the same size*) from the 8 to add to it, and then subtract: $\frac{8}{6} - \frac{3}{6} = \frac{5}{6}$. Write $\frac{5}{6}$. Now, since 1 of the 8 has been used in order to make the upper fraction large enough to subtract from, we have 7 to subtract from. Subtract 5 from 7. The answer is $2\frac{5}{6}$.

3. Subtract $5\frac{3}{5}$ from 8.

8

$5\frac{3}{5}$

$2\frac{2}{5}$

Use 1 (changed to fifths) in the minuend. Subtract $\frac{3}{5}$ from $\frac{5}{5}$. Write $\frac{2}{5}$. Since one has been used, seven are left. Subtract 5 from 7. The answer is $2\frac{2}{5}$.

6. Multiplying Fractions

The order of presentation of the various phases of the multiplication of fractions is: (1) a fraction multiplied by a whole number, (2) a whole number multiplied by a fraction, (3) a fraction multiplied by a fraction, (4) a whole number multiplied by a mixed number, and the reverse, and (5) a mixed number multiplied by a mixed number.

In taking up formal work in the multiplication of fractions, time is saved by presenting *first* the repetition of a fraction a given number of times, $4 \times \frac{2}{3}$; or the multiplication of a fraction by a whole number.[1]

Each step should be presented with as much of objective demonstration as is necessary for the pupils to understand what is required in the multiplication and how to proceed. When they understand, they should be provided with plenty of practice in carrying through the given step before proceeding to the next. Illustrations will be given of the first and third steps.

Teaching How to Multiply a Fraction by a Whole Number

1. How many grape fruits will it take to serve 6 persons if each person gets $\frac{1}{2}$ of a grape fruit?

It will take as many halves as this for all:

The problem can be worked either way, as follows:

$$\frac{\frac{1}{2}}{\frac{6}{\frac{6}{2}}} = 2\overline{)6} \qquad \text{or} \quad 6 \times \frac{1}{2} = \frac{6}{2} = 3$$

2. Susan needs 4 strips of edging to go round a pillow she is making. Each strip must be $\frac{2}{3}$ yard long. How many yards of edging does she need?

How much she will need can be shown by a diagram, like this:

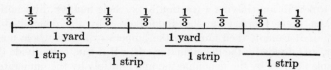

The 4 strips needed make $2\frac{2}{3}$ yards.

The problem can be worked either way, as follows:

$$\frac{\overset{\frac{2}{3}}{4}}{\frac{8}{3}} = 3\overline{)8} \quad \begin{array}{c} 2\frac{2}{3} \\ \hline \\ 6 \\ \hline 2 \end{array}$$

or $4 \times \frac{2}{3} = \frac{8}{3} = 3\overline{)8} \quad \begin{array}{c} 2\frac{2}{3} \\ \hline \\ 6 \\ \hline 2 \end{array}$

3. Multiply $\frac{3}{4}$ by 12.

Notice the two methods. Which is the easier?

$$A$$

$$12 \times \frac{3}{4} = \frac{36}{4} = 4\overline{)36} \quad \begin{array}{c} 9 \\ \hline 36 \end{array}$$

$$B$$

$$\cancel{12} \times \frac{3}{4} = 9 \quad ^3$$

In Method A, we first multiply 3 by 12, then divide by 4.

In Method B, we first divide 12 by 4, then multiply by 3.

4. Multiply $\frac{3}{5}$ by 25.

$$A$$

$$25 \times \frac{3}{5} = \frac{75}{5} = 5\overline{)75} \quad \begin{array}{c} 15 \\ \hline 5 \\ 25 \\ 25 \end{array}$$

$$B$$

$$\cancel{25} \times \frac{3}{\cancel{5}} = 15 \quad ^5$$

5. Multiply $\frac{2}{3}$ by 14.

$$A$$

$$14 \times \frac{2}{3} = \frac{28}{3} = 3\overline{)28} \quad \begin{array}{c} 9\frac{1}{3} \\ \hline 27 \\ \hline 1 \end{array}$$

$$B$$

$$\cancel{14} \times \frac{2}{3} = \quad ^{4\frac{2}{3}} \text{(See the trouble this method sometimes gives.)}$$

Method B is the easier when the whole number can be divided even by the denominator. Method A is the easier when the whole number cannot be divided even.

Rule: In multiplying a fraction by a whole number, first notice if the whole number can be divided even by the denominator. A. If it cannot, then multiply the numerator by the whole number, and divide by the denominator. B. If it can, then divide the whole number by the denominator, and multiply by the numerator.

Teaching How to Multiply a Fraction by a Fraction

1. How much is $\frac{2}{3} \times \frac{4}{5}$? Or how much is $\frac{2}{3}$ of $\frac{4}{5}$?

Let us use a diagram. Suppose we draw a line and divide it into 15 equal parts, or fifteenths:

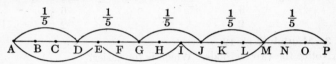

From A to D is $\frac{1}{5}$ of the line.

From A to M is $\frac{4}{5}$ of the line.

(Let us note $\frac{2}{3}$ of $\frac{4}{5}$ of the line, or $\frac{2}{3}$ of the part A to M.)

From A to E is $\frac{1}{3}$ of the part A to M.

From A to I is $\frac{2}{3}$ of the part A to M.

Counting from A to I we have $\frac{8}{15}$ of the whole line.

$$\frac{2}{3} \times \frac{4}{5} = \frac{8}{15}, \text{ or } \frac{2}{3} \text{ of } \frac{4}{5} = \frac{8}{15} \qquad \left(\text{Note: } \frac{2 \text{ 4's are } 8}{3 \text{ 5's are } 15}\right)$$

In multiplying a fraction by a fraction, multiply the numerators, then multiply the denominators.

2. Multiply, $\frac{2}{3} \times \frac{3}{4}$.

$$\overset{A}{\frac{2}{3} \times \frac{3}{4} = \frac{6}{12} = \frac{1}{2}} \quad \text{or} \quad \overset{B}{\frac{\overset{1}{\cancel{2}}}{\underset{1}{\cancel{3}}} \times \frac{\overset{1}{\cancel{3}}}{\underset{2}{\cancel{4}}} = \frac{1}{2}}$$

Method B is the method of cancelling. 2 will divide the 2 in the numerator of one fraction and the 4 in the denominator of the other, and 3 will divide the 3 in the numerator of one fraction and the 3 in the denominator of the other.

3. Multiply, $\frac{3}{5} \times \frac{10}{13}$. $\quad \frac{3}{\cancel{5}} \times \frac{\overset{2}{\cancel{10}}}{13} = \frac{6}{13}$

4. Multiply, $\frac{3}{8} \times \frac{2}{3}$. $\quad \frac{\overset{1}{\cancel{3}}}{\underset{4}{\cancel{8}}} \times \frac{\overset{1}{\cancel{2}}}{\cancel{3}} = \frac{1}{4}$

In multiplying a fraction by a fraction, cancel as much as you can; that is, divide the numerators and denominators by the same numbers as much as you can. Next, multiply the numerators, and then multiply the denominators.

In the multiplication of whole numbers and mixed numbers (listed as a fourth phase of the multiplication of fractions) the pupil is given further practice in what he has already learned, and at the same time he is required to keep his wits about him in order to realize the fact that he secures two or more partial products that must be added.

$$
\begin{array}{r}
24 \\
5\frac{2}{3} \\
\hline
16 \\
120 \\
\hline
136
\end{array}
\qquad
\begin{array}{r}
37\frac{1}{2} \\
18 \\
\hline
9 \\
296 \\
37 \\
\hline
675
\end{array}
$$

In the multiplication of mixed numbers (listed as fifth phase) the pupil is given additional practice in multiplying fractions, in the changing of mixed numbers to improper fractions, and in the changing of improper fractions to mixed numbers.

$$2\frac{1}{2} \times 4\frac{1}{4} \qquad \frac{5}{2} \times \frac{17}{4} = \frac{85}{8} = 10\frac{5}{8}$$

The method of changing a mixed number to an improper fraction should be demonstrated objectively, as in the following example:

Teaching How to Change a Mixed Number to a Fraction

1. Suppose we want to change $2\frac{1}{4}$ to a fraction; that is, to find how many fourths in $2\frac{1}{4}$.

We know that in 1 there are four fourths, $1 = \frac{4}{4}$

Then in 2 there are eight fourths, $2 = \frac{8}{4}$

$\frac{8}{4}$ and $\frac{1}{4}$ are $\frac{9}{4}$.

We can change $2\frac{1}{4}$ to fourths more quickly by thinking: "Four twos are eight and one are nine *fourths*," $\frac{9}{4}$.

2. Let us change $3\frac{5}{8}$ to a fraction.

We think, "Eight threes are twenty-four and five are twenty-nine *eighths*," $\frac{29}{8}$.

7. Dividing Fractions

Since the method of dividing by a fraction is the same as the method of multiplication, except that the divisor is inverted, it follows that the pupil should first be well acquainted with the process of multiplication and then should be made to understand the reason why the inversion of the divisor is necessary. To accomplish the latter, he must review the meaning of division and keep the meaning consciously before him as he proceeds to divide.

The following sample lessons are included in order to illustrate the means of reviewing the meaning of division as a prelude to division.

Teaching the Dividing of Fractions

After learning to multiply fractions, you will find it very easy to divide fractions. The rule in dividing by a fraction is easy to remember and to use. *In dividing by a fraction, invert the divisor and multiply.*

Invert means to *turn over.*

When $\frac{2}{3}$ is inverted, it becomes $\frac{3}{2}$.

When $\frac{3}{8}$ is inverted, it becomes $\frac{8}{3}$.

When $\frac{5}{6}$ is inverted, it becomes $\frac{6}{5}$.

When $\frac{1}{2}$ is inverted, it becomes $\frac{2}{1}$, or **2.**

When $\frac{1}{3}$ is inverted, it becomes $\frac{3}{1}$, or **3.**

When $\frac{8}{5}$ is inverted, it becomes $\frac{5}{8}$.

When $\frac{12}{7}$ is inverted, it becomes $\frac{7}{12}$.

Let us see why, when *dividing by a fraction*, we *invert* the divisor and multiply. We will first review what division means.

In the second and third grades you learned that division always *asks a question*. You learned that

$2\overline{)6}$ asks, "How many twos in six?"

$3\overline{)15}$ asks, "How many threes in fifteen?"

$4\overline{)60}$ asks, "How many fours in sixty?"

$17\overline{)850}$ asks, "How many seventeens in eight hundred fifty?"

In dividing by a fraction, we use a different *form* of asking the question, but the kind of question asked is exactly the same. In dividing 5 by $\frac{1}{4}$, for example, instead of using this form, $\frac{1}{4}\overline{)5}$, to ask the question, we use this form, $5 \div \frac{1}{4}$.

$6 \div 2$ asks the same question as $2\overline{)6}$

$15 \div 3$ asks the same question as $3\overline{)15}$

$60 \div 4$ asks the same question as $4\overline{)60}$

$850 \div 17$ asks the same question as $17\overline{)850}$

$5 \div \frac{1}{4}$ asks the same question as $\frac{1}{4}\overline{)5}$

What question does $5 \div \frac{1}{4}$ ask?

Let us see how to find the answer.

NUMBER OF OBJECTS   NUMBER OF FOURTHS

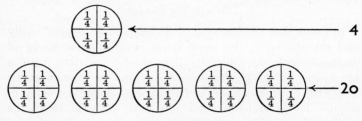

In order to find how many fourths there are in 5, we first ask ourselves how many fourths there are in 1.

Since there are 4 fourths in 1, in 5 there are as many fourths as 5×4, or 20.

$5 \div \frac{1}{4}$

$5 \times \frac{4}{1} = 20$. (We can write the answer $\frac{20}{1}$, but we know that $20 \div 1 = 20$.)

1. Helen uses $\frac{1}{3}$ of a yard of crepe paper to make a paper doll. How many dolls can she make with 5 yards of crepe paper?

$5 \div \frac{1}{3} = \qquad 5 \times 3 = 15$

2. Find, $7 \div \frac{1}{2}$. $\qquad 7 \div \frac{1}{2} = \qquad 7 \times 2 = 14$

Teaching the Dividing of a Fraction by a Fraction

The rule is the same: *In dividing by a fraction, invert the divisor and multiply.*

Mother has $\frac{2}{3}$ of a pie. How many people can she serve if she gives each person $\frac{1}{6}$ of a pie?

The real question is, "How many sixths are there in $\frac{2}{3}$? In 1 there are 6 sixths. In $\frac{2}{3}$ there are how many sixths? The answer is $\frac{2}{3}$ times 6, or 4. The problem is worked like this:

$$\frac{2}{3} \div \frac{1}{6} = \qquad\qquad \frac{2}{3} \times \frac{\overset{2}{\cancel{6}}}{1} = 4$$

VI. Decimal Fractions

1. Introducing Decimals

In order that the learning of decimals may proceed easily and expeditiously, the pupil must approach the study of decimals with an understanding of the fraction, with a knowledge of the significance of size and number of parts, and with the idea of ten and the use of position clearly in mind. To be launched upon his work with decimals, the pupil will need then only to review the things he has already learned and to be introduced to the conventional way of setting off the decimal from the whole number. Our discussion of decimals and our illustrations of typical sample lessons will proceed on the assumption that the pupil has come to an understanding of the work that has been outlined in preceding discussions. Where our assumption is justified, the pupil can proceed to learn something that at the outset appears new, but that is really only a new way of using the ideas he has been gaining in his preceding work. As such a pupil moves from one stage of his work to another in the study of decimals, he will constantly discover his own ability to explain to himself the 'new' things to be learned. As he proceeds, he will be able to do so with more and more confidence in his ability to do what he has to do; and he may learn to be on the lookout for familiar elements in each new undertaking.

What follows illustrates the relations between the new work with decimals and the ideas the pupil should bring from his earlier work to the study of decimals.

Teaching the General Idea of Decimals

In your study of fractions, you have learned about *parts* of many different *sizes*, such as *halves, thirds, fourths, fifths, tenths, twelfths,* etc. You found it difficult sometimes to compare them because the *parts* were *of different sizes,* and because the parts to be compared were often *not related.* Now you are to study about *parts* that are of only three different *sizes* — *tenths, hundredths, thousandths* — and, what is more, about *parts* that are *closely related.*

The fractions to be studied now are called *decimals.* The word 'decimal' may be a new word to you, but its meaning is not so new, because you began to learn it as far back as the first grade. 'Decimal' is a word which is taken from an old Latin word *decem,* and *decem* means *ten.* (March used to be considered the first month of the year. Which month was then the *tenth* one? How did it get its name?) In using decimals you will be using the *idea of ten* and the *idea of position* in exactly the same way that you have been using these ideas in all of your previous work in arithmetic.

In your earlier work in arithmetic, after you had learned to add, subtract, multiply, and divide *units*, you learned that *tens, hundreds*, and *thousands* were added, subtracted, multiplied, and divided just like units. So in your work now with *decimals*, you will find that *tenths, hundredths*, and *thousandths* are added, subtracted, multiplied, and divided just like units. In your earlier work in arithmetic, you found that you did not need to be thinking all the time you were doing something with *tens, hundreds*, and *thousands* about doing it just like units, but that if you were careful to put each part of the answer *in its proper place* that *position* would take care of everything for you. So in doing various things with *tenths, hundredths*, and *thousandths*, you will not need to be thinking about 'just like units,' but will only need to write each part of the answer *in its proper place*. In working with *decimals, proper position* will take care of everything for you.

Really, there is not anything new to learn in working with *decimals*, unless it is to be *very careful* about writing everything *in its proper place*, and that is not so new if you have already learned to be careful about numbers in their proper places.

Teaching the Writing and Reading of Decimals

11 is not 2 ones, but 1 *ten* and 1 *unit*.

111 is not 3 ones, but 1 *hundred*, 1 *ten*, and 1 *unit*.

1111 is not 4 ones, but 1 *thousand*, 1 *hundred*, 1 *ten*, and 1 *unit* — and so on.

In the number, 1111, the second 1 to the left is *ten* times the first 1. It is in *ten's* position, and shows 1 *ten*. The third 1 is *ten* times the second 1. It shows *ten tens*, or 1 *hundred*, and is in *hundred's* position. The fourth 1 is *ten* times the third 1. It shows *ten hundreds*, or 1 *thousand*, and is in *thousand's* position. Each position *to the left* means *ten times* the position to the right of it.

Let us now start with the 1 *thousand* in 1111, and go *to the right*, seeing how the positions compare. The second 1 to the right of 1 *thousand* is 1 *hundred*, which is 1 *tenth* of the 1 to the left of it. The third 1 is 1 *ten*, which is 1 *tenth* of the 1 to the left of it. The fourth 1 is 1 *unit*, which is 1 *tenth* of the 1 to the left of it. Each position *to the right* means 1 *tenth* of the position to the left of it.

Let us now start with 1 *unit* and write 1 and 1 and 1 to the right of it to show 1 *tenth*, 1 *hundredth*, and 1 *thousandth*. Suppose we write the 1's like this:

1111

We can see at once that this is not the way to write 1 *unit*, 1 *tenth*, 1 *hundredth*, and 1 *thousandth*, because it is the same as 1 *thousand*, 1 *hundred eleven*. We need something to show that the first 1 on the left is 1 *unit* and that the next 1 to the right is 1 *tenth*. This is the way to write what we wish:

1.111

Notice the *decimal point* (.) to the right of the 1 *unit* and to the left of the 1 *tenth*. The point (.) is not a number. It is only a means of showing the *position* that is to be taken by the number that shows *tenths*.

When we have the number

1.111

we have 1 at the left of the *point* to show 1 *unit*. The next 1 *to the right*, next to the *point* and at the right of the *point*, is 1 *tenth* of 1 *unit*, or 1 *tenth*, and is in *tenth's* position. The next 1 *to the right* is 1 *tenth* of the 1 on its left, that is, 1 *tenth* of 1 *tenth*, or 1 *hundredth*, and is in *hundredth's* position. The last 1 *to the right* is 1 *tenth* of the 1 on its left; that is, 1 *tenth* of 1 *hundredth*, or 1 *thousandth*, and is in *thousandth's* position.

Showing the Number and Size of Parts

In writing a fraction, as you will remember, we have to show the *number of parts*, and the *size of the parts*. In the writing of ordinary, or *common*, fractions, like $\frac{3}{10}$, for example, we write 3 as a *numerator* to show *number* of parts, and 10 as a *denominator* to show *size* of parts.

In writing *decimal* fractions, we also have to show the *number of parts*, and the *size of the parts*. In the writing of a decimal, however, we write only *one* number, and that shows *number of parts*. But we have to have some way of showing *size of parts* also. In writing a *decimal*, we just let *position* show *size*.

If, in writing a decimal, the number ends *one place* to the right of the point (.); that is, in *tenth's position*, the *position* of the number that is written shows the *size* of the parts to be *tenths*.

.1 is read *one tenth*.

.2 is read *two tenths*.

.7 is read *seven tenths*.

6.1 is read *six and one tenth*.

25.3 is read *twenty-five and three tenths*.

562.4 is read *five hundred sixty-two and four tenths*.

If, in writing a decimal, the number ends *two places* to the right of the point (.); that is, in *hundredth's position*, the positions of the numbers written show the *size* of the parts to be *hundredths*.

.15 is read *fifteen hundredths*.

.63 is read *sixty-three hundredths*.

.50 is read *fifty hundredths*.

.04 is read *four hundredths*. (Notice that we use a zero to hold *tenth's* place when we have no *tenths* to write.)

6.09 is read *six and nine hundredths*.

30.45 is read *thirty and forty-five hundredths*.

If in writing a decimal the number ends *three places* to the right of the point (.); that is, in *thousandth's position*, the positions of the numbers written show the *size* of the parts to be *thousandths*.

.275 is read *two hundred seventy-five thousandths*.

.506 is read *five hundred six thousandths*.

.042 is read *forty-two thousandths*.

.007 is read *seven thousandths*. (Notice that the zero is used to hold a place when we have nothing to write in it.)

.500 is read *five hundred thousandths*.

30.025 is read *thirty and twenty-five thousandths*.

Notice that we read *and* only between the whole number and the decimal.

Zeros written after a decimal do not change its value. .5 = .50 = .500 = .5000, and so on. Six dollars may be written as $6 or as $6.00.

To add a point (.) at the end of a whole number, followed by zeros, does not change its value. 3 may be written as 3.0, 3.00, 3.000. Usually we add no point (.), followed by zeros, at the end of whole numbers. Sometimes, however, it is convenient to do so when we are dealing with whole numbers and decimals, as we shall presently see.

2. The Addition and Subtraction of Decimals

The addition and subtraction of decimals give further opportunity for the pupil to employ his ideas about the importance of position and about the general principle that parts of the same size must be dealt with together. Moreover, the relations between tenths, and hundredths, and thousandths, as being the same as the relations between thousands, and hundreds, and tens, are impressed as the pupil learns to deal with them alike, or just like units, in adding and subtracting.

Teaching the Addition and Subtraction of Decimals

Decimals are added and subtracted exactly the way whole numbers are added and subtracted. In the addition and subtraction of whole numbers one must always be careful to write each part of each number *in its proper place*, in order that *units* may be added to or subtracted from *units*, *tens* added to or subtracted from *tens*, and so on. And one must be careful, too, to write each part of the answer *in its proper place*. So in the addition and subtraction of decimals, one needs to be very careful to write each part of each number *in its proper place*, in order that *thousandths* may be added to or subtracted from *thousandths*, *hundredths* added to or subtracted from *hundredths*, and *tenths* added to or subtracted from *tenths*. And one must be very careful to write each part of the answer *in its proper place*. *If one takes care of position, he can add and subtract decimals just as though they were whole numbers.*

1. Let us add .25, .5, .375, and .075.

.25
.5
.375
.075
———
1.200

Notice how we place *tenths* under *tenths*, *hundredths* under *hundredths*, and *thousandths* under *thousandths*. Although the method used is correct, one sometimes finds it hard to keep the columns straight when he starts to add. So as an *aid to the eye* in looking up and down the columns, it is advisable to add zeros to the right of the shorter decimals in order to make full columns. (Making .25 into .250, and .5 into .500 does not change their values.) So in setting down our example, we may write it as shown on the next page.

.250
.500
.375
.075
─────
1.200

Read the answer, 1.200. It is usually better to strike off the zeros that come at the end, 1.200, and give the answer as 1.2. Notice that we *add* and *carry* just as we do in adding whole numbers. Notice in adding the *tenth's* column we get 12, which we know to be 12 *tenths*. Since we can write only one figure in *tenth's* column, we write the .2 there and *carry* the 10, which is 10 *tenths*, or 1, to the *unit's* position, and write it there.

2. Let us subtract .625 from .75.

.75
.625
────

We may set the example down like this, but to *aid the eye* we attach a zero to the right of the .75; then our example will look like this:

.750
.625
────
.125

Read the answer. Notice that we *subtract* and *carry* just as we do in subtracting whole numbers.

3. Let us subtract .675 from .75.

.750
.675
────
.075

To *aid the eye* we write the example as shown. We *subtract* and *carry* just the way we do in subtracting whole numbers. When we get to the *tenth's* column, we subtract, "Six from six." It is necessary that we write the 0 in the *tenth's position* in the answer, in order to keep the 7 and the 5 *in their proper places*. The 7 is *hundredths* and the 5 is *thousandths*; so we need a 0 in *tenth's* place to make the 7 and the 5 show what they really are.

4. Let us add 20.5, 6.75, 14.825, and 16.7.

20.5
6.75
14.825
16.7
──────

We can add as the example stands, but to *aid the eye* we attach zeros to fill the columns on the right before adding.

20.500
6.750
14.825
16.700
──────
58.775

Notice that we *add* and *carry* just as we do in adding whole numbers.

5. Let us subtract 6.875 from 17.5.

17.500   It is more convenient to fill the columns on the right
 6.875   with zeros. Notice that we *subtract* and *carry* just as we
10.625   do in subtracting whole numbers.

6. Let us subtract 7.25 from 16.

16.00   Sometimes a pupil, when he is not wide awake, makes
 7.25   the mistake of thinking that 7.25 is larger than 16. But
        anyone who really looks at the two numbers can easily
 8.75   tell that 16 is larger than 7 and 25 *hundredths*. To *aid
the eye*, we attach zeros in *tenth's* and *hundredth's* places to the
right of 16. Notice that we *subtract* and *carry* just as we do in
subtracting whole numbers.

3. The Multiplication of Decimals

The rule for 'pointing off' in the multiplication of decimals is useful as a thought-saver, but to be used intelligently, it must be evolved by thinking it out. The pupil
may be led to evolve the rule by first proceeding to multiply
with a full understanding of what he is undertaking to do
and of the terms in which his answer should appear when
he gets it. The following material will illustrate one way to
introduce multiplication of decimals.

Teaching the Multiplication of Decimals

In multiplying a decimal by a whole number or a whole number
by a decimal, all one needs to do is multiply just the way he does
in multiplying whole numbers and to write each part of the answer
in its proper place.

1. Multiply .375 by 7.

 .375   Notice that we *multiply* and *carry* just as we do in multi-
    7   plying whole numbers. Notice the last multiplication,
        "Seven threes are twenty-one and five are twenty-six."
2.625   Since this is 3 *tenths* being multiplied, the answer is twenty-
six *tenths*. We write the 6 *tenths* in *tenth's* position, and the 2,
since it is 20 *tenths*, or 2 *units*, in *unit's* position.

2. Multiply 423 by .75.

```
 423
  .75
21 15
296 1
317.25
```

Notice that we *multiply* and *carry* just as we do in multiplying whole numbers. When we multiply a number like 423 by a number *less than 1* like .75, will the answer be more or less than the multiplicand?

3. Multiply 42.25 by 26.

```
 42.25
    26
 253 50
 845 0
1098.50
```

Notice that we *multiply* and *carry* just as we do in multiplying whole numbers. We may strike off the last zero and give our answer as 1098.5 .

4. Multiply 367 by 2.5

```
  367
  2.5
 183 5
 734
917.5
```

Notice that we *multiply* and *carry* just as we do in multiplying whole numbers.

5. Multiply 25.75 by 8.

```
 25.75
     8
206.00
```

Notice that we *multiply* and *carry* just as we do in multiplying whole numbers. We may strike off the zeros in our answer, and give it as 206.

Notice these points:

(1) That in Example 1 we multiply *thousandths* by a whole number and get *thousandths;*

(2) That in Example 2 we multiply a whole number by *hundredths* and get *hundredths;*

(3) That in Example 3 we multiply *hundredths* by a whole number and get *hundredths;*

(4) That in Example 4 we multiply a whole number by *tenths* and get *tenths;*

(5) That in Example 5 we multiply *hundredths* by a whole number and get *hundredths.*

(6) That we use decimals in multiplication just as we use whole numbers.

Teaching the Multiplying of Decimals by Decimals

In multiplying decimals by whole numbers or whole numbers by decimals, we can let *position* take care of our answers for us, because *tenths*, or *hundredths*, or *thousandths*, multiplied by a whole number will give *tenths*, or *hundredths*, or *thousandths* in the answer; and a whole number multiplied by *tenths*, or *hundredths*, or *thousandths* will give *tenths*, or *hundredths*, or *thousandths* in the answer.

But in multiplying a decimal by a decimal, although we multiply them just as though they were whole numbers, we cannot rely upon *position* to take care of our answer for us. We have to *think* for ourselves what the answer should be. However, there is an easy rule to follow that will do our thinking for us. Let us see if we can find the rule.

1. Multiply .5 by .5.

.5
.5
—
.25

We multiply "Five fives are twenty-five," just as though they were whole numbers. We remember that we are multiplying *tenths* by *tenths* and that *tenths* multiplied by *tenths* give *hundredths*. So we have to fix our answer, 25, to make it show 25 *hundredths*.

2. Multiply 2.5 by 2.5.

2.5
2.5
—
1 25
5 0
—
6.25

We first multiply as though we were multiplying whole numbers. We notice that we are multiplying *tenths* by *tenths*, and that the answer must show *hundredths*. So we place the point (.) in the answer to show 6.25. Or we notice that we multiply 2 and a little more by 2 and a little more. Since two twos are *four*, our answer must be slightly more than 4. Neither 625., nor 62.5, nor .625 is slightly more than 4. Only 6.25 is slightly more than 4.

3. Multiply 3.75 by 5.3.

3.75
5.3
—
1 125
18 75
—
19.875

We first multiply as though we were multiplying whole numbers. We notice that our answer has to be in the neighborhood of 15, since we are multiplying 3 and a little more by 5 and a little more. Or we notice that we are multiplying *hundredths* by *tenths*, which gives *thousandths*. So we make our answer show *thousandths*. 19.875 must be the correct answer, since it is in the neighborhood of 15, and since it shows *thousandths*.

We can by *reasoning* or *thinking* always decide just where to place the point in our answer. In Examples 1, 2, and 3 we have *reasoned* out just where to place the point in the answer in each case. We *know* that our answers are correct. Now let us look at these examples and see whether we can *find the rule*.

In Example 1, count the places to the right of the decimal point in both multiplier and multiplicand together. There are *two* places to the right in both. Count the places to the right of the point in the answer. There are *two* places to the right of the point in the product. How do they compare?

Do the same in Example 2. You find *two* places to the right of the point in the product, and *two* places to the right of the point in the multiplier and the multiplicand taken together.

Do the same in Example 3. How many places to the right of the point in the multiplier and the multiplicand? How many places to the right of the point in the product?

Rule: *In multiplying decimals, first multiply as you do with whole numbers. Next, point off in the product as many places as there are decimal places in both multiplier and multiplicand taken together.*

4. The Division of Decimals

If the pupil has learned to divide tens, hundreds, etc., 'just like units,' by relying upon the position in which the various partial answers are written to aid in thinking, he will have no difficulty in learning to divide decimals. He proceeds, first, to divide decimals by whole numbers, and, next, to divide decimals by decimals. In the latter divisions, he may profit by the former if in each case he changes the divisor to a whole number. Such change in the divisor means that it has been multiplied by ten or by a power of ten, which requires that the dividend must be multiplied by the same number. Since the multiplications require nothing more than 'moving the point to the right' the required number of places, he will encounter no difficulty on that score. If, as he proceeds, he is conscious of what is required and of the purpose of each step of procedure, he will quickly learn to bring to bear upon this 'new' task the ideas and procedures he learned in previous lessons. The following paragraphs will illustrate some of the outstanding stages of procedure that may be presented.

Teaching the Division of a Decimal by a Whole Number

In dividing a decimal by a whole number, all one needs to do is to place each part of the answer *in its proper place*. One divides exactly as he would when dividing a whole number by a whole number. If he is careful about *position, position* will take care of the answer for him.

1. Divide 52.75 by 25. **2.** Divide 5.275 by 25. **3.** Divide .5275 by 25.

Notice how these three examples are worked:

1.	**2.**	**3.**
2.11	.211	.0211
25)52.75	25)5.275	25).5275
50	5 0	50
27	27	27
25	25	25
25	25	25
25	25	25

In each example, notice the position of each part of the answer. Notice that the point in each answer is just above the point in the dividend. Notice in the answer in Example 3 that we have to write a zero in *tenth's* place to hold that place. In Example 1, how many 25's in 52.75? Is the answer 2.11 a reasonable one? Would the answers .211 or 21.1 be reasonable? In Example 2, how many 25's in 5.2 (that is, 52 *tenths*)? Is .2 reasonable for the first quotient answer? In Example 3, how many 25's in 52 *hundredths*? Is 2 *hundredths* (that is, .02) reasonable for the first quotient answer?

Teaching Division by Decimals

In dividing *by a decimal*, since you already know how to divide by a whole number, it is a good plan right at the start to make the decimal in the divisor a whole number. This you can do by moving the point the required number of places to the right. When the point is moved to the right, it is the same as multiplying by 10, or 100, or 1000, etc., as the case may be. So, if you multiply the divisor, you will need to balance things up by multiplying the dividend by the same number. This you can do by moving the point an equal number of places to the right. Now, when you have made the divisor a whole number and moved the point in the dividend accordingly, you can divide as usual.

1. Divide 4.075 by 2.5.   **2.** Divide 4.075 by .25.

3. Divide 4.075 by .025.

Things to do:

(1) Make the divisor a whole number by moving the point to the right. Make a caret ($\wedge$) to show where the point has been moved.

(2) Move the point in the dividend the same number of places to the right. Show by a caret ($\wedge$) where the point has been moved.

(3) Divide as usual.

(4) Place the point in the quotient just above the caret ($\wedge$) in the dividend.

1.	**2.**	**3.**
1 . 63	16 . 3	163 .
2.5$_\wedge$)4.0$_\wedge$75	.25$_\wedge$)4.07$_\wedge$5	.025$_\wedge$)4.075$_\wedge$
2 5	2 5	2 5
1 57	1 57	1 57
1 50	1 50	1 50
75	75	75
75	75	75

Teaching the Adding of Zeros in the Dividend

Adding zeros *to the right of the decimal point* does not change the value of a number. 25.8 is not changed in value when we make it 25.80, or 25.800, or 25.8000, etc. 885. is not changed in value when we make it 885.0, or 885.00, or 885.000, etc. Sometimes we find it convenient to add one or more zeros *to the right of the point* in the dividend in order to complete our division.

1. Divide .885 by .375.

We first make .375 a whole number by moving the point to the right, and next we move the point to the right in the dividend an equal number of places. We now divide. Our first quotient answer is 2.

```
        2 . 36
.375∧).885∧00
        750
        135 0
        112 5
        22 50
        22 50
```

When we multiply and subtract, we have a remainder of 135. But since adding zeros *to the right of the point* does not change the value of a number, we write as many zeros to the right of 885∧ as we need to complete our division. We place the point in the quotient just above the caret (∧) in the dividend, and our answer is 2.36.

2. Divide 1.71 by .54.

```
        3 . 166
.54∧)1.71∧000
        1 62
        9 0
        5 4
        3 60
        3 ' 24
        360
        324
```

We first make .54 a whole number by moving the point to the right, and next we move the point in the dividend an equal number of places. We now divide. Our first quotient answer is 3. When we multiply and subtract, we have a remainder of 9. By adding zeros to the right of the point in the dividend, we can continue our division. In this particular example we could keep on adding zeros in the dividend, and dividing, and still have a remainder. If we wanted our answer to include *hundredths* only, we could divide as we have done until we get our quotient answer for *thousandth's* place, which we note is more than 5. Since it is 6, we would write our answer as 3.17. If we should want our answer to be still more exact by including *thousandths*, we would add another zero in the dividend and find the quotient figure for *ten thousandth's* place. Our answer would be 3.1666, which we would write as 3.167.

3. Divide .1185 by .625.

```
            . 1896
.625∧).118∧5000
        62 5
        56 00
        50 00
        6 000
        5 625
        3750
        3750
```

We change the divisor to a whole number by moving the point to the right, and moving the point in the dividend an equal number of places. In order to complete our division, we add zeros to the right of the point in the dividend. Had we wanted our answer in a decimal of two places — *hundredths* — we would have stopped dividing when we had .189 in the answer, and noticing that the 9 in *thousandth's* place is more than 5, we would have made our answer read .19.

It is seldom necessary to carry an answer beyond *hundredth's* place, since *thousandths* are very small parts. When we want our answer to be extra exact, we carry our work to *ten thousandth's* place, and if the number in that place is less than 5, we strike it off. If it is 5 or more, we drop it and add 1 to the figure we have in *thousandth's* place.

The point to remember is that we can add as many zeros as we need to the right of the point in the dividend.

4. Divide 54.6 by .156.

$$.156_\wedge\overline{)54.600_\wedge}$$

$$\begin{array}{r} 350\ . \\ \hline 46\ 8 \\ \hline 7\ 80 \\ 7\ 80 \\ \hline 0 \end{array}$$

We first change the divisor to a whole number by moving the point to the right. We next move the point in the dividend to the right an equal number of places. In order to do that, we have to add two extra zeros to provide enough places. We now divide as usual, and place the point in the quotient just above the caret in the dividend.

Teaching Fractional Equivalents

Equivalent is a double word. The part *equi* means equal; the part *valent* means value. *Equivalent* means 'of equal value.' Let us find the equivalents of some of the common fractions you have learned to use.

One of the things that you learned about a fraction when you began to study them was that a fraction means *to divide*. $\frac{1}{2}$ shows that 1 has been divided into 2 equal parts; $\frac{1}{4}$ shows that 1 has been divided into 4 equal parts, and so on. When such fractions as $\frac{12}{4}$, $\frac{30}{6}$, $\frac{42}{7}$, etc., are shown, we can find the answer by dividing, thus:

$$\begin{array}{r} 3 \\ 4\overline{)12} \\ 12 \\ \hline \end{array} \qquad \begin{array}{r} 5 \\ 6\overline{)30} \\ 30 \\ \hline \end{array} \qquad \begin{array}{r} 6 \\ 7\overline{)42} \\ 42 \\ \hline \end{array}$$

Now that you have learned how to divide a smaller number, like 3, for example, by a larger number, like 4, for example, by adding zeros to the right of the point in the dividend as they are needed, you are able to find the equivalents of common fractions, like $\frac{1}{2}$, $\frac{1}{4}$, etc., by dividing.

We know that 1 can be written as 1.0, or 1.00, or 1.000; that 3 can be written as 3.0, 3.00, or 3.000, etc. Let us then in dividing

add a point (.) followed by enough zeros to enable us to divide by
the denominator.

$$\frac{1}{2} = 2\overline{)1.0}^{\;.5} \qquad \text{or } 2\overline{)1.00}^{\;.50} \qquad \text{or } 2\overline{)1.000}^{\;.500}$$

$$\begin{array}{c} .5 \\ \frac{1}{2} = 2\overline{)1.0} \\ \underline{1\,0} \end{array} \qquad \begin{array}{c} .50 \\ 2\overline{)1.00} \\ \underline{1\,0} \\ 0 \end{array} \qquad \begin{array}{c} .500 \\ 2\overline{)1.000} \\ \underline{1\,0} \\ 00 \end{array}$$

Thus we divide and find that $\frac{1}{2}$ is the same as .5, or .50, or .500.

Usually we just make the one division, $2\overline{)1.0}^{\;.5}$, to discover that $\frac{1}{2}$
equals .5. If, in using .5 with other decimals, we wish to write it
as *hundredths*, or *thousandths*, we can easily change it by adding
zeros: .50, or .500.

$$\begin{array}{c} .25 \\ \frac{1}{4} = 4\overline{)1.00} \\ \underline{8} \\ 20 \\ \underline{20} \end{array} \qquad \begin{array}{c} .666 \\ \frac{2}{3} = 3\overline{)2.000} \\ \underline{1\,8} \\ 20 \\ \underline{18} \\ 20 \\ \underline{18} \end{array}$$

.67 or .667 or .6667. Each is about
the same as $\frac{2}{3}$. To be exact, we
may write it: $\frac{2}{3} = .66\frac{2}{3}$.

Since $\frac{1}{2}$ is the same as .5 or .50, $\frac{1}{2}$ of a number is the same as
multiplying it by .5 or .50.

$$\begin{array}{c} 48 \\ \underline{.5} \\ 24.0 \end{array} \qquad \frac{1}{2} \text{ of } 48 = 24 \qquad \begin{array}{c} 24 \\ 2\overline{)48} \\ 4 \\ \underline{8} \\ 8 \end{array}$$

Since $\frac{1}{3}$ is the same as .33$\frac{1}{3}$, $\frac{1}{3}$ of a number is the same as multiplying it by .33$\frac{1}{3}$.

$$\begin{array}{c} 48 \\ .33\frac{1}{3} \\ 16 \\ 1\,44 \\ 14\,4 \\ 16.00 \end{array} \qquad \frac{1}{3} \text{ of } 48 = 16 \qquad \begin{array}{c} 16 \\ 3\overline{)48} \\ 3 \\ 18 \\ \underline{18} \end{array}$$

VII. Percentage

1. The Hundredth Part

Immediately following the study of decimals, percentage should be introduced as another way of writing and speaking of the hundredth. Instead of being widely separated from the study of decimals, percentage should be intimately related to decimals. The pupils should be made to feel that they are undertaking nothing new other than the learning of the method of writing and speaking of the decimal fraction — hundredth — commonly used in business and practical affairs.

Percentage is a continuation of fractions. It is a special case of the subject and it may be made to afford excellent practice in enlarging the ideas of fractions and in securing greater facility in using them. The following illustration will serve to show the language change in the transition from fractions to percentage. A man had 700 chickens and sold 1 out of every 2, or 1 out of every 10, or 1 out of every 50, or 1 out of every 100, or 1 out of every 350, how many were sold? The above problem would be classified under the subject of fractions. Since 1 out of 2 was sold, the number sold was $\frac{1}{2}$ of 700; or since 1 out of 10 was sold, the number sold was $\frac{1}{10}$ of 700; or since 1 out of 100 was sold, the number sold was $\frac{1}{100}$ of 700.

If we agree that the word *per* shall mean *out of* when used in this connection, the above statements would be: 1 per 2, or 1 per 10, or 1 per 100. If we substitute the Latin word *decem* for *ten*, our statement becomes 1 *per decem;* if we substitute the Latin word *centum* for *hundred*, our statement becomes, 1 *per centum*. If we abbreviate the word *centum* by cutting off the last two letters we have 1 per cent. We frequently abbreviate words in this way in arithmetic; for example, we write *int.* for *interest*, and *fract.* for *fraction*. Therefore 1 per cent means 1 out of every 100. If a problem involving 1 out of every 100 is properly classified as a problem in fractions, it is certain that a problem involving 1 per cent is also a problem in fractions. Percentage came in as a separate topic about the beginning of the nineteenth century.

The fact that a quantity is measured off into hundredths instead of into any other possible number of parts appears to be no valid reason for considering percentage as a new phase in the development of number.[2]

The following sample materials are included in order to illustrate the introduction of percentage as a special phase of the general topic of fractions.

Teaching the Relation of Percents to Fractions

In your work with fractions, you studied about *parts* of many different sizes, such as *halves, thirds, fourths, fifths, twelfths, sixteenths*, etc. In your work with decimals, you studied about *parts* of only three or four different sizes, such as *tenths, hundredths*, and *thousandths*, and occasionally about *parts* as small as *ten thousandths*. In the work you will now begin, you will have to study about *parts* that are of *one special size* — hundredths.

In your work with *hundredths*, you will have really nothing new to learn about *parts*, since you already have learned in your work with decimals how to add, subtract, multiply, and divide *hundredths*. The only reason why you will now have to make a special study of *hundredths* is that *hundredths* have a special use in business and everyday life. In business and in everyday life *hundredths* are spoken of, written, referred to, and used very commonly, while the other decimals, like *tenths* and *thousandths*, are used only as they relate to, or as they connect with, *hundredths*.

In business and in everyday life *hundredths* are spoken of, written, and referred to as *percent*. (*Percent* is a single term which means *hundredth*. One does not think of the coin 'cent' when he uses the term 'percent.' One does not think of a 'doll' when he uses the term 'dollar.' A cent is a coin. It is called a 'cent' because it is a *hundredth* part of a dollar. *Percent* means *hundredth* when applied to anything. A 'cent' refers to money only. *Percent* refers to the *size* of a *part* of anything that is a *hundredth*. Do not confuse *percent* with dollars and *cents*.)

[2] J. C. Brown and L. D. Coffman. *The Teaching of Arithmetic*. (Row, Peterson and Company, Chicago, 1924), pp. 254–255.

Instead of writing the word 'percent,' the sign % is usually written. Thus 75% is read "75 percent."

Illustrating Common Uses of Percent

1. The children had 100 words to spell in a review lesson. Robert spelled 87 of them. Since he spelled .87 of all the words, he was given a grade of 87%.

2. In his history work last month, Sam did only .8, or .80, as well as he should have done. The teacher gave him a grade of 80% in history.

3. Last month nine-tenths of all the children in the fifth grade were neither absent nor tardy. This was, of course, .90 of them. And so, when the report went in, the fifth grade was mentioned as having 90% of the children neither absent nor tardy.

4. Mr. Simpson bought some cement to use in putting a floor in his garage. When the dealer sent the bill for it, he said he would take 10% off for cash. Mr. Simpson paid cash for the cement, and so his bill was one-tenth, or 10%, less than if he had waited until the next month to pay the bill.

5. The Wright Clothing Store had the following advertisement in the papers: "Summer Suits, 25% off." What was meant was that the price of summer suits had been reduced one-fourth, or .25, or 25%.

6. The College Book Store received a bill from the publishing company for books bought. The bill showed that the Book Store owed $36.78. The bill was marked: "Discount, 20%." This meant that the price charged, $36.78, had been reduced one-fifth, or .20, or 20%.

7. John's brother had to borrow $150 in order to help pay his expenses at college. He agreed to pay 6% of the $150 each year for the use of the money. That is, he agreed to pay .06 of the $150 each year for the use of the money.

8. The Creamery Company tested the milk it was buying, and found that .04 of the milk was butter fat. In keeping a record of the test, the clerk wrote it like this: Butter fat = 4%.

9. 60% of the crowd at a football game were high-school students. This means that .60, or .6, of the crowd were high-school students.

10. Last fall the local high-school football team won 50% of all

games played, tied 30%, and lost 20%. What is meant by the expression 50%? How much is 30%? How much is 20%?

11. James was writing to his mother about his new job. He said, "I try to save 45% of what I am making." He meant that he tried to save .45 of what he made.

12. Mr. Johnson was saving 20% of his salary toward buying a home. That is, he was saving .2, or .20, of his salary toward buying a home.

Changing Percents and Decimals

When one has a problem in *percent*, either in business or in daily life, he finds that the fractional *parts* that he has to use are stated not as a decimal, but as percent. In working the problem, since one has learned how to use decimals, he first changes the percent that is given to a decimal. Sometimes, one wishes to find the answer to a problem in percent. In working the problem, one gets the answer first as a decimal. He then must change the decimal to percent. Let us see how to change each to the other.

(1) *The way to change a percent to a decimal is to drop the percent sign, %, and move the decimal point two places to the left. Annex zeros when necessary.*

$$25\% = .25 \qquad 62.5\% = .625$$
$$60\% = .60 \qquad 37.5\% = .375$$

(2) *The way to change a decimal to a percent is to move the decimal point two places to the right, annex zeros when necessary, and add the sign %.*

$$.14 = 14\% \qquad .95 = 95\%$$
$$.2 = 20\% \qquad .045 = 4.5\%$$

A Table of Equivalents

Sometimes it is helpful in thinking "just how much is 50% of anything?" to think that 50% is the same as $\frac{1}{2}$; in thinking "just how much is 25% of anything?" to think that 25% is the same as $\frac{1}{4}$, and so on.

Here is an important table of *equivalents*. It will be helpful if you learn all of them.

$$50\% = \tfrac{1}{2} \qquad 12\tfrac{1}{2}\% = \tfrac{1}{8} \qquad 40\% = \tfrac{2}{5} \qquad 8\tfrac{1}{3}\% = \tfrac{1}{12}$$

$$33\tfrac{1}{3}\% = \tfrac{1}{3} \qquad 37\tfrac{1}{2}\% = \tfrac{3}{8} \qquad 60\% = \tfrac{3}{5} \qquad 6\tfrac{1}{4}\% = \tfrac{1}{16}$$

$$66\tfrac{2}{3}\% = \tfrac{2}{3} \qquad 62\tfrac{1}{2}\% = \tfrac{5}{8} \qquad 80\% = \tfrac{4}{5} \qquad 5\% = \tfrac{1}{20}$$

$$25\% = \tfrac{1}{4} \qquad 87\tfrac{1}{2}\% = \tfrac{7}{8} \qquad 16\tfrac{2}{3}\% = \tfrac{1}{6} \qquad 4\% = \tfrac{1}{25}$$

$$75\% = \tfrac{3}{4} \qquad 20\% = \tfrac{1}{5} \qquad 83\tfrac{1}{3}\% = \tfrac{5}{6} \qquad 2\% = \tfrac{1}{50}$$

CHAPTER XVIII

THE THREE KINDS OF PROBLEMS

ARGUMENT

1. The three kinds of problems provide a new and a more productive means of studying the relations between numbers than do earlier activities.

2. They appear again and again in fractions, in decimals, in percentage, and in the practical applications of percentage.

3. Each kind of problem should be studied separately. Later, each should be studied in its relations to the other two.

4. The second kind of problem performs a special function as a means of comparing two numbers. The other two kinds give illustration of contrasting ways of stating comparisons.

5. Learning to deal with the three kinds of problems is in the main the learning of distinctions, including practice in looking for and making such distinctions.

6. Special practice should be provided in looking for and noticing the relations between numbers.

I. METHODS OF STUDYING RELATIONS

The systematic study of parts begins with a consideration of the part in its relation to the whole, and gradually leads to the ability to deal with each fractional expression and its corresponding idea of the part as an independent item with characteristics of its own. Beginning with the concrete, the pupil proceeds to the abstract. Through the comparing of one part with another and through the use of fractions in his various computations, the pupil learns to neglect, temporarily at least, the relations with particular wholes and to concentrate upon the various ways the given part (of anything or of nothing in particular) may be handled. By such means the pupil acquires familiarity with the fraction and with the rules that govern its use. By dealing with it as an independent abstraction, he acquires facility in dealing with it as it may be applied to anything and everything.

The relational idea of the fraction is, however, never completely lost. The necessity of giving attention to the size of the part enforces attention upon relations. Moreover, the practical applications that the pupil is called upon to make from time to time call attention to relations. In the midst of, or immediately following, his study of each of the three ways of dealing with parts — namely, common fractions, decimals, and percentage — the pupil is introduced to the applications that are commonly called "the three kinds of problems." These are:

(1) Finding the part, or percent, of a number;

(2) Finding what part, or percent, one number is of another;

(3) Finding a number when a part, or percent, of it is given.

The three kinds of problems are called 'problems in fractions' simply for the pupil's convenience. They are in reality methods of studying relations between numbers. They serve to carry the pupil back, after his excursions into the study of parts, to a more complete, as well as a more useful, study of groups than he has heretofore been able to pursue. After learning to deal with the part as an independent abstraction, the pupil receives training by means of the three kinds of problems in dealing with groups upon a higher level than has hitherto been possible without the use of the fractional idea.

II. A Continuation of Earlier Studies

Studying the relations between numbers is no new activity for the pupil. In the first grade he engaged in the comparison of groups; later he analyzed certain larger groups into smaller equal groups and noted the number of smaller groups resulting from the analysis; still later he extended his studies

of equal groups to the finding of how many times one number
is another number. After learning division, he learned to
use the process of division as a means of partition; and, most
recently, the pupil has been learning, through his studies
in fractions, decimals, and percentage, how to manipulate
the machinery of dealing more explicitly with the relations
between numbers. So, when the pupil is introduced to 'the
three kinds of problems,' he is not suddenly thrust into an
entirely new enterprise. He is merely led to undertake more
explicit and more exact studies of matters that have been
his concern from the outset of his studies of groups.

As indicated in Chapter VIII, the three kinds of problems
are often introduced as three different methods of computation, and each upon three separate occasions, so that they
give the appearance of nine separate methods. It is to be
expected that the so-called 'problems' will appear at first as
ways of finding answers, but if each is considered in its relations and contrasts with the others, each will help the others
to develop an understanding of relationship between numbers. Moreover, if the attempt is made to recall what the
pupil already knows about the relations between numbers as
means of introducing the new ways of studying relations,
the new ways will appear less and less as methods of computation and more and more as different ways of looking at
number relations and speaking about them.

III. THE EARLIER PRESENTATION

The earlier presentation of 'the three kinds of problems'
follows the study of common fractions and is made for the
purpose of introducing the various methods of computation
required in the three solutions. The later presentations,
made in connection with decimals and percentage, and
designed to give larger opportunity for the use of the methods
of computation, are especially useful in making them more
understandable through comparisons and contrasts. Although comparison and contrast between the three problems

are important from the beginning, not a great deal can be undertaken until the pupils develop an understanding of the method of performance that belongs with each kind of problem. Thus, at the outset each problem must be considered pretty much as a special one; later each problem is considered in its relation to the others.

In connection with their work in the multiplication of fractions, the pupils have learned about the 'problems of the first kind,' for example:

Find $\frac{2}{5}$ of 25.

A yard of dress goods costs $1.60. How much will $\frac{3}{4}$ of a yard cost?

All the pupils need is to classify the kind of multiplication indicated under its appropriate designation. They can quickly proceed to 'problems of the second kind,' which may be presented somewhat as follows:

Presenting Problems of the Second Kind: Finding What Part One Number Is of Another Number

The purpose of this kind of a problem is to compare one number with another, or to see how one number is related to another. In this kind of problem, one wishes to find out what part a smaller number is of a larger one.

Let us compare 5 with 15; that is, see how 5 is related to 15, or find what part 5 is of 15.

A smaller number, like 5, must always be a *fractional part* of a larger number, like 15. It cannot be 3 *times* 15, or 2 times 15, or 1 times 15; it must be a *part* of 15, since it is smaller. Therefore, one should remember that when the question, "what part?" is asked, the answer must be expressed, not as a whole number, but as a fraction. Since *part* means *fraction*, the question, "what part?" suggests that the answer wanted is a fraction.

The question may be asked either way, as follows:

1. 5 is *what part* of 15?
2. *What part* of 15 is 5?   *What part* suggests that the answer
3. *What part* is 5 of 15?   is a fraction.

We already know that $\frac{1}{3}$ of 15 is 5, and from that we know that 5 is $\frac{1}{3}$ of 15. Let us see how we can fix the numbers 5 and 15 to show $\frac{1}{3}$. This is the way.

When such a question as 1, 2, or 3 is asked, we find the answer by *dividing the smaller number by the larger*. Since a fraction shows division, and since we have not yet learned to divide a smaller number by a larger one, we show 5 divided by 15 as a fraction, thus $\frac{5}{15}$.

The fraction $\frac{5}{15}$, when reduced, is $\frac{1}{3}$.

In the presentation of the 'third kind' of problems, enough of contrast must be made with those of the 'first kind' for the pupil to distinguish the difference. For example, in the problem:

"James solved 12 of his problems, which was $\frac{2}{5}$ of all he had been assigned to solve. How many had he been assigned?"

the pupil must be able to note that the statement does not tell him to find $\frac{2}{5}$ of 12, but gives him an entirely different kind of direction. When the pupil has discovered the fact that a different requirement is made in the type of problem indicated, he may be led to an understanding of the method of procedure. The method is illustrated herewith.

Presenting Problems of the Third Kind: Finding a Number When a Fractional Part of It Is Given

1. James had been assigned a number of arithmetic problems to solve. This afternoon he solved 12 of them, which was $\frac{2}{5}$ of all he had been assigned to solve. How many problems had he been assigned?

Notice what the problem tells: James' problems were in 5 parts. He solved 2 parts of all his problems, or 12 problems.

Notice how it may be solved:

If 2 parts of all the problems = 12 problems,
then 1 part of all the problems = $\frac{1}{2}$ of 12, or 6 problems,
and 5 parts, or all the problems = 5×6, or 30 problems.

2. Edith had just finished reading 240 pages of her book. She said, "I have finished reading about $\frac{3}{4}$ of the book." If that is so, about how many pages are there in the entire book?

If 3 parts of the entire book = 240 pages,
then 1 part of the entire book = $\frac{1}{3}$ of 240, or 80 pages,
and 4 parts, or the entire book = 4 × 80, or 320 pages.

3. Helen was looking at a new dress that cost $12.60. She thought, "If I buy this, it will take $\frac{2}{3}$ of all the money I have." How much money had she?

If 2 parts of Helen's money = $12.60,
then 1 part of Helen's money = $\frac{1}{2}$ of $12.60, or $6.30,
and 3 parts, or all Helen's money = 3 × $6.30, or $18.90.

4. $\frac{1}{5}$ of a certain number is 14. Find the number.

1 part of the number = 14,
5 parts of the number = 5 × 14 = 70.

5. $\frac{3}{8}$ of a certain number is 36. Find the number.

If 3 parts of the number = 36,
then 1 part of the number = $\frac{1}{3}$ of 36, or 12,
and 8 parts, or all the number = 8 × 12, or 96.

Whenever you have given the fractional part of a number, you can always find the number by *thinking it out* as you have just been shown and as you have been doing.

There is a shorter way of finding the number when a fractional part of it is given that does not require so much thinking or so much writing. It is the *method of division*.

Turn back to Problem 1, and read it. Notice how it may be solved:

$$12 \div \tfrac{2}{5} = \overset{6}{\cancel{12}} \times \tfrac{5}{\cancel{2}} = 30$$

Read Problem 2, and notice:

$$240 \div \tfrac{2}{3} = \overset{120}{\cancel{240}} \times \tfrac{3}{\cancel{2}} = 360$$

Read Problem 3, and notice:

$$\$12.60 \div \tfrac{2}{3} = \overset{6.30}{\cancel{\$12.60}} \times \tfrac{3}{\cancel{2}} = \$18.90$$

Notice Example 4:

$$14 \div \tfrac{1}{5} = 14 \times \tfrac{5}{1} = 70$$

Notice Example 5:

$$36 \div \tfrac{3}{8} = \overset{12}{\cancel{36}} \times \tfrac{8}{3} = 96$$

Following the presentation of the three kinds of problems, as indicated above, the pupil should be given ample practice with each kind separately and with all three kinds together. The outcomes of the presentation and the practice should be (1) the ability to distinguish the difference between the first and third kinds of problems, (2) the understanding of the method of division used in solving the third kind, and (3) the ability to indicate one number as the fractional part of another. The abilities and the understanding indicated will not be fully developed, and the pupil will need help and guidance in making the necessary distinctions. He will receive, however, a type of preparation for a continuation of similar studies and for the extended studies of the same three kinds of problems in connection with decimals and percentage.

IV. LATER PRESENTATIONS

In the later presentations the pupil has the benefit of having learned the methods of performance required in problems of the first and third kinds, as well as of having learned the method of completing the indicated division when one number is stated as the fractional part of another. The methods of performance need first to be reviewed so that the pupil may proceed with these at his command to the comparisons and contrasts that are necessary to bring him to an independent mastery of all three kinds of problems. The methods suggested in what follows may be used in connection with the three kinds of problems in decimals and percentage. The contrast between the first and the third kinds will help to bring each to the level of clear understanding, and the comparisons undertaken in connection with the second kind will help the pupil to avoid such confusion as often results when he needs to find what percent a larger number is of a smaller one and attempts a solution by dividing the smaller by the larger, as is usually required. The pupil should be made aware from the outset of each presentation that he is undertaking to study the same three kinds of problems he studied in the earlier presentations.

Teaching the Comparing of Numbers

The methods of comparing any two numbers are *subtraction* and *division*. When one wishes to find out 'how much more' or 'how much less' one number is than another, he uses *subtraction*. When one wishes to find out 'what part of' or 'how many times' one number is another, he uses *division*.

The *second kind* of fraction (or decimal) problem that you have just been learning uses *division* to find what part one number is of another. In this kind of problem you were comparing a *smaller* number with a *larger* one to find what part the *smaller* is of the *larger*.

A very similar kind of comparison is made when one compares a *larger* number with a *smaller* one. The question to be answered is 'how many times' the *smaller* is the *larger*. The method is to divide the *larger* by the *smaller*.

In these two kinds of comparison problems the method is *division*. In both kinds the *number being compared*, or *being asked about*, is put *in the numerator* to be divided. In both kinds the *number* which goes in the blank when the question is asked, 'what part of ——?' or 'how many times ——?' is put *in the denominator*, to be used as the divisor.

When the question 'what part of' is asked, the answer is a fraction, or a decimal. When the question 'how many times' is asked, the answer is a whole number or a mixed number.

Let us compare a smaller number with a larger one.

1. 6 is what part of 15?

$$\frac{6}{15} = \frac{2}{5} \qquad\qquad \text{or} \qquad \frac{6}{15} = 15\overline{)\begin{array}{c}.4\\6.0\\6\ 0\end{array}}$$

The answer is a fraction, $\frac{2}{5}$, or a decimal, .4, depending on the kind of answer one wants.

Let us compare a larger number with a smaller one.

2. 15 is how many times 6?

$$\frac{15}{6} = 6)\overline{15}^{\,2\frac{1}{2}} \qquad \text{or} \qquad \frac{15}{6} = 6)\overline{15.0}^{\,2.5}$$

$$\begin{array}{r} 2\frac{1}{2} \\ \frac{15}{6} = 6)\overline{15} \\ 12 \\ \hline \frac{3}{6} = \frac{1}{2} \end{array} \qquad \text{or} \qquad \begin{array}{r} 2.5 \\ \frac{15}{6} = 6)\overline{15.0} \\ 12 \\ \hline 3\ 0 \\ 3\ 0 \end{array}$$

In the solving of many kinds of problems in arithmetic it is often very convenient and useful to compare one number with another; that is, to find *what part* or *what per cent* one number is of another or to find *how many times* one number equals the other. The method of comparison that is used in either case is the *method of division.*

It often happens, however, when the numbers are large and the relation between them is difficult to see, that one is a little confused as to which number to use in the divisor and which one to use in the dividend. There is a rule, which you have had a good deal of practice in using, that always works, and that, if one follows it, always helps one out of his confusion. This is the rule:

In comparing one number with another one, always place the number being compared in the dividend.

1. 6 is what part of 24? The question asks about 6; so we put 6 in the dividend, and get the answer we desire:

$$\frac{6}{24} = \frac{1}{4} \qquad \text{or} \qquad \begin{array}{r} .25 \\ 24)\overline{6.00} \\ 4\ 8 \\ \hline 1\ 20 \\ 1\ 20 \end{array}$$

2. How many times 6 is 24? The question asks about 24; so we put 24 in the dividend, and find that 24 is 4 times 6:

$$\begin{array}{r} 4 \\ 6)\overline{24} \\ 24 \end{array}$$

3. What percent of 140 is 112? The question asks about 112; so we put 112 in the dividend:

$$
\begin{array}{r}
.80,\text{ or }80\% \\
140\overline{)112.00} \\
112\,0 \\
\hline
0
\end{array}
$$

4. What percent of 112 is 140? The question asks about 140; so we put 140 in the dividend:

$$
\begin{array}{r}
1.25,\text{ or }125\% \\
112\overline{)140.00} \\
112 \\
\hline
28\,0 \\
22\,4 \\
\hline
5\,60 \\
5\,60
\end{array}
$$

In Example 1, we compare *6* with 24.
In Example 2, we compare *24* with 6.
In Example 3, we compare *112* with 140.
In Example 4, we compare *140* with 112.

In working any example or problem in which two numbers are to be compared by division, always ask yourself one of these questions: (1) "About which number does the question ask?" (2) "Which number is the one being compared with the other?"

Teaching the Solution of Mixed Problems

Let us compare the three kinds of problems in percent:

1. Bettie has 96 books all her own in her library at home. 75% of them are storybooks. How many storybooks does Bettie have? (First kind)

2. Bettie has 96 books all her own in her library at home. 72 of them are storybooks. What percent of all Bettie's books are storybooks? (Second kind)

3. Bettie has 72 storybooks in her library at home. This is 75% of all the books in her library. How many books does Bettie have in her library? (Third kind)

In Problems 1 and 3, a percent and a number are given, and you are asked to *find the other number*. In Problem 2, two numbers are given, and you are asked to *find the percent*. It will be easy, therefore, to note the difference between a problem like Problem 2 and a problem like either of the others, and to recognize a problem like Problem 2. In Problem 2 you are asked to find out about the 72 storybooks; 72 is the number being asked about. In any problem like Problem 2, *one must put the number being asked about in the dividend*. In any problem, when two numbers are given and you are asked to find the percent, always ask yourself first of all, "About which of the two numbers is the question being asked?" Then you will know which one goes in the dividend.

Problems 1 and 3 are easy to tell from Problem 2, but sometimes they are not so easy to tell one from the other. In each a number and a percent are given, and in each you are asked to find the other number. You know, of course, that in Problem 1 the other number is found by *multiplying by the percent*, and in Problem 3 the other number is found by *dividing by the percent*. Let us see how to tell Problem 1 from Problem 3.

Notice in Problem 1 that it says "75% of them" (meaning the 96 books) of a number *that is given*, and in Problem 3 that it says "75% of all the books," which is of a number *that is not given*, but is to be found. If you can see this difference between Problem 1 and Problem 3, you can make your rules for solving these problems and all others like them:

Rule: When a percent is given of a number that is given, *multiply* by the percent. (First kind)

Rule: When a percent is given of a number that is not given, *divide* by the percent. (Third kind)

Rule: When two numbers are given to find the percent, put the number being asked about in the dividend. (Second kind)

Notice how we follow these rules in working Problems 1, 2 and 3:

Problem 1	*Problem 2*	*Problem 3*
96	.75, or 75%	96 .
.75	96)72.00	.75$_\wedge$)72.00$_\wedge$
4 80	67 2	67 5
67 2	4 80	4 50
72.0̸0̸	4 80	4 50

In the practice exercises that follow the presentations, the 'problems' should be presented in mixed order, so that the pupil will be required, when he comes to each one, to distinguish its characteristics and to decide upon its kind. Very beneficial practice may be had in the requirement that, when the pupil has solved a problem of a given kind, he should use all the facts at hand and turn it into a problem of each of the other two kinds.   The general directions given the pupil for attacking the practice exercises should be such as to aid him in making distinctions.   They may take the form illustrated below.   They should be supplemented by the teacher according to the pupils' needs.

Illustrative Problems

These problems with percent are not all alike. Some are problems of the first kind, some are problems of the second kind, and some are problems of the third kind. Read each problem carefully, so that you will know *exactly* what it tells you to do.   When a percent and a number are given, and you are asked to find another number, look at the percent and decide whether the percent is of the number that is given or of the number that is not given, but to be found.   When two numbers are given, and you are asked to find the percent, look at the numbers and decide which of them the problem is asking about or asking you to find out about.

1. There are 24,600 books in the city library.   Of these, 2952 are books on history and biography.   What percent of the books in the library are books on history and biography?

2. In a certain school library there are 13,500 books.   Of these, 55% are storybooks.   How many storybooks are there in this school library?

3. Farmer Brown has found that about 80% of the apples he picks from the trees are good apples.   He has just received an order from a city merchant for 40 bushels of good apples.   How many bushels will he have to pick from the trees to get enough to fill the order?

Which is a problem of the first kind?   Which is one of the second kind?   Which is one of the third kind?

V. FURTHER PRACTICE IN STUDYING RELATIONS

Following the training and practice in finding the numbers when the relations are expressed, either as a part or as a percent, and in stating the relation when the numbers are given, the pupil should be given some training and practice in determining relations between numbers when the relations need not be explicitly stated. This is training and practice in 'seeing' relations, and understanding and using them without going to the trouble of undertaking their statement and without running into the danger of being distracted by the necessity of giving them explicit statement. Such is training and practice in ratio and proportion without resort to the formal language that is frequently used to state ratio and proportion. It is further practice in studying relations, which was begun in earlier grades. The method is illustrated below.

Teaching Pupils to See Relations in Problems

It often happens, in solving certain kinds of problems, that a comparison between two of the numbers that are given is very helpful. Usually, however, when such a comparison is helpful, the problem itself neither tells you what the comparison is nor asks you to find the comparison. Usually the problem leaves you to ask the question yourself and to find the answer for yourself. Of course, in every case the comparison between the two numbers is there for one to see, if he can see it, but he has to *read between the lines* to see it.

1. If 2 oranges cost 5¢, how much will 20 oranges cost?

One may, of course, *read between the lines* and make the problem into two problems, as follows:

1a. If 2 oranges cost 5¢, how much will 1 orange cost?
1b. If 1 orange costs 2½¢, how much will 20 oranges cost?

This is a good way to *read between the lines*, but there is another way that is often easier. It will be easier in this problem in *reading between the lines* to notice the relation between 20 and 2, making the problem into two problems, as follows:

1a. 20 is how many times 2? Now you can make the second part of the problem read:

1b. If a certain number of oranges cost 5¢, how much will 10 times that number cost?

Here are the two solutions of Problem 1:

Solution I	*Solution II*
Finding the cost of one	Seeing the relation between numbers

$$\begin{array}{r} 2\tfrac{1}{2} \\ 2\overline{)5} \end{array} \qquad \begin{array}{r} 2\tfrac{1}{2}¢ \\ 20 \\ \hline 40 \\ 10 \\ \hline 50¢ \end{array} \qquad\qquad \begin{array}{r} 10 \\ 2\overline{)20} \end{array} \qquad \begin{array}{r} 5¢ \\ 10 \\ \hline 50¢ \end{array}$$

In many problems Solution II is the easier. Often you can do most of Solution II 'in your head.'

2. If bananas are selling at 30¢ a dozen, how many can be bought for 5¢?

Solution I	*Solution II*

$$\begin{array}{r} 2\tfrac{1}{2} \\ 12\overline{)30} \\ 24 \\ \hline 6 \\ \hline 12 \end{array} = \tfrac{1}{2}$$

$$5 \div 2\tfrac{1}{2} =$$
$$5 \div \tfrac{5}{2} =$$
$$5 \times \tfrac{2}{5} = 2$$

$$\tfrac{5}{30} = \tfrac{1}{6}$$
$$\tfrac{1}{6} \text{ of } 12 = 2$$

Often one does not need pencil and paper, if he can just see the relation between the numbers. In solving Problem 2, one could think the solution to himself, like this: 5¢ is $\tfrac{1}{6}$ of 30¢; $\tfrac{1}{6}$ of 12 is 2.

3. Last week Mrs. Jones bought $2\tfrac{1}{2}$ yards of muslin for 90¢. Now she thinks she can use 10 yards more. How much will the 10 yards cost?

Ask yourself, 10 is how many times $2\tfrac{1}{2}$? If you can *see* that 10 is 4 times $2\tfrac{1}{2}$, you can easily find the answer by multiplying 90¢ by 4.

4. If the price of lemons is 40¢ a dozen, how much will 3 lemons cost?

Ask yourself, 3 is what part of 12? If you can *see* that 3 is $\tfrac{1}{4}$ of a dozen, you can easily find the answer.

5. If crayon pencils sell 3 for 10¢, how much will an assortment of 24 cost?

Ask yourself, 24 is how many times 3?   If you can *see* the relation between 24 and 3, you can easily multiply and get the answer.

6. Mrs. Stewart remembered that when she made her last meat loaf the $1\frac{3}{4}$ pounds of beef she used cost 56¢.   She now wishes to make a larger one, and needs to buy $3\frac{1}{2}$ pounds of beef.   How much will the $3\frac{1}{2}$ pounds of beef cost?

Ask yourself, $3\frac{1}{2}$ is how many times $1\frac{3}{4}$?

In the pupil's earlier work in studying relations, he was directed by the questions of the teacher and of the book, as "What part or percent of 24 is 6?"   "How many times 5 is 35?" etc.   In the exercises just presented the pupil is required to answer the same kinds of questions; but instead of being asked by the teacher or book, the questions are asked by the situations with which he has to deal.   However practical or impractical the situations may be, they serve the very practical purpose of enforcing upon the pupil the necessity of looking for the questions indicated as an independent activity.   Such situations serve to transfer the practice upon the 'second kind of problems' to a higher level.

CHAPTER XIX

THE APPLICATIONS OF PERCENTAGE

ARGUMENT

1. There are many situations in which the idea of percent is an element that the pupil should study.

2. Such situations involve other elements that are unknown to the uninitiated. To learn the situations, such other elements must become familiar.

3. Such other elements do not illustrate or apply percentage; an understanding of percentage helps to make the other elements understandable.

4. To view such situations merely as means of developing or applying computational ability is to miss their real worth.

5. Each situation should be studied as a matter of importance in its own right.

6. The idea of percent is helpful both in making a given situation understandable and in establishing relations between various situations that otherwise are not related.

7. Lesson materials are offered to illustrate:
   (a) The method of studying the various elements of a given situation;
   (b) The way the idea of percent, as represented in the 'three kinds of problems,' may be used to relate and classify otherwise diverse situations.

I. THE STUDY OF SITUATIONS

From the activities set up for the purpose of developing an understanding of percentage as the expression of relations between quantities, the pupil proceeds to the study of the personal, practical, and human situations of life in which the form of percentage is used as a means of expression and the idea of percentage is used as a means of comprehension. Such situations are not the familiar ones of the pupil's everyday experiences. Though he has lived in the midst of them and though the currents of his life have been determined by the way the adult world has learned to use them, they have hitherto gone unrecognized by him. Sooner or later, however, he must be made conscious of such situations because the influences they exert upon his manner of life change more and more from the indirect to the direct. He must be made to look ahead a bit and to take a larger view of the world in which he has been living and in which he is going to live.

The situations to which reference has been made provide 'applications' of what the pupil has been learning about percentage. They serve to enlarge his ideas about percentage and to reveal to him something of its practical importance and use in the larger world around him. They are the situations that have come into being and that are constantly handled and solved, through the borrowing and lending of money, the investment of savings, the insurance of property against destruction and theft, the insurance of one's dependents against lack of support, the determination of reasonable profit in the buying and selling of goods, the payment for services in business transactions in proportion to the money value of the services rendered, the levying of taxes for the support of government, and the like. They apply percentage in the ways they are developed and handled in the affairs of life.

The 'applications' of percentage must not be thought of, however, as taking place automatically and as reacting upon the individual without his intelligent, active coöperation. Though they affect his life whether he is intelligent about them or not, he is not the master of his actions in the midst of their influences upon him if he does not have an intelligent understanding of them; and to gain such understanding, he must study their operations and attack the questions they raise. Having learned percentage, which is a characteristic of all these situations, or an idea of relations that makes them intelligible, or a method of statement that serves to describe them, the pupil is ready to proceed to a study of the other characteristics of the various applications that are intimately related to the idea of percentage and stated in the language of percentage. These 'other characteristics' are not at first mere illustrations of percentage; indeed, they cannot serve as illustrations of anything until they are known. They are, rather, activities of the larger life surrounding the pupil in which he has not as yet been engaging. His introduction to these other characteristics is facilitated by his knowledge and understanding of percentage, which is intimately a part of all of them.

II. Computational Ability versus Understanding

The 'applications of percentage' are frequently presented as methods of finding answers to the 'problems' they serve to classify. Having learned to compute in terms of percents, the pupil is shown how answers are computed, first in this 'application,' then in that one. It seems as if those who follow this type of teaching believe that the pupil will be called upon to spend his days figuring interest on notes, determining the amount of discount on bills, computing the premiums on his fire and life insurance policies, finding the tax levy, and summing up the tax forms.

The truth of the matter is that one very rarely has to figure the interest on a note, or determine the amount of discount, or compute the premiums upon insurance policies, or decide exactly what the tax levy shall be. All such computations are made for one by the companies, firms, associations, and levying bodies with which one deals; and the computations are made in accordance with tables and charts prepared for such purposes. It is true, of course, that in one's personal and business budgeting he must be able to determine costs in advance or to check the correctness of various kinds of bills presented to him for payment; but such computations and such checking present little difficulty so far as the computational and checking processes are concerned. All one needs to do in such matters is to employ the four fundamental processes with decimals. The essence of the total procedure, however, is *understanding*, for without understanding one is unable to determine what computations are required.

The situations to which reference has been made involve a great deal more than mere computation. They involve the ability to detect hidden issues, to seek them out, and to weigh them; the sense to suspend judgment until all necessary facts have been taken into account; and the power to make decisions. They constantly surround the adult in his personal, civic, and business life, and in one way or another they enforce their demands upon him. Their external features are presented by one's friends, by one's business associates, and by various civic and political organizations. Shall one buy for cash or buy on the installment plan? Shall one carry this kind of insurance or that? Shall one leave his savings in the bank or buy a bond? Shall one cast his vote for this plan of tax revision or for some other plan? Is it cheaper, more convenient, and more satisfactory to rent a house or to buy one? These and many other similar questions confront the adult — or rather, are presented through various channels for his consideration — and often their attractive features are emphasized and played up in the presentation. The adult must be able, while his attention is caught by the attractive features, to recognize that a given situation possesses also certain other, less attractive features; and he must seek them out and weigh all together. In short, the adult must understand the situations in question if he is to be intelligently discriminative about their values.

So, if the pupil is to be instructed in the ways of the larger world into which he must eventually enter, he must be led to consider more than certain rule-of-thumb methods of finding the answers to particular questions; he must be led to study the situations that his previous training has prepared him to study.

If the topic is insurance, for example, the pupil must be led to study the topic, not as a matter solely of number operations, but as a matter of human interest and of intense personal concern as well. What insurance is, why one insures his life or his property, the advantages and obligations of insurance, insurance as a business, insurance as a matter of mutual benefit, both to the company and to the insured, the kinds of insurance and the purpose of each, policies, premiums, and the like are all topics for study and discussion until the personal, human, and business aspects of insurance are understood as well as the ordinary individual who buys insurance needs to understand them. The procedure needed is not merely one of acquiring information; the pupil must gain a view of insurance as a great coöperative enterprise in which he is reimbursed for his losses in turn for his share of the expenses of reimbursing others for their losses. He must gain the view of insurance as a business arrangement of individuals through the medium of a company of qualified officers and directors, in which the obligations and benefits of all are pretty evenly balanced.

Similarly, if the topic is interest, the pupil must become informed of the needs of individuals and of business firms for the use of ready money, of the risks of lenders, of the obligations of borrowers, of the advantages the borrowers gain, of provisions for safety and security, of the similarity between using another's money and using another's property, of the methods of reimbursing the lender for the use of his money, and of like matters. How interest is computed is a matter of secondary concern; but what interest is, why it is charged and paid, the situation that involves it, and the people involved in it are the matters of first importance.

Again, if the topic is taxation, the pupil will need to develop a view of the government as a money-spending organization that pays out money for services rendered the people; or of the people paying through the agency of government for services they desire and need. He must gain a view of the people paying for what they get and getting, it is assumed, what they pay for. He must contrast the benefits of the right kinds and right amounts of services with the disadvantages of the wrong kinds and of too much or too little service. He must consider the variations in benefits of different kinds of service to different persons and the variations in amounts paid by different persons to their government for services rendered. He must contrast the conditions that render taxation a benefit with those that render taxation a burden. In short, the study of taxation is a study of the operations of government, not of rule-of-thumb methods of computation.

III. RELATING THE SITUATIONS

As the pupil is brought to the study of each of the situations to which reference has been made, he must attack it as a separate undertaking. Around each situation are a number of experiences, activities, and connections that are in a sense peculiar to it alone. All these must be studied in their relations to the given situation and distinguished from those that relate to other situations. Later, when the pupil gains a larger view of the adult world and of the work of the world, he will gain the insight that will enable him to bring all these separate situations into a single scheme of thinking. For the present, however, he must be content to study first one, then another, learning each as best he can, and developing such relations as are possible as he proceeds from one to another. Or, it may be pointed out, as the pupil gains an understanding of the different situations, he will receive the training in certain of his subjects other than arithmetic that will enable him to relate the different situations, as they really belong together, into a single pattern.

Though an understanding of the relations between the

situations is in the main a later development, the pupil need not be compelled to wait; he is at the moment in possession of an idea of number relations that will enable him, as he moves along, to bring the various situations together into certain understandable relations. The various situations may be held together in thought, for the time being at least, and until later studies provide better methods, by the method of referring each situation to the appropriate one of the 'three kinds of problems.' The common idea of percentage runs through all the situations to which we have been referring, and this common idea may be made to stand out with sufficient clearness, when each situation is studied, to bring them all together in thought. With the common idea in clear consciousness, the pupil may observe how the individual, in one situation after another, employs the common idea as a means of handling his personal, business, and civic affairs. For example, the pupil may view the use of one aspect of the common idea in the situation of paying for the use of money, the use of a second aspect in determining the value of an investment, and the use of a third aspect in the manner of accounting profit as a percent of the selling price. As the pupil proceeds, he gains new illustrations of his general idea of percentage, and his general idea suggests a method of attack upon each situation as he comes to it.

IV. ILLUSTRATIVE LESSONS ON APPLICATIONS OF PERCENTAGE

Our exposition emphasizes two points to be observed in guiding pupils in the study of the applications of percentage:

First, lead the pupils to study a situation as a matter of importance in its own right. Help them to view the situation from various angles. Let them observe the situation as an affair of life, as a matter of human interest and of personal, business, or civic concern.

Second, help the pupils to employ their idea of percentage as much as possible in interpreting each situation by itself and to bring the various situations under the common bond of the idea of number relations that runs through them all.

The first point is illustrated in the following suggested method of presenting the subject of interest. The discussion of interest there is by no means complete. Enough is presented, however, to call attention to the fact that the subject of interest in arithmetic involves a good deal more than mastering certain methods of computation. The material may give some hint also of the manner of helping the pupil to refer to his well-known 'three kinds of problems' in the study of a situation.

A Lesson on Renting Property

When a person needs the *use* of something he does not own and it is not convenient or advisable for him to buy it, he may *rent* the use of it from someone who has it to rent. When one arranges to *rent* a thing, he agrees to *pay for its use*. Houses, apartments, storerooms, offices, cars, garages, and many other things are *rented* by persons who do not own them, but need to use them. The money they pay for the use of a thing is called *rent*.

The amount of rent that is charged is determined in part by the value of the property that is rented.

1. Mr. Law, Mr. Black, and Mr. Hooper live side by side in rented houses on a certain street in our town. Mr. Law lives in a 6-room frame house and pays $40 a month rent. Mr. Black lives in a 6-room brick house and pays $50 a month rent. Mr. Hooper lives in a larger 7-room brick house and pays $65 a month rent. Why are the three men charged different amounts for rent?

2. Mr. Greenburg, who owns the U-Drive-It Automobile Company, rents the use of cars by the day to anyone who may need them. Among the cars he rents is a second-hand one that cost $200, one that he bought new for $675, and a more expensive one that cost $950. Do you think that he charges the same rent for each of these three cars? Why?

Find out the different rents that are charged for houses, stores, garages, etc., in your neighborhood. See if you can tell why different rents are charged.

The amount of rent that is charged is determined in part by the risk the owner takes when he rents the property.

1. Mr. Greenburg charges $5 a day rent for the automobile that cost $675. On the rear of the lot where he lives is a double frame garage that cost about $700 to build. For the two stalls in this garage he gets $8 a month rent, which is about 27¢ a day. Why does he charge so much more rent for the car?

2. Near the Iota Iron Works is a small one-story frame building. Mr. Reeser wants to rent it to use as a restaurant, and Mr. Keeney wants to rent it for a small grocery store. If Mr. Reeser gets it, he will, of course, fit up the back part as a kitchen and put in a large stove for cooking. The owner will rent it to Mr. Reeser for $40 a month, or to Mr. Keeney for $35 a month. Do you think the owner is doing right to ask different rents for the same building? Why?

3. Mr. Wilson owned a vacant house that he was trying to rent. Mr. Good and Mr. Blank both had looked the house over, but neither had decided to ask to rent it. Mr. Good had the reputation of taking good care of the houses where he had lived and of paying his rent promptly. Mr. Blank had the reputation of being careless about the way he looked after the houses where he had lived and of not being prompt in paying his rent. Mr. Wilson decided if Mr. Good wanted the house, to charge $30 a month rent, but if Mr. Blank wanted it, to charge $40 a month. Why?

What things determine the amount of rent one should receive? Do not forget them: the *value* of the property and the *risk* the owner takes in renting it.

A Lesson on Renting Money

When a person works and makes money and saves part of it, he can use what he has saved to buy property of some kind that he can either use himself or rent to someone else. Or, if he does not buy property with the money he has saved, he can keep the money for his own use. But, if he does not have any use for his money at the time, he can 'rent' it to someone else who may need to use it. The one to whom money is rented pays for the use of it just the same as a person to whom a house is rented pays for the use of the house.

Money that is paid for the use of property is called *rent*.

Money that is paid for the use of money is called *interest*.

The amount of interest that is charged is determined in part by the value (amount) of the money that is loaned or borrowed.

1. Mr. Wilson borrowed $250 from his insurance company. At the end of one year he paid back $265. The insurance company charged $15 for the use of the $250 for one year, or $15 interest.

2. Henry borrowed $150 from his uncle to finish his last year in college. At the end of a year he paid back $159. The amount of interest paid for the use of $150 was $9.

3. A business firm had to borrow $10,000 in order to enlarge its store. The firm had to pay $600 a year interest for the use of the money.

4. At the end of a year the firm paid back $5000 of the $10,000 loan. For the use of the remaining $5000 for another year the interest charge was $300.

The amount of interest that is charged is determined in part by the length of time the money is used when borrowed.

1. On several occasions the Atwood Wholesale Company has had to borrow money to use in running the business. At one time the company borrowed $5000 for 1 year. The interest that had to be paid was $300. At another time the company borrowed the same amount for $1\frac{1}{2}$ years. This time the interest that had to be paid was $450. At another time the company needed to use $5000 for 6 months. The interest this time was $150. Once the company borrowed $5000 for 3 months and paid $75 interest.

2. If the interest that is charged for $750 for 1 year is $45, how much interest should be charged for 2 years? For $2\frac{1}{2}$ years? For $1\frac{1}{4}$ years? For 6 months? For 1 month? For 4 months?

3. If the rent for a house is $480 for 1 year, how much is the rent for 2 years? For $2\frac{1}{2}$ years? For $1\frac{1}{4}$ years? For 6 months? For 1 month? For 4 months?

A Lesson on the Rate of Interest

The amount of interest that is charged is determined in part by the rate of interest.

Rate of interest means the percent of the whole amount that is loaned, or borrowed, for one year. It is usually spoken of, or described, as "interest at so many percent." Thus, if the *rate of interest* is 6% for 1 year, the *rate* is spoken of, or described, as "interest at 6%," or "at 6% interest." "Interest at $3\frac{1}{2}$%" means a *rate* of $3\frac{1}{2}$% a year. "Interest at 5" means a *rate* of 5% a year, and so on.

1. Kelton Farley needed $300 to help pay his expenses during his last year in college. He learned that the college would lend him the money from the Students' Loan Fund at 6% interest. He thought that it might be 2 or 3 years before he could pay back the money. How much interest would he have to pay each year?

This is the way to answer the question:

$300	The amount he wanted to borrow
.06	The rate of interest
$18.00	The amount of interest for 1 year

2. Suppose Kelton had borrowed the money from the Students' Loan Fund, and had paid it back at the end of $2\frac{1}{2}$ years. How much interest would he have had to pay for that length of time?

$300	The amount borrowed
.06	The rate of interest
$18.00	The amount of interest for 1 year
$2\frac{1}{2}$	The time the money was borrowed
9 00	
36 00	
$45.00	The amount of interest for $2\frac{1}{2}$ years

3. Kelton's uncle learned that Kelton needed some money and offered to lend him the $300 at 4% interest. Kelton decided to borrow the money from his uncle. He paid back the money at the end of 2 years. How much interest did he have to pay?

Notice how the problem is worked:

$$\begin{array}{r} \$300 \\ .04 \\ \hline \$12.00 \\ 2 \\ \hline \$24.00 \end{array}$$

Remember that "at 6% interest," "or interest at 6%" means 6% for 1 year; "at 5% interest" means 5% for 1 year; and so on.

4. A college chum of Kelton's borrowed $850 at 5% interest and kept the money for $3\frac{1}{2}$ years. How much interest did Kelton's chum have to pay?

<table>
<tr><td align="center">(1)</td><td align="center">(2)</td></tr>
<tr><td>Find the interest for 1 year</td><td>Find the interest for the whole time</td></tr>
</table>

(1) Find the interest for 1 year

$850
.05
‾‾‾‾‾‾
$42.50

(2) Find the interest for the whole time

$42.50
$3\frac{1}{2}$
‾‾‾‾‾‾
21 25
127 50
‾‾‾‾‾‾
$148.75

Kelton's chum had to pay $148.75 interest for the use of $850 for $3\frac{1}{2}$ years.

(1) Find the interest for 1 year by multiplying by the percent.

(2) Find the interest for the whole time by multiplying by the number of years.

A Lesson on Short Loans

Usually, when money is borrowed for personal or business use, it is borrowed for periods shorter than a year — sometimes for 30 days (1 month), sometimes for 60 days (2 months), sometimes for 90 days (3 months), sometimes for 4, 5, or 6 months, and so on.

1. Mr. Brown, the grocer, had just bought a supply of groceries. By paying for them within 10 days, he can get them a little cheaper. But his customers will not be paying their bills before the end of the month, and he does not have enough money now to pay for the supply of groceries. He is especially anxious to pay cash for his supply of groceries, so that he can get them a little cheaper than usual. In order to pay for his supply of groceries now, he may borrow some money for 30 days, and by that time his customers will have paid him enough on their bills to pay back what he needs to borrow.

2. Mr. Jenkins owns an orchard. In August, he wishes to buy some baskets and barrels for the fruit he will pack for sale. During the early fall he will have to hire several persons to help him pick and pack the fruit. By November, he expects to have his fruit, at least most of it, marketed. But he does not have enough ready money in August to pay for the baskets and barrels and for the help he must hire, and he does not expect to collect much pay for the fruit he will sell until the middle of October. He may borrow enough money in August, to be paid back in 3 months, to see him through.

3. Mr. Warth, who is a contractor and builder, tries to be prompt about paying for the materials he has to buy, and he has to pay the men who work for him regularly each week. He is building a school for the Board of Education. He knows that the Board will not pay for the remainder they will owe him, until the building is finished two months from now. But he needs $12,500 now to pay his bills for materials and labor. What can he do? He may borrow $12,500 for 3 months, and by that time he can pay back what he has to borrow with part of the money the Board of Education will pay him for finishing the work on the schoolhouse.

4. Mr. Hall had some extra household expenses; so he borrowed some money from his insurance company. He thus was able to pay for his extra household expenses at once. He was able at the end of 8 months to pay back the money he had to borrow.

5. Mr. Brown borrowed $750 for 1 month at 6% interest. How much did the interest cost him?

$$\begin{array}{r} \$3.75 \\ \hline 12)\$45.00 \\ 36 \\ \hline 9\,0 \\ 8\,4 \\ \hline 60 \\ 60 \end{array}$$

interest for $\frac{1}{12}$ of a year, or 1 month

$750
.06
$45.00 interest for 1 year

6. Mr. Jenkins borrowed $1250 for 3 months at 6% interest. How much interest did he have to pay?

$$\begin{array}{r} \$18.75 \\ \hline 4)\$75.00 \\ 4 \\ \hline 35 \\ 32 \\ \hline 3\,0 \\ 2\,8 \\ \hline 20 \\ 20 \end{array}$$

interest for $\frac{1}{4}$ of a year, or 3 months

$ 1250
.06
$75.00 interest for 1 year

A Lesson on Lending Money and Investing Mo

Whenever the owner of a house rents the use of it
else, he tries to make sure that the renter will take good ca...
He wishes not only to be paid rent for the use of the house, but
also to have the house kept in good condition. Likewise, whenever
the owner of some money rents the use of it (lends it) to someone
else, he always tries to make sure that the renter of the money
(the borrower) will take good care of it. He wishes not only to be
paid interest for the use of the money, but also to have all the
money paid back to him. As the owner of a house wishes to rent
it to one who is reliable; so the owner of money wishes to lend it
to one who is reliable. But unless a person is in the business of
lending money, he cannot always be sure about who is reliable and
who is not. So, instead of *lending* money to anyone who may
want to borrow it, one usually finds that it is safer and more convenient to *invest* his money in some good and reliable business.

Investing money is very much the same as lending money. In
both cases one *rents the use* of his money to someone else. However, one goes about *investing* in a different way, and he *invests*
for a longer period of time. Also, when one *invests*, he has to be
content to take whatever interest the *investment* can pay him; but
when one *lends*, he can charge a reasonable interest.

*The amount of interest that is paid is determined in part by the
risk the owner of the money takes when he invests.*

There are many different kinds of investments. Here are some
examples of common ones:

1. Each week Florence Harvey saves 30¢ of her allowance. She
does not want to keep it in her coin box at home, because she
knows she will be tempted to spend it, and the amount is too
small, she thinks, for a savings account at the bank. And, of
course, it is hardly large enough for anyone in business to want to
borrow it. So each week she buys Postal Savings Stamps at 10¢
each, and pastes them on a card. When she has a card full of 10
stamps, or a dollar's worth, she turns it in at the post office, and a
dollar is added to her Postal Savings account. The United States
Government, through the Post Office, takes care of her money for
her, and in addition pays her 2% each year for the use of it.

2. Willard Crum delivers papers and sells magazines in our neighborhood, and deposits most of the money he makes in a savings account at the bank. The bank takes care of Willard's money for him, and besides pays him 3% interest for the use of it. The bank pays the interest each January 1 and each July 1. Since the interest the bank pays is 3% a year, the interest it pays for 6 months is $1\frac{1}{2}$%.

This is a fine way for Willard to save and *invest* his money. He is sure of getting it when he needs it, and he is paid for the use of it.

3. In order to get money when it is needed for use, states, counties, cities, school districts, railroads, large business firms, and other organizations sell *bonds* that promise to pay various amounts of interest. For example, a state will sell bonds to get money to build roads, a county to get money to build a bridge, a city to pay for street paving, a school district to pay for a new building, a railroad to buy new engines and cars, a large business firm to build a new factory, etc.

Mr. Johnson had $1200 to invest. He decided to buy bonds. At the time he could buy bonds from his state that paid 4% interest, or from a local manufacturing company which paid $5\frac{1}{2}$% interest. Which is better — 4% of $1200, or $5\frac{1}{2}$% of $1200? Mr. Johnson decided to buy the 4% bonds from his state. Why?

4. Sometimes people buy *stock* as an investment. *Stock* means a *share in the business*. When a person buys *stock*, or a share in a business, he gets his share of all the company makes. If the company makes much money, his share of the profits is large; if the company makes only a little, his share amount is small. If the company does not make any profit, the one who has bought stock makes none. If the company fails, the owner of the stock loses what he has invested.

Stock in a reliable, successful company is a good investment, but it is not easy to tell just how reliable a company is or just how successful it will be in the future. It is not advisable for a person who knows but little about business to buy stock.

a. Mr. Wheaton bought $300 worth of stock in a local oil and gas company. For $2\frac{1}{2}$ years the company paid a *dividend* of 20%. (*Dividend* means a share of the profits; it is the same as *interest* for the use of money invested. Do not confuse with the *dividend* one speaks of in division.) How much is 20% of $300 for $2\frac{1}{2}$

years? This was a fine investment, was it not? But at the end of $2\frac{1}{2}$ years, the company failed, and Mr. Wheaton lost the $300 he had invested. Not so good!

b. Mr. Rauden bought $500 worth of stock in a local news company. The *dividend*, or interest on the investment, was 8%. Mr. Rauden received 8% for 3 years. During the fourth and fifth years, he received no dividend, because the company was not making any profits. The sixth year the company failed.

c. Mr. Ruddel bought $2200 worth of stock in a very large company that does business over the whole country. For three years his dividend was $6\frac{1}{2}$%, for two years it was 7%, and now he is getting a dividend each year of 8%. The company has a growing business, and it looks as though the dividends in the future will be larger than 8%. Because the company seems to be such a reliable one, Mr. Ruddel could now sell the stock that cost him $2200 to someone else who had money to invest for $2750.

A Lesson on Finding How Much Interest

Sometimes in making an investment a person knows how much it will cost him and how much the investment will pay him each year, and he wishes to find out *how much interest* he would get on his money if he should make the investment.

1. You remember that Mr. Ruddel, who bought $2200 worth of stock in a good company, was finally getting 8% interest on his investment. Each year Mr. Ruddel was getting 8% of $2200, or $176. Let us suppose that Mr. Smith buys Mr. Ruddel's stock from him for $2750. Mr. Smith will then be getting the same amount of dividend each year from the company for the same shares of stock — $176. (The fact that Mr. Smith buys Mr. Ruddel's shares of stock does not have anything to do with the amount of business the company is doing, and the company, of course, does not raise its dividend just because Mr. Smith pays Mr. Ruddel more for the stock than Mr. Ruddel paid for it.) Mr. Smith has to pay $2750 to get a dividend of $176, and he would like to know just *how much interest* $176 is on $2750. In other words, he would like to know what percent $176 is of $2750.

(When we want to find what percent one number is of another, we put the number asked about in the dividend.)

This is the way he finds out:

$$
\begin{array}{r}
.064, \text{ or } 6.4\% \\
\$2750\overline{)\$176.000} \\
165\ 00 \\
\hline
11\ 000 \\
11\ 000 \\
\hline
\end{array}
$$

So, by buying the stock for $2750 that pays a dividend of $176, Mr. Smith will be making 6.4% interest on his investment.

2. Mr. Jones reads in the paper that he can buy stock in a certain company for $180 a share, and that he would be paid $9 a share in dividends each year by the company. He wants to know what percent interest that would be. In other words, he wants to know what percent $9 is of $180.

$$
\begin{array}{r}
.05, \text{ or } 5\% \\
\$180\overline{)\$9.00} \\
9\ 00 \\
\hline
\end{array}
$$

3. Mr. Johnson paid $1200 for a small share in a certain business. Each year he is paid about $90 as his share of the profits. What percent of interest does he get on his investment?

4. Mr. Davis reads in his newspaper the prices that are being charged for shares of stock in various companies, and the amount of dividend each different share is paying. He makes a little table like the one shown below. He labels each company A, B, and C, and so on, and opposite each he writes the cost of a share of stock and the amount of the dividend that is paid. He next finds the percent of interest each of the different shares will pay. Find the percents for him. (Do not carry the division beyond tenths of percent. Notice how A is worked.)

$$
\begin{array}{r}
.0438 = 4.38\%, \text{ or } 4.4\% \\
\$57\overline{)\$2.5000} \\
2\ 28 \\
\hline
220 \\
171 \\
\hline
490 \\
456 \\
\hline
\end{array}
$$

Company	Amount charged for each share	Dividend paid on each share	Percent interest
A	$57	$2.50	4.4%
B	$167	$7.00	?
C	$98	$5.00	?
D	$36	$2.00	?
E	$124	$6.00	?

5. Suppose all of the companies are good, reliable companies. Which one offers the best investment? Why?

6. Suppose Mr. Davis had $1250 to invest. How many shares of stock can he buy in the company that offers the best investment?

7. Suppose Mr. Davis does not know anything about any of the companies. Should he invest in any one of them? Why?

8. Suppose Mr. Davis knows that Companies A, B, and C are good, reliable companies, and that he cannot be sure about the rest. Which company offers the best investment? Why? How many shares of stock can he buy with his $1250 in this company?

A Lesson on the Value of an Investment

What a thing is worth is not always the same as what it costs. Sometimes a thing is worth more than it costs; sometimes it is worth less; but usually the value and the cost are just about the same.

The value, or the worth, of a thing is shown by the service it gives. The pair of shoes or the suit of clothes that wears well and gives good service is worth more than the one that wears out quickly even though the price may be no higher. The automobile tire that gives the greatest service has the greatest value. If two investments are equally safe, the one that brings the higher percent of interest has the higher value.

Often a person is mistaken about the value of a thing because the cost of it is high. Mr. Rader had been buying a certain brand of shoes for $6.50 a pair and was very well satisfied with them. Last fall he liked the looks of another brand that was being sold for $9.00 a pair. He thought he would try a pair of them. Since they cost more than the ones he had been wearing, he thought they surely were worth more. When he bought a pair and wore them, he found that they wore no longer and gave no better service than the $6.50 kind he had been wearing. Did he find that the $9.00 shoes were worth more than the $6.50 shoes? Why?

Henry Smith is a traveling salesman. He drives his car to call on his customers in different towns in the state, and he keeps account of all of his expenses. He has used three kinds of tires on his car. One kind cost him $5.50 each; another cost him $6.98 each; and a third kind cost him $9.00 each. The following table shows how he compared the costs and the values of the three kinds of tires:

Kind of tire	Cost	Miles of service before replaced
First kind	$5.50 each	10,000 miles
Second kind	$6.98 each	4,000 miles
Third kind	$9.00 each	14,000 miles

Which kind of tire was worth least?

Which kind had the greatest value?

Does the cost of a thing give any idea of its value?

Does the cost tell exactly what the value is?

Sometimes when a person tries to buy a thing the owner will ask a price that is more than the thing is worth. The person who wants to do the buying has to keep in mind that the price of a thing does not always tell exactly what the value is. Sometimes when a person has money to invest, the owner of the property, or of the stock, or of the bonds will ask a price that is more than the value. The person who has money to invest must remember that the price of an investment does not always tell exactly what the value of the investment is.

How does a person tell the value of an investment? He must think not so much about the *cost* of it as about the *service* it ought to give. Now, as you know, the *service* that an investment gives is the interest, or dividends, it brings the owner each year. If this service is less than it ought to be, the value of the investment is lower than the price of it. If this service is more than one should reasonably expect, the value is higher than the price. The question that one has to ask is: How much interest, or dividends, should one reasonably expect when he invests? Or, what percent of interest, or dividends, is reasonable?

1. Mr. Bloom knows of an investment that pays $75 a year in dividends. He believes that this kind of an investment ought to pay 6%. In other words, he thinks that the dividend of $75 is 6% of the value of the investment. What is the value of this investment?

Notice: When a percent (6%) is given of a number (value of investment) that is *not given*, divide by the percent.

$$
\begin{array}{r}
\$12\ 50\,.\\
.06_\wedge\overline{)\$75.00_\wedge}\\
\end{array}
$$

6	Mr. Bloom figures that this investment
$\overline{15}$	would be worth $1250 to him.
12	
$\overline{3\ 0}$	
3\ 0	
$\overline{0}$	

2. Mr. Hendrickson is thinking about buying a house to rent. That is, he wishes to buy a house as an investment. He believes that the rent one gets each year should be 10% of what the house is worth. The house he is thinking of buying rents for $35 a month, or $420 a year. How much does Mr. Hendrickson figure he can pay for the house?

According to the way Mr. Hendrickson figures it, the $420 yearly rent is 10% of the value of the house, or of what he can afford to pay. Thus, he figures that the value of the house is $4200, and that he can afford to pay $4200 for it, and no more.

$$
\begin{array}{r}
\$4200\,.\\
.10_\wedge\overline{)\$420.00_\wedge}\\
\underline{40}\\
20\\
\underline{20}\\
00
\end{array}
$$

3. Mr. Jones reads in his paper that he can buy stock in a certain well-known company for $195 a share. He is interested, not only in what the stock costs a share, but also in *what it is worth* a share. He knows that the company pays $8 a share dividends each year. Mr. Jones figures that he should get 5% interest for money invested in the stock of this company. What is a share of this stock worth to Mr. Jones?

Pay attention, not to the cost, but to the value.

Notice: The $8 a share is 5% of what Mr. Jones thinks the stock is worth to him. He figures that the stock is worth $160 a share, and that the price of $195 a share is too high.

$$
\begin{array}{r}
\$1\,60. \\
.05_{\wedge}\,)\overline{\$8.00_{\wedge}} \\
5 \\
\hline
3\,0 \\
3\,0 \\
\hline
0
\end{array}
$$

4. Below are given the costs and the yearly dividends of some investments. Figuring the yearly dividend in each case as 6% of the value of the investment, find the values of the investments. Pay no attention to the cost in finding the value. Pay attention to the service in finding the value. When you have found the value of an investment, compare it with the cost, and tell whether or not the investment is a bargain.

Cost of Investment	Yearly Dividend	Value	Is it a bargain? Yes or No
a. $24 a share	$1.50 a share	?	?
b. $105 a share	$5.50 a share	?	?
c. $43 a share	$3.00 a share	?	?
d. $195 a share	$8.00 a share	?	?
e. $50 a share	$3.50 a share	?	?

5. Copy the costs and the yearly dividends in another table, and find the answers to the questions if the dividend in each case is thought to be 5% of the value.

6. Find the answers if the dividend in each case is thought to be 7% of the value.

7. A small apartment house is for sale, and can be bought for $30,000. The six families who live in the apartments pay rents that amount to $3600 a year. Figuring the yearly rents as 10% of the value of the apartment, what is the value? Do you think that the price of $30,000 is too high?

V. Illustrative Lessons on the Three Kinds of Problems

How pupils may be aided in employing their ideas of the three kinds of problems is illustrated in the following suggested material. It will be observed that pupils have to learn something more than methods of procedure. The material serves also to illustrate the fact that the situation must be studied until the ability to note distinctions, or to choose between various possible modes of procedure, has been developed.

Explaining the Use of Percents in the Three Kinds of Problems

Sometimes a person knows the cost of a thing, and the percent of gain or loss, and wants to find the selling price. Or he knows the former number, and the percent of increase or decrease, and wants to find the present number. In such a case he has a 'problem of the first kind.'

Sometimes he knows the cost and the selling price, and wants to find the percent of gain or loss. Or he knows the former number and the present number, and wants to find the percent of increase or decrease. In such a case he has a 'problem of the second kind.'

Sometimes he knows the selling price and the percent of gain or loss, and wants to find the cost. Or he knows the present number, and the percent of increase or decrease, and wants to find the former number. In such a case he has a 'problem of the third kind.'

There are just three kinds of problems in gain or loss in which percents are used. These "three kinds" are the same three kinds that you learned to work with in fractions, decimals, and percents. Remember how each is worked:

First kind: When a percent is given of a number that is given, multiply by the percent.

Second kind: When two numbers are given and you are asked to find the percent, place the number being asked about in the dividend.

Third kind: When a percent is given of a number that is not given, divide by the percent.

A Lesson on Problems of the First Kind

1. A druggist bought some hot-water bottles at a cost of $1.80 each. He sold them so as to gain 35%. At what price did he sell them?

This is a two-step problem. First we must find how much gain the druggist made on each bottle; then we must add this gain to the cost of each to find the price at which each was sold. The "35% gain" means 35% of the cost.

$1.80 $1.80 cost
 .35   .63 gain
────   ──────
 900          $2.43 selling price
540
──────
$.6300 gain

Or we can think and solve the problem this way: Cost is 100% of the cost; gain is 35% of the cost. Cost and gain added give the selling price. So the selling price is 135% of the cost.

$1.80   100%
 1.35 (1.35 is the same as 135%)   35%
────   ────
 900   135%
540
1 80   This is the 'short way.' Think, "Gain of 35%
────
$2.4300   makes selling price 135% of cost."

2. The Horace Mann School was built to take care of 500 pupils. Last summer it was enlarged so that it could take care of 25% more pupils. How many pupils will it now take care of?

"25% more" means an increase of 25% of 500.

500	500	former number
.25	125	increase
25 00	625	present number
100 0		
125.00		

Or we may solve the problem the 'short way' by thinking, "25% more makes the present number 125% of the former number," and finding 125% of 500:

$$
\begin{array}{r}
500 \\
1.25 \\
\hline
25\ 00 \\
100\ 0 \\
500 \\
\hline
625.00
\end{array}
$$

3. After the fire at the clothing store a quantity of clothing that cost $840 was sold at a loss of 65%. How much did the store get for the clothing?

This is a two-step problem. First we must find how much the clothing store lost on the sale of goods, then we must subtract the amount that was lost from the cost to find the selling price. "Loss of 65%" means 65% of the cost.

$840	$840	cost
.65	546	loss
42 00	$294	selling price
504 0		
$546.00	Cost − Loss = Selling Price	

Or we can think and solve the problem this way: Cost is 100% of the cost; loss is 65% of the cost. The loss subtracted from the cost gives the selling price. So the selling price is 35% of the cost.

$840	100%
.35	65%
42 00	35%
252 0	This is the short way. Think, "Loss of 65%
$294.00	makes the selling price 35% of the cost."

4. The population of a certain town was 3240 in 1920. In 1930 the population had decreased 25%. What was the population of the town in 1930?

The decrease of 25% means 25% of the former number.

A Lesson on Problems of the Second Kind

1. A grocer bought apples at $1.60 a bushel and sold them at $2.00 a bushel. What percent of the cost did he gain?

In this problem we have two things to do. First we must find how much was gained on a bushel; then we must find what percent this gain is of the cost of a bushel.

The first question is, "How much was the gain?" This is the way we find it:

$$\text{Selling price} - \text{Cost} = \text{Gain}$$

$$\begin{array}{ll} \$2.00 & \text{selling price} \\ \underline{1.60} & \text{cost} \\ \$\ .40 & \text{gain} \end{array}$$

The next question is, "What percent of the cost ($1.60) is the gain ($.40)?"

$$\begin{array}{r} .25,\ \text{or}\ 25\% \\ 1.60_{\wedge})\overline{.40_{\wedge}00} \\ \underline{32\ 0} \\ 8\ 00 \\ \underline{8\ 00} \end{array}$$

Or we can solve the problem this way: First find what percent the selling price is of the cost, and then subtract 100% of the cost to find the percent gained.

$$\begin{array}{r} 1\ .\ 25,\ \text{or}\ 125\% \\ 1.60_{\wedge})\overline{2.00_{\wedge}00} \\ \underline{1.60} \\ 40\ 0 \\ \underline{32\ 0} \\ 8\ 00 \\ \underline{8\ 00} \end{array}$$

Thus we find that the selling price is 125% of the cost. The cost, we know, is 100% of itself. So the gain is:

$$\text{Selling price} - \text{Cost} = \text{Gain}$$
$$125\% - 100\% = 25\%$$

Which of the two ways of solving the problem is the easier?

2. Last year the enrollment at the Jefferson School was 432. This year the enrollment is 486. What is the percent of increase?

Notice the two ways of solving the problem:

$$
\begin{array}{r}
486 \\
432 \\
\hline
54 \text{ increase}
\end{array}
\qquad
\begin{array}{r}
.125, \text{ or } 12.5\% \\
432\overline{)54.000} \\
43\ 2 \\
\hline
10\ 80 \\
8\ 64 \\
\hline
2\ 160 \\
2\ 160 \\
\hline
\end{array}
$$

The increase (54) is 12.5% of last year's enrollment (432).

$$
\begin{array}{r}
1.125, \text{ or } 112.5\% \\
432\overline{)486.000} \\
432 \\
\hline
54\ 0 \\
43\ 2 \\
\hline
10\ 80 \\
8\ 64 \\
\hline
2\ 160 \\
2\ 160 \\
\hline
\end{array}
$$

Thus we find that this year's enrollment (486) is 112.5% of last year's enrollment (432).

$$
\begin{array}{ll}
112.5\% & \text{present number} \\
100 & \text{former number} \\
\hline
12.5\% & \text{increase}
\end{array}
$$

Which way is the easier?

3. In the latter part of the summer the department store had a number of hats that cost $58.00. The store put on a special sale and sold these hats for $34.80. What percent of the cost did the store lose?

In this problem we have two things to do: First we must find how much the store lost on the hats; then we must find what percent this loss is of the cost of the hats.

The first question is, "How much was the loss?" This is the way we find it.

$$
\text{Cost} - \text{Selling price} = \text{Loss}
$$

$$
\begin{array}{rl}
\$58.00 & \text{cost} \\
34.80 & \text{selling price} \\
\hline
\$23.20 & \text{loss}
\end{array}
$$

The next question is, "What percent of the cost ($58.00) is the loss ($23.20)?"

$$\underline{.40,\ or\ 40\%}$$
$$\$58.\overline{)\$23.20}$$
$$\underline{23\ 2}$$
$$0$$

Or we can solve the problem this way: First find what percent the selling price is of the cost, and then subtract this percent from 100% of the cost to find the percent loss.

$$\underline{.60,\ or\ 60\%}$$
$$\$58.\overline{)\$34.80}$$ Thus we find that the selling price is 60% of the
$$\underline{34\ 8}$$ cost. The cost, we know is 100% of itself, so the
$$0$$ loss is:

Cost − Selling price = Loss
100% − 60% = 40%

Which way of solving the problem is the easier?

4. Last year Mr. Johnson raised 1072 bushels of corn. On account of the dry weather this year he raised only 670 bushels. What was the percent of decrease?

Notice the two ways of solving the problem:

```
1072                    .375, or 37.5%
 670           1072)402.000
 402 decrease       321 6
                     80 40
                     75 04
                      5 360
                      5 360
```

```
        .625, or 62.5%
1072)670.000
      643 2              100.0%
       26 80              62.5
       21 44              37.5%
        5 360
        5 360
```

Which way is the easier?

A Lesson on Problems of the Third Kind

1. A real estate dealer sold a house for $9600. By selling the house at this price he gained 20% of what the house cost. How much did the house cost?

In working this problem, we must keep in mind that the word 'gain' is an important one. The 20% gain is not 20% of $9600, but is 20% of the cost. The selling price — $9600 — is not 20% of the cost, because it would then be much less than the cost, and 'gain' means that the selling price is more than the cost. The $9600, which is the selling price, is the cost and the gain added; and since the gain is 20% of the cost, the cost and gain added equal 120% of the cost. So $9600 is 120% of the cost, which is *not given*. So, really, the problem tells us that the selling price of $9600 is 120% of the cost. We can now find the cost by following the rule: *When a percent is given of a number that is not given, divide by the percent.*

We think, "Gain of 20% makes selling price 120% of the cost." and find the cost as follows:

$$\begin{array}{r} \$80\;00\;. \\ \overline{1.20_\wedge\,)\$9600.00_\wedge} \\ 960 \\ \overline{0\;00} \end{array}$$

2. The enrollment at State College is 1540. This is an increase of 10% of the enrollment of last year. What was the enrollment last year?

Think, "Increase of 10% makes present number 110% of former number."

$$\begin{array}{r} 14\;00\;. \\ \overline{1.10_\wedge\,)\,1540.00_\wedge} \\ 110 \\ \overline{440} \\ 440 \\ \overline{00} \end{array}$$

3. On account of the drought a farmer had to sell some of his cattle at a loss. He received $1284 for the cattle he sold. This was at a loss of 20% of the cost of the cattle. What was the cost of the cattle the farmer sold?

In working this problem we must keep in mind that the word 'loss' is an important one. The 20% loss is not 20% of $1284, but is 20% of the cost of the cattle that were sold. The selling price, $1284, is not 20% of the cost. The problem states that the selling price, $1284, made the sale a loss. We must keep in mind that the selling price is the cost less the amount lost; that is, 20% of the cost subtracted from the cost, which is 100% − 20%, or 80% of the cost. Now, since we know that $1284 is 80% of the cost, which is *not given*, we can find the cost by *dividing by the percent.*

We think, "Loss of 20% makes selling price 80% of the cost," and solve as follows:

$$
\begin{array}{r}
\$1605. \\
.80_{\wedge}\overline{)\$1284.00_{\wedge}} \\
80 \\
\hline
484 \\
480 \\
\hline
4\ 00 \\
4\ 00 \\
\hline
\end{array}
$$

4. There are 49 members in the high-school band this year. This is a decrease of 12.5% of the number of members in the band last year. How many members were in the band last year?

Think, "Decrease of 12.5% makes the present number 87.5% of the former number."

$$
\begin{array}{r}
56. \\
.875_{\wedge}\overline{)49.000_{\wedge}} \\
43\ 75 \\
\hline
5\ 250 \\
5\ 250 \\
\hline
\end{array}
$$

A Lesson on Figuring Profit on the Selling Price

In the problems you have just been having, the percent of profit was figured on the cost of the goods that were sold. This is the usual way of figuring the profit. Often, however, a merchant or a business firm wishes to figure the profit as a certain percent of the selling price. There is a perfectly good reason for figuring the profit this way. The reason is that at the end of a day's sales — or at the end of a week's or a month's, for that matter — the business man knows just how much money has been taken in for the various sales, and he would like to be able to tell at once just what part, or what percent, of the money taken in he can call his profit. For example, suppose the cash register at the grocery store shows at the end of the day that $176.80 is the amount that has been received for the groceries sold during the day. If the grocer has his business so planned that he can say, "25% of this is profit," he can tell at once just what amount his profit is. He would know, of course, in this case, that $44.20 of the $176.80 is profit. Or, if the week's sales in a clothing store amounts to $1728, let us say, and the owner knows that he can figure his profit as 20% of his sales, he can tell at once just how much his profit has been for the week.

So because of the advantage of being able to tell quickly just how much of the amount of sales is to be considered as profit, merchants and business firms often fix the prices of their goods so that they can figure their profits as a certain percent of the selling price. To do this, they have to know how to fix the price of their goods. Let us find out how they do this.

1. The manager of a clothing store bought some caps for $1.20 each. He wanted to know what price to charge for each cap so that his profit would be 40% of the selling price. What price did he charge for each cap?

Let us help this manager to solve his problem. We will review the problem and see (a) what the manager knows, and (b) what he wants to find out.

(a) What the manager knows:

The *cost* of each cap — $1.20

The percent *profit* he wants to make — 40% of the *selling price*

(b) What the manager wants to find out:

The price to charge — the selling price — for each cap

The problem *does not say* that the selling price is 40% *of the cost*, so we cannot find 40% of $1.20, or 48¢, and use that in any way.

The problem *does not say* that the *cost* is 40% of the selling price; so we cannot divide $1.20 by .40 to get $3.00 as the selling price.

The problem *does say* that the *profit* is to be 40% of the *selling price*. If we knew the profit we could divide it by .40 to find the selling price. But instead of knowing the profit, we know the cost.

Here is one other thing the manager knows:

$$\text{Cost} = \text{Selling price} - \text{Profit}$$

So the manager would think to himself: "The selling price is 100% of itself, and the profit is 40% of the selling price; so the cost must be 60% (100% − 40%) of the selling price. The cost is \$1.20, and this is 60% of the selling price. So the selling price is \$1.20 divided by .60, or \$2.00."

$$
\begin{array}{r}
100\% \\
40 \\
\hline
60\%
\end{array}
\qquad
\begin{array}{r}
\$2. \\
.60_\wedge\overline{)\$1.20_\wedge} \\
1\,20 \\
\hline
\end{array}
$$

If, then, we are to help the manager to solve his problem, we need to know that

$$\text{Cost} = \text{Selling price} - \text{Profit}$$

2. When the profit is 40% of the selling price, the cost is 100% − 40%, or 60% of the selling price.

Fill the blanks:

3. When the profit is 35% of the selling price, the cost is ____% of the selling price.

4. When the profit is 25% of the selling price, the cost is ____% of the selling price.

5. When the profit is 20% of the selling price, the cost is ____% of the selling price.

When a person figures his profit as a certain percent of the selling price, he finds what the selling price of his goods ought to be, as follows:

(1) He subtracts the percent of profit from 100%.

(2) He divides the cost by this percent.

He does these two things because

(*a*) Cost = Selling price − Profit

(*b*) When a percent is given of a number that is not given, one should divide by the percent.

A Lesson on Figuring Profit by Different Methods

Some merchants like to figure their profit as a certain percent of the selling price; others like to figure their profit as a certain percent of the cost. Mr. Bowman and Mr. Henson both sell shoes in our city. They both buy and sell, among others, a certain brand of shoes. They pay the same for these shoes, and they sell them for the same price.

1. Mr. Bowman buys this brand of shoes for $4.80 a pair. He sells these shoes so as to make a profit of 20% of the selling price. How much does he charge for these shoes?

2. Mr. Henson buys this brand of shoes for $4.80 a pair. He sells these shoes so as to make a profit of 25% of the cost. How much does he charge for these shoes?

Notice how the two problems are worked:

Problem 1		*Problem 2*	
100%	$6 .	100%	$4.80
20	.80∧)$4.80∧	25	1.25
80%	4 80	125%	24 00
			96 0
			4 80
			$6.00 ∅∅

Study Problems 1 and 2 carefully, and note how each one is worked. Be sure to notice that in Problem 1 the profit is 20% *of the selling price* and that in Problem 2 the profit is 25% *of the cost.*

In solving the following problems, *note carefully* whether the profit is described as a certain percent of the selling price, or as a certain percent of the cost.

3. A hardware dealer paid $35 for a certain kind of stove. He sold the stove so as to make a profit of 30% of the selling price. How much did he charge for the stove?

4. A furniture dealer bought a certain style of writing desk for $28.20. He sold the desk so as to make a profit of 40% of the cost. How much did he charge for each desk?

5. A grocer bought some canned peaches for $1.76 a dozen cans. He sold them so as to make a profit of 37.5% of the cost. How much did he charge for each dozen cans?

6. Another grocer bought some canned corn for $1.17 a dozen cans. He sold the corn so as to make a profit of 35% of the selling price. How much did he charge for each dozen cans?

Find the selling price in each of the following cases:

	Cost	Profit	Selling price
7.	68¢	25% of the cost	?
8.	$28.00	30% of the selling price	?
9.	$28.00	30% of the cost	?
10.	$1.50	40% of the cost	?
11.	$1.26	40% of the selling price	?
12.	$12.00	25% of the selling price	?

CHAPTER XX

MEASURES AND WEIGHTS

1. The uses and relations of measures and weights are not revealed by their appearances.

2. Number ideas do not depend upon measurement for their development. Ideas of the relations between measures and weights depend upon number ideas.

3. Measures and weights must be studied as situations in which number ideas constitute a major element.

4. The study of the diversity of early measures helps to set off by way of contrast the uniformity of present-day measures.

5. Present-day measures, though exactly related, are characterized by diversity with respect to their uses and the ways they are understood.

6. The course of development of measures and weights may be traced from early diversity to later uniformity.

7. The full meaning of measures in common use is not derived from the study of their common uses, since their common uses do not impress the idea of exactness.

8. The study of relations that exist between common measures is not impressive, because there is no ordered scheme by which such relations may be stated.

9. The study of diversity of early measures illustrates the steps of procedure one must follow in measuring; namely,

    (*a*) Choosing a measure,

    (*b*) Applying the measure.

10. The value of the metric system is not revealed in its everyday uses.

11. The metric system is not merely an exactly related one; its relations are established and stated in the well-ordered and assumedly familiar decimal system. It provides the clearest possible illustration of the relations between measures and weights.

12. A chief difficulty of pupils is explained by the fact that they frequently fail to derive from their study of familiar measures a method of studying those that are not familiar.

13. Lesson material is offered to illustrate how pupils may be made conscious of a method of attack upon the problem of measuring, in their study of linear measure and of the measurement of rectangles.

14. Further material is offered to illustrate the use of the method of attack to make intelligent the measurement of triangles, circles, etc.

15. Measurement may come to mean to the pupil a social institution, a means and a record of man's progress.

16. Measurement will, however, not mean more than the teacher undertakes to have it mean.

Measures and weights may be considered from the standpoints of their place in the curriculum in arithmetic, of their historical development and present characteristics, of the demands they make upon the individual who sets out to understand them, of the difficulties pupils encounter in trying to learn them, of the progress of pupils in dealing with them, and of the influence they exert upon the methods of thinking of the modern world. These various points of view are so intimately interrelated as to make it difficult to give explicit treatment of any one of them. We shall content ourselves with the attempt to touch upon the various points of view and to give attention in passing to their relations, similarities, and mutual interdependencies.

I. The Place of Measures and Weights in the Curriculum

One of the first considerations to take the attention of the teacher who gives thought to measures and weights is their place in the curriculum. Although not logically the first question to be asked about them, yet actually the first one to occur to the teacher, whose major interest is to keep the work of the school moving steadily ahead, is the question: "When shall we begin teaching measures and weights?"

1. A Common False Assumption

For an answer one may turn to textbooks and courses of study. One finds very frequently that the teaching of measures and weights begins in the early part of the primary grades. It is very commonly assumed that, because measures and weights play such a prominent part in the activities of the modern world in which the child who enters school has been living for six years, they of necessity are very familiar to him. For example, the child must certainly have seen and handled pint bottles and quart bottles of milk, the yardstick, the tape measure, and the foot rule; consequently, these all must be well-known instruments. On the basis of the assumption that the relations between the pint and the quart, and between the foot and the yard, are perfectly clear, the school often attempts at the very beginning of number work to recall these relations to the child and to use these assumedly familiar relations as illustrations of the activities of multiplying and dividing by two and three and of the ideas of the half and the third. It appears to be assumed that because the pint bottle and the quart bottle, for example, are concrete objects that may be seen and handled, they may serve as perfectly obvious illustrations of the number relations that the child has to learn in connection with multiplications and divisions. The teacher who labors under such assumptions is frequently very much disturbed when the pupil fails to understand multiplication and division, and appears at the same time to be more confused than helped by the concrete collection of pint and quart bottles that has been used for purposes of demonstration.

Although the pint and quart measures, the yardstick, and the foot rule are all concrete objects, their relations and uses are to be discovered, not in concrete appearances, but in the realm of the abstract. A yardstick to the child is just a

stick. Its use is not obvious, and what it signifies is the outgrowth of a long line of human experiences that are wholly
unfamiliar to the child who merely views the stick. How
the yardstick may be used is really controlled by an idea in
the mind. It is this idea that is unfamiliar in the beginning,
and that must be made to develop before the child can use
the yardstick with intelligence or can be referred to its use as
an illustration of number relations.

2. Historical Development

Although some form of crude measurement must have been
used by primitive peoples from the earliest beginnings of
human development; although measurement and number
experienced a parallel and concurrent development in the
history of human progress; although number may have been
used from the outset to count the crude measures that were
made by early peoples; although measurement and number
must have been intimately related from the beginning, owing
to the fact that the development of the former depended
upon the development of the latter; the fact remains that
number ideas do not depend upon measurement for their
development. When one has learned to count, for example,
he can count his measures if he has any to count; his development of counting may proceed, however, entirely apart from
his development and use of measures. Our present discussions, however inadequate and ineffective they may be, may
be referred to as a very impressive illustration of the fact that
number ideas may develop independently of ideas of measurement. We have proceeded up to the present chapter in this
book, dealing with the development of number ideas in the
history of the race and in the progress of the individual child
through the elementary school, without once having to refer
to the development and use of measures and weights for purposes of illustration.

The teacher who undertakes to illustrate number relations
by reference to measures, even the most commonly used

ones, assumes falsely. He assumes an understanding of measures that the child who has merely seen and handled them cannot possess, and he assumes a dependence of number upon measurement that has never existed.

3. Grade Placement Must Be Determined By Number Development

The relation between number and measurement needs to be clear to the teacher. The pupil can make no progress in his study of measures and weights without number ideas; he can proceed to great lengths in his study of number without any reference whatsoever to measures and weights. The idea of number is not wrapped up in measurement; it may be developed without thought of measurement, and then applied to a thousand things other than measures. Because the idea of number is so unrelated to measurement as well as to other activities; that is, because it is so abstract in its very nature, it may be applied, when developed, to measurement and to anything else with equal ease.

Our discussions of the double purposes of the so-called 'problem-solving' activity give us an answer to the question, "When shall we begin teaching measures and weights?" It has been pointed out that the purpose of problem-solving in the early stages of the learning of arithmetic is to develop an acquaintance with such general ideas as addition, subtraction, multiplication, division, the fraction, etc., through practice in recognizing these ideas as they are made clear in familiar situations; and that the purpose of problem-solving in the later stages of the learning of arithmetic, after the general ideas have become familiar, is to give opportunity to view, through the use of the ideas, new and relatively unfamiliar situations that now may become the subjects of special study. Our earlier discussions called attention to the distinction between the earlier and the later stages of arithmetic in order both to impress the point that the problems of the former period must be presented in situations that are familiar, and to indicate the folly of attempting to teach new situations before the general ideas that apply in them have been acquired. We do not attempt to illustrate the idea of percentage, for example, by reference to the paying of interest on borrowed money, the levying of taxes, the value of an investment, and the like, which are wholly unfamiliar situations before the pupil has studied them; we rather delay the so-called 'applications' until the pupil has learned something about percentage. Likewise, we must not attempt to illustrate such number relations as are expressed in multiplications and divisions by reference to measures and weights whose relations are unknown and not at all evident in their appearances. It is necessary that the study of measures and weights be delayed until the pupil has acquired by other means the ideas of number relations that appear in them and that help to make them understandable and usable.

All this does not mean that the study of measures and weights be delayed until the end of the elementary-school period; there is no intention to suggest that measures and weights must be the last chapter in the pupil's arithmetic. It is the intention, rather, to suggest that the study of measures and weights be delayed until the ideas necessary for their study have been acquired. This means that the early stages of measures and weights may be undertaken when the ideas necessary for their study have been gained, and that the later stages must be postponed until the ideas necessary for their study have had a chance to develop.

II. The Development of Measures and Weights

Our question about the grade placement of measures and weights may be answered in another way if we now turn our attention to the historical development of measures and weights and to the characteristic features of their present state of development.

We find that diversity is the outstanding characteristic of measures and weights in their earlier stages of development, and that comparative uniformity is the characteristic in the later stages. We find, moreover, that uniformity characterizes their present stage of development and that they appear in well-established relations in the situations of modern life. It would appear, then, that the child must come to an understanding of measures and weights as now used — that is, in respect to their uniformity — and that, if there is any parallel between individual development and racial development, the child must be brought to a view of the earlier diversity of measures and weights. Of one thing we can be certain: that is, that uniformity will be understood the better if it is set over in contrast against diversity. The answer, then, with respect to the question of grade placement that is suggested is that discussions of measures and weights must be delayed until the child is prepared through the study of number relations to understand present uniformity and to appreciate earlier diversity.

III. The Diversity of Early Measures

When savage man began to measure, he selected as his instruments of measurement those objects of his possessions that were readily available, and consequently familiar to him, and that appeared to be the most directly applicable to the things to be measured. Thus, the savage used his own body as an instrument of measurement when he was converting the skin of an animal into an article of clothing, or the extension of his arms in drawing the bow when he was shaping the length of an arrow, or his own height or his arm's reach when he was constructing a rude shelter for himself.[1] Short distances, since they applied directly to the use of the feet, were measured in steps or paces, and later, actually by means of the feet; longer distances were measured in terms of so many days' journeys. The lengths of things that were handled were measured in terms of the bodily

[1] See J. Q. Adams. *Report of the Secretary of State upon Weights and Measures* (Gales and Seaton, 1821).

part that seemed to be suggested as the most convenient in-strument — sometimes the span between thumb and middle finger, sometimes the width of the hand, sometimes the length between elbow and tip of finger, sometimes the ex-tension of the arms, and so on.

> Here then is a source of *diversity*, to the standards even of linear measure, flowing from the difference of the relations between man and physical nature. It would be as incon-venient and unnatural to the organization of the human body to measure a bow and arrow for instance, the first furniture of solitary man, by his foot or pace, as to measure the distance of a day's journey, or a morning's walk to the hunting ground, by his arm or hand.[2]

Thus, we see that the first measures used by solitary man for his own individual and personal uses differed among them-selves. There is, to be sure, no noticeable relation between the hand and the pace, or between the span and the step, as instruments of measure; but even where obvious relations exist, as in measures of time, diversity characterizes the early stages of measurement. Early man was cognizant of the difference between night and day, of the appearances of the new moon, and of the changes in the seasons, yet he used these for a long time as separate and unrelated measures of the passage of time. A short time was reckoned in days; a longer time in moons; and a still longer time in so many summers or winters. The relations between the three did not become apparent until society reached the point in its de-velopment where records were kept and made the subject of comparison. Even then man was confused in bringing the three measures into their exact relations, as may be witnessed by the facts that the early Jewish calendars varied the length of the year between the extremes of 353 days and of 385 days, that the number of days in the month is variable, and

---

[2] Adams. *Op. cit.*, p. 7.

that there are thirteen lunar months in the year instead of the twelve that are named on the calendar.

For the measurement of liquids, such containers as were readily available were used. These were either the shell of an egg, the hollowed gourd, or the prepared skin of an animal. Like the pace or the cubit, these measures were at first used for man's individual convenience and varied both among themselves and from person to person. The shell, or skin bottle, of one man was no more closely related to the shell, or skin bottle, of another than were the lengths of their respective paces, cubits, feet, or hands. Diversity as between the same measures of different people was unimportant until people came together into societies and engaged in exchange with one another.

IV. Progress Toward Uniformity

When people began to engage in barter and exchange, it became necessary to bring diverse measures into some semblance of uniformity. It would not do to use the hand's breadth of the large man in buying a string of beads and the hand's breadth of the small man in selling them; and it was not productive of common understanding or fair dealing to use cups or weights of different sizes to measure the commodities being traded. It became necessary to agree upon common measures. In the measuring of one thing against another in an exchange of goods, a common standard had to be selected as a basis. At first this was the grains of the field; later, it was the precious metals, which themselves were measured in terms of grains of the field. Grains of barley, seeds of the rati, carat beans, and the like were used. Later, so many of these grains constituted an ounce, and so many a pound.

The Roman pound consisted of 5204 grains, and each pound was divided into 12 unciae, or ounces. Henry III, in the thirteenth century, decreed that "an English penny, called a sterling, sound and without clipping, shall weigh 32 wheat corris in the midst of the ear; and 20 pennies do make an ounce; and 12 ounces one pound." There is no need of additional evidence to show that the primary unit of weight was a grain, sometimes barley, sometimes rati-seed, sometimes wheat.[3]

Common standards of length were often derived from the person of the chieftain of the group, the foot of the king, for example, being taken as the standard foot for the measurement of length.

. . . . Common standards will then be assumed from the person of some distinguished individual; but accidental circumstance, rather than any law of nature, will determine whether identity or proportion will be the character of their uniformity. If, pursuing the first and original dictate of nature, the cubit should be assumed as the standard of linear measure for the use of the hand, and the pace for the measure of motion, or linear measure upon earth, there will be two units of long measure; one for the measure of matter, and another for the measure of motion. Nor will they be reducible to one; because neither the cubit nor the pace is an aliquot part or a multiple of the other. But, should the discovery have been made, that the *foot* is at once an aliquot part of the pace, for the mensuration of motion, and of the ell and fathom, for the mensuration of matter, the foot will be made the common standard measure for both: and, thenceforth, there will be only one standard unit of long measure, and its uniformity will be that of identity.[4]

Some semblance of relationship between the various measures crept slowly into general usage. For example, old English law gives us the following tables that show the carrying of relationship back to the use of the grain in weighing:

[3] J. C. Brown and L. D. Coffman. *How To Teach Arithmetic* (Row, Peterson and Company, Chicago, 1914), p. 173.
Adams. *Op. cit.*, p. 24.
[4] Adams. *Op. cit.*, p. 11.

32 grains.............. 1 sterling
20 sterlings............ 1 ounce
12 ounces .... 1 pound
 8 pounds............. 1 gallon
 8 gallons............. 1 bushel

3 barley corns (end to end)...... 1 inch
12 inches...................... 1 foot

One can readily note that such relations were more apparent than real, since the grains were used in the one case as a standard of weight, and in the other as a standard of size. One can see how such relations could easily lead into error, for while a gallon of water may weigh 8 pounds, a gallon of some different substance may weigh either more or less than 8 pounds. Later regulations have corrected the errors of earlier relations, either by establishing new and accurate ones, by legislating older ones out of existence, or by distinguishing the confusions of earlier relations by different names.

Thus, by legislation the yard has been defined, first, as 36 of the 39.1393 parts of a second's pendulum, and later, as $\frac{3600}{3937}$ of a meter; the gallon as 231 cubic inches; and the pound as 7,000 of the 252.422 parts of the weight of a cubic inch of distilled water. Thus, the different weights of the ton have been distinguished by the names *long* and *short*. The *long* ton originated in the crude approximation of the hundred-weight. The English *stone* was 14 pounds. The nearest approximation to the hundred-weight in terms of *stones* was 8, or 112 pounds. Since the ton is 20 hundred-weight, it would normally be 2,000 pounds, but, in terms of stones, 2240 pounds. The needs of society for ordered social and economic relations between people have finally expressed themselves through the legislation of government in bringing uniformity out of diversity between the measures and weights in common use. It is now possible to evaluate the measures that are used for diverse purposes in terms of common standards.

V. The Diversity of Present Measures

Although the regulations of government have succeeded in bringing the various measures and weights into clearly stated relationships, and in enforcing strict observance of the established relationships by all tradesmen, great diversity continues to exist with respect to the way the various measures and weights are understood and used. The diversity may be explained in two ways.

In the first place, the various measures are used for different purposes and in different ways. Distance, for example, is measured in miles, and length in feet, yards, or inches. One does not gauge the height of a room or the width of a street as a part of a mile, nor does he speak of the distance between towns in terms of feet. Moreover, the relation between the mile and the foot is hard to grasp. One may note that there are 5,280 feet in a mile, but the number is not very helpful, since it is too large to be readily understood. The number may be used in computations quite as readily as a smaller one, like 528, or 52.8, but when thought of as 5,280 separate feet, the units are too numerous for ready comprehension. One may have fairly definitely in mind the distance of a mile, and may be able readily to estimate short distances, such as 20 feet, 100 feet, 20 yards, and so on; but when he attempts to measure off in his mind 600 yards, let us say, he is helpless until he remembers, or someone suggests to him, that 600 yards is slightly more than one third of a mile. The point is that the two units, the mile and the foot, have separate uses, and are brought into their relations through computations, and through computations only.

Moreover, one learns to use the pound and the gallon for such diverse purposes that he is usually at a loss in estimating the weight of a gallon of water, milk, preserved fruit, etc., until he brings himself to the point of recalling the rhyme, "A pint's a pound, the world around." The ordinary individual is usually somewhat at a loss when he must select from the storage room a half-gallon jar out of a miscellaneous collection. He is not helped by remembering that there are 231 cubic inches in a gallon, and about 115 in a half-gallon. Though pints and pounds, gallons and cubic inches, may be very familiar to the ordinary individual, he will find it a task to estimate with the help of a yardstick whether the iceman has placed 50 pounds of ice in his refrigerator, 35 pounds, or 25 pounds.

In the second place, the diversity of common measures in the mind of the common man is explicable because their relations are expressed in uncommon numbers that are unrelated and difficult to remember. The number system the individual has learned to use is a system of tens. He has learned to translate all quantities and groups into tens and multiples of ten, so that any other set of multiples is relatively difficult to keep in mind. The relations between various measures are neither expressed in multiples of ten, nor regularly in multiples of any other number. One finds the relations between the various units of length expressed by the numbers, 12, 3, $5\frac{1}{2}$, etc.; those between the units of capacity by 2, 8, and 4, and so on; the relation between the cubic inch and the gallon by 231; that between the pound and the cubic foot by $62\frac{1}{2}$; and other relations by other numbers that bear no observable relation to those already mentioned. One may learn the various relations mentioned, and keep them in memory, if he will, but he is always at a loss when he tries to call them out for use, any one in relation to any other, because they do not possess the quality of an ordered series. The quality of an ordered series of numbers was absent from the relations between measures from the beginning of their development, just as it is absent today. The following quotation from Adams is very suggestive:

> The proportions of the human body, and of its members, are in other than decimal numbers. The first unit of measures, for the use of the hand, is the *cubit*, or extent from the tip of the elbow to the end of the middle finger; the motives

for choosing which, are, that it presents more definite termi-
nations at both ends than any of the superior limbs, and
gives a measure easily handled and carried about the person.
By doubling this measure is given the ell, or arm, including
the hand, and half the width of the body, to the middle of the
breast; and, by doubling that, the fathom, or extent from
the extremity of one middle finger to that of the other, with
expanded arms, an exact equivalent to the stature of man, or
extension from the crown of the head to the sole of the foot.
For subdivisions and smaller measures, the span is found
equal to half the cubit, the palm to one-third of the span, and
the finger to one-fourth of the palm. The cubit is thus, for
the mensuration of matter, naturally divided into 24 equal
parts, with subdivisions of which 2, 3, and 4 are the factors;
while, for the mensuration of distance, the foot will be found
at once equal to one-fifth of the pace, and one-sixth of the
fathom.[5]

VI. Learning the Measures and Weights

Some idea of the peculiar difficulties that the pupil encounters in learning the various measures and weights has
been indicated in the foregoing paragraphs. We note that
the task is one of learning measures that in their later development have been brought into exactly defined relations,
but that in their common and everyday uses are entirely
lacking in relations. We note that the measures to be learned
possess both the quality of diversity and the quality of
uniformity, and that in their common and everyday uses
neither quality appears to bring the other to attention; or,
in other words, we note that the pupil may be brought to
give attention to both qualities without being helped in his
study of the one by what he has learned of the other.

For example, the full meaning of the measures in common
use is not derived from the study of their common uses, since
their common uses do not impress the idea of exactness. One
may ask to purchase a pound of butter, a peck of potatoes,

[5] Adams. *Op. cit.*, p. 8.

or a quart of vinegar; but, so far as the thinking of the individual is concerned, he refers to the measures indicated in about the same way as he would to other commonly, but not exactly, understood amounts. His needs would be met quite as well if he asked to purchase a roll of butter, a bag of potatoes, or a bottle of vinegar. The ordinary use of measures does not impress their relations; indeed, it could be pointed out that to learn to use measures in the ordinary way, one would not need to be sent to school to study measures and weights, since the ordinary uses impress themselves sufficiently well. Moreover, the use of a given measure is usually without reference to any other, and its relation to any other need not be considered by the user. Even when the relation between the measures used is their most striking characteristic, it may be readily forgotten, indeed never conceived, under the influence of the superficial demands of their common uses. The use of non-metric measures in metric Europe [6] illustrates in a very impressive way the fact that the relations between measures are not significant for common usage or demanded by it.

The pound is a commonly used measure in the retail markets of Belgium, France, and Germany. The store window and market labels in Germany are lb., and *Pfund* (pound) is employed as the oral designation.

In France the use of the common terms is strictly forbidden, so the pound labels are usually (not always) "$\frac{1}{2}$ Kilo." But the conversation is "la livre" (pound), and if you go into any store or retail market in Paris and ask for a "pound" of apples, or nuts, or meat, you are understood and accommodated. The pound you get is the modified French pound of 500 grams, but it is the old term that persists and forms the basis of thinking. The difference is small. The customary pound contains 453.6 grams.

The makers of the metric scheme designated the *gram* as

[6] G. M. Wilson. "Why non-metric measures in metric Europe?" *Education*, 52: February, 1932, 319–324.

the unit of weight, but later recognized their mistake and changed to the kilogram. But the kilogram does not fit well into customary thinking and convenience in trading. The housewife does not want a kilogram of butter; she wants a pound. The pound is a convenient unit. So the French people, compelled by severe penalties to use metric terms, took the one-half kilogram (note the "$\frac{1}{2}$" please, a common fraction) and called it a "pound."

In the rural districts of France, the *argent*, the old French acre, is still the basis of thinking in land measure, and this after 100 years of compulsion, and 125 years of exclusive teaching of the metric system in the schools.

In Germany the metric scheme has been official and taught in the schools since 1870. But the penalties have not been severe, so the old customary terms are used freely. The market and stores everywhere use the pound. The farmer thinks in acres (*Morgen*) and bushels and uses these terms. He also uses feet, inches, and yards, particularly *feet*, in connection with buildings, bins, farm machinery, gates, fences, etc.[7]

The following conclusions from an article on units of measurement in industry [8] by a writer who appears to be interested only in the common uses of measures illustrate the fact that if the only aim of the study of measures and weights is to teach common uses, they might just as well not be included in the course in arithmetic.

As a result of this study, it is proposed that the following tentative suggestions should have consideration by the committee that determines the curriculum in arithmetic:

1. It is not profitable for children in the elementary grades to spend time committing to memory tables of weights and measures.

2. When one understands the commodity, it is not difficult for him to apply the preferred unit of measurement to that commodity.

[7] Wilson. *Op. cit.*, p. 319.

[8] M. deS. Louth. "Units of measurement in industry." *Education*, 52: February, 1932, 315–318.

3. The teaching of addition, subtraction, multiplication, and division of compound denominate numbers has little, if any, value.

4. Reduction ascending and reduction descending have little value in industry, with the exception of the estimating department, whose personnel consists of highly-trained experts.[9]

The two quotations serve to make impressive the lack of dependence of common usage of weights and measures upon an understanding of their relations. If intelligence about measures is not important and if the ordinary individual is not supposed either to be precise in his own thinking or to understand the precise thinking of the world in which he lives — that is, if common usage is the only matter of importance — he will not need to study the relations between measures. And, it may be added, he will not need to study the common usage of measures, since he can pick that up in the workaday world without difficulty.

VII. The Study of Relations between Measures

The study of the relations between measures that the pupil is frequently called upon to undertake turns out not to be very impressive. One reason is the lack of any ordered scheme into which the various relations may be arranged as they are being learned. Reference has been made to this deficiency in a preceding topic. Another reason is that when the relations are learned, they are taken as a matter of course and often without attempt to grasp their significance. In other words, the pupil is often called upon, when he learns a table of measures, merely to attend to, and to learn, the various expressions of relationship. Thus, for example, he learns the number, $5\frac{1}{2}$, which states the relation between the yard and the rod, and makes use of the number in a variety of computations, without having very clearly in

[9] Louth. *Op. cit.*, p. 318.

mind just how long the yard is and how long the rod is; or he learns that there are 4 quarts in a gallon without any clear conception of the size of either. Foregoing paragraphs have pointed out that common usage does not lead to any great familiarity with the various units of measure. Consequently, when the relation between any two units that have been viewed only in terms of common usage is stated, the relation fails to add to the meaning of the units, simply because the relation, however accurately it may be expressed, between any two vaguely conceived units is itself without meaning.

The matter may be stated in another way. Ordinary usage of measures, as the preceding topic has indicated, can get along very well without any suggestion of relations; and so, any suggestion of relations that may be imposed becomes just so much extra to remember, because it makes no contribution to common usage, which, in a sense, is self-sufficient. Common usage, moreover, employs the various units as diverse units, and being self-sufficient, does not impress the common user with the deficiencies of diversity. Consequently, the significance of any relation that may be imposed upon the learner is lost because there is no place in his scheme of handling measures into which the relation may be fitted. The significance of the relations between measures can hardly be well understood until one begins to appreciate the shortcomings and peculiarities of diverse measures.

VIII. The Study of Diversities

The study of early measures is almost a necessary prelude to the study of present relations. The study, for one thing, makes the pupil conscious of diversity, and, with this consciousness, appreciative of the difficulties of earlier peoples who had nothing but diverse measures to use. The study leads, moreover, to an insight into the crude, but easily understood, efforts of early peoples to bring their various measures into relationship; it makes clear the significance of the various relations that were eventually developed; and it develops a scheme of thinking, or point of view, about measures that requires an understanding of relations for its completion.

The study of early measures makes two other closely related contributions. First, it serves to bring the various measures now in common use each into clear perspective by demonstrating the various stages of their development. Since the measures used by early man had to be readily available and were, necessarily, parts of his body or objects of his immediate environment, their concreteness is a most striking characteristic; and their concreteness serves to make clear their proportions and to give meaning to those of our present measures that have been derived from them.

Second, the study of early measures serves to bring to consciousness the method of procedure that one has to follow in undertaking to measure the amount or quantity of anything. The pupil may observe that the estimate of amount that is derived from measurement is more accurate than any other estimate because it is derived by comparing the thing to be measured, or about which an estimate of amount or quantity is to be made, with something whose size, or amount, or quantity, is familiar or relatively familiar. The pupil can easily note that the available objects, which were selected in the beginning as units of measure, were also familiar objects; and moreover, that the measurement consisted in applying the unit chosen to the thing to be measured. Thus, the two steps — namely, (1) choosing a measure and (2) applying the measure — may be brought to the level of clear consciousness. If the teacher desires, the steps may be made to stand out as ideas of procedure that the pupil can use in his succeeding studies of measures, and that can receive further demonstration in the succeeding studies. Sooner or later in the pupil's progress, he will have to do some thinking of his own in coming to an understanding of derived measures, like square and cubic measure. If he can come to such task with a clearly defined method of attack, he may be able to understand the better the things he is called upon to learn.

Reference will be made in the illustrative exercises that are presented further on to the development and use of a method of attack upon square measure.

IX. USING THE METRIC SYSTEM

When the pupil has studied the diversity of early measures and has seen, by way of striking contrast with the measures of the present, the need for their development toward uniformity, he may continue his studies of relations by viewing a system in which relations are not only obvious but indeed the most characteristic feature. The system to which reference has just been made is the metric system of measures and weights. It is proposed that the metric system be included in the curriculum in arithmetic, not for the value of its content, but for the value of its training.

1. Often Rejected as 'Useless'

The metric system, insofar as the curriculum of the elementary school is concerned, is frequently disposed of by the statement that its only use is in the study of science, and that the pupil can learn as much as he needs of it later on when his courses in science begin. It is suggested that when the pupil studies the system in the elementary school, he forgets it, and must study it again in the high school. It is pointed out, and entirely correctly, that the uses of the system can be readily learned in connection with its actual uses in scientific measurement; and, it is added, perhaps not entirely correctly, that unless the pupil studies science he has no need for the system. Wilson [10] has suggested that the system's popularity in Europe is more apparent than real, and that the spread of the system has been accomplished by compulsion

[10] Wilson. *Op. cit.*, 319–324.

and propaganda. The following paragraphs are indicative of his generalizations and of his point of view:

> Any metric unit which has been readily accepted is a close approximation to a customary unit.
>
> Metric units which do not closely approximate customary units have been accepted slowly and unwillingly, if at all.
>
> Metric units are halved and quartered exactly as the customary units. Decimalization is used in statistics and refined measurement, but is not more used with metric units than with customary units.
>
> Thus it gradually becomes clear why customary, or non-metric measures, persist in metric Europe. The customary units are more convenient and better suited to trade conditions. They persist because of inherent merit and in spite of compulsion.
>
> The manufacturing and trade of the world are still largely non-metric. It would be simpler and easier to get along without metric units than without customary ones. We need not ask that the metric units be abandoned or legislated against. We can reasonably ask that metric propaganda cease and that metric units be left to win or lose on merit. We should avoid compulsion.[11]

If the value of the metric system were determined only by the usefulness of its units as instruments of measurement, one would be justified in disposing of it, with respect to the arithmetic of the elementary school, in any one or in all of the ways indicated above. If one accepts as correct the point of view that value is determined by common usage, he may conclude with Wilson that the metric system might just as well be abandoned. There is no advantage in measuring with a meter stick in preference to the yardstick; in dropping gram and kilogram weights into the balance in preference to ounce and pound weights; or in using a liter bottle as a container of liquids in preference to the quart bottle. One can use the one kind of measure just as well as the other, and no

[11] Wilson. *Op. cit.*, 323–324

better. Usage is common to all systems of measure; once a system has been decided upon, its use is like the use of any other system. There is no gain in turning to the metric system for information or instruction about the way measures may be used.

2. Positive Values Often Overlooked

Let us, then, cease to turn to the metric system for mere information about kinds of measures and for suggestions about the ways various measures are used. Let us turn to it, if at all, for values that may not be so apparent in our own system or so readily gained from our own system. In learning to use our own system of measurement, we would seek to be intelligent, not only about the various measures themselves, but also about the relations between them. From the point of view of the teacher who may be in possession of an understanding of relations, there is no purpose in seeking elsewhere for an illustration of relations. The teacher must bear in mind, however, that the pupil is not conscious of the relations between the measures he has to learn, and that the measures in common use furnish within themselves a rather poor means of demonstrating relations or even of bringing relations to the level of consciousness. If the teacher is interested in teaching the relations between measures, he had better seek a means of illustration.

The metric system provides just the kind of illustration of relations that is needed. The one standard unit that has been adopted, for each kind of measure stands out with perfect clearness, and its name is not lost in its divisions and multiples. Smaller and larger units, even though they are given separate and unrelated uses — the *centimeter*, for example, in measuring short lengths, and the *kilometer* in measuring distances — are held together by the retention of the name of the standard. The name, *meter*, for instance, is evident to the pupil in both *centimeter* and *kilometer*, and the name is useful in suggesting and in emphasizing relations.

Moreover, the exactness of the relations is both suggested and emphasized by the names of the divisions and multiples of the standard unit. The name *centi* denotes one hundredth, and the name *kilo* denotes one thousand. Compounded with the name of the standard unit, *meter*, these names provide names for smaller and larger units that, though used for widely different purposes, retain their relations with the standard in a way that no one can fail to observe; and the compounded names express an exactness of relationship with the standard that impresses itself upon the attention.

The metric system also serves to illustrate in a most impressive way the relations between the measures of length and the measures of weight and capacity. The latter measures were derived from the measure of length; they did not grow up as separate measures to be brought finally into relations with the measure of length. The relation between the *gram* and the *centimeter* is easy to grasp; and the relation between the kilogram and the liter is also easy to grasp. Moreover, the relations are so simple that the pupil can move back and forth in his thinking from one kind of measure to another. Once he has visualized a centimeter, and then, ten centimeters, in length, he can visualize a kilogram, or a liter, without difficulty, and shift his attention from one to the other with ease. He is aided in doing this, not merely by what he remembers and understands about relations, but also by the fact that he can easily carry the relations in his mind. They all are stated in the decimal system. Since the idea of ten has become so familiar, and since the metric system is a decimal system, the pupil does not need to hesitate in transferring his attention from one measure to another, or from one unit within a measure to another, until he can use pencil and paper computations to aid him. The presence of the idea of ten in the system invites an easy movement of thought from one measure, or any part of one measure, to another or to any part of another.

3. Importance of the Method of Teaching

Much depends, of course, upon how the metric system is taught. If the teacher is interested only in values that are derived from use, he will find little of value to make impressive. Indeed, the metric system is so lacking in usefulness to the pupil of the elementary school as to make the teaching of what little use it may ever have an extraordinarily difficult task. The teacher who tries to teach usefulness will usually find himself so engrossed in the task of trying to discover uses to exhibit and illustrate as to forget entirely the valuable relations between measures that the system can make clear. Thus, the teacher may come actually to hide from the pupil's view the valuable relations that otherwise are so obvious and so clearly evident.

On the other hand, if the teacher is interested in helping pupils to develop an understanding of measurement, of what measurement involves, of the precise thinking that originates in measurement, and of how the work of the world has moved in the direction of precision through the development of measurement, he will use every means possible to call attention to the relations between measures and to illustrate such relations. He will refer to ancient measures whose use has long since been abandoned, in order to suggest the need of relations; he will indicate the slow development of measures from diversity to uniformity, in order to impress the importance of growing relations upon the development of precision; and he will introduce his pupils to a system of measurement in which the relations are so obvious and so clearly expressed as to make the transition of thought from one measure to another a matter of comparative ease, in order to provide needed practice in thinking the relations between measures. The teacher who is interested in transmitting to the pupil an idea of how the race has progressed toward precision in thinking through the development of standard measures that make possible the translation of the amount of one kind of substance into terms expressing the amount of another kind is not really interested in whether the metric system is gaining or losing as a means of common measurement. If the use of the metric system were by some trick of fate suddenly abandoned the world over, such a teacher might well continue to include the metric system in his course because of its great value as an instrument of instruction.

X. The Difficulties Met by Pupils and the Stages of Their Progress

Something of the difficulties encountered by pupils and of the stages of their progress in learning measures and weights has been indicated in what has already been said. One of their chief difficulties is to be explained by the fact that they are inclined to be neglectful of the obvious uses of the measures in common use, and that they often fail to develop, in connection with their studies of the common measures, a method of attack upon the measures that are not so common. For example, the yardstick, or the quart measure, is so common as to fail to attract attention to its significance as a means of measurement; and the way each of these measures is used is so obvious as to cause one to neglect the peculiar manner in which all measures are used. Some means must be used to assist the pupil to develop a method of attack upon the general problem of measurement he will encounter in the later stages of his work. The following lesson material is included to illustrate a means of aiding the pupil to develop a method of attack, or a general idea of procedure in measurement. The material is not included to suggest completeness of content, but rather a method of procedure.

The method of attack that the pupil may derive is the two–step method to which reference has already been made, namely, (1) decide upon a measure that can be used, and (2) apply the measure.

1. Methods of Procedure in Linear Measure

The material begins with a review of linear measure as an introduction to square measure.

An Illustrative Lesson on Measuring Lengths

You have already learned a good deal about how to measure. You know, for example (although you may not have thought about it just like this), that the way to measure the amount of a certain thing is to take the *right kind of a measure* and *apply it* to the thing to be measured. Thus, the way to measure liquids is to take a quart, pint, or gallon measure and *apply it* (count the times the liquid fills the quart, pint, or gallon measure). The way to measure grains, vegetables, etc., is to take the quart, peck, or bushel measure and *apply it* (count the times the material fills the quart, peck, or bushel measure). The way to measure lengths is to take the *foot, yard,* or *rod measure* and *apply it* (count the times the length being measured, not exactly fills, but extends over the foot, yard, or rod measure).

In order to measure lengths one must first have the right kind of a measure — the inch, foot, yard, or rod. Next, he must *apply the measure* to the length, and count the times the measure has to be applied to cover the length. Let us see:

In order to measure his height, Jack stood up against the wall and marked on the wall level with the top of his head. He took a foot rule, *applied it* to the length from the floor to the mark on the wall, and *counted the feet* as he covered the distance: one, two, three, four, and a half — $4\frac{1}{2}$ *feet;* or he *counted the inches* as he covered the distance: 12, 24, 36, 48, and 6 are 54 *inches.*

In order to measure the width of the vegetable garden, Bob took the yardstick, and *applied it* to the distance from corner stake to corner stake, and *counted the yards,* or the *feet,* as he covered the distance: 1, 2, 3, 4, 5, 6, 7, 8, *9 yards* — or 3, 6, 9, 12, 15, 18, 21, 24, *27 feet.*

That is the way people always have measured lengths or distances: *Take a measure and apply it.* Of course, in olden days the measures were not so exact as the ones we use now; yet we have got our modern measures and the method of applying them from the measures and method of former times.

In olden times, when one wanted to measure a short length, or distance, he would use his *foot*, or his *feet*, as a measure, and apply it, or them. He *applied* his measures by placing his feet heel to toe from one end of the length to the other, and counting the times (*feet*) he set down a foot to cover the distance.

To measure longer distances, the people of olden times used a *rod*, or a *pole*, and *applied* it to the distance. Of course, you know what a *pole* is and what a *rod* is. Sometimes they used a stick of shorter length that they called a *yard*. The old meaning of *yard* is stick, rod, or measure. We still speak of the *yardstick*. The point for us to remember is that they *applied* the *rod, pole, yard*, or their *feet*, just as we *apply* our measures today.

We can understand how the use of such measures led to many disputes about lengths and distances. The *poles, rods,* and *yards* (sticks) they used were of no established lengths, and two persons using different length sticks to measure the length of a piece of land could easily get into a dispute about it. The sizes of *feet* differed also, as they do today, so that two people could hardly settle a dispute about a distance by stepping it off. Such disputes could hardly be avoided until the *exact lengths* of various measures were decided upon.

The *yard* of length, as we use it today, is the distance between two gold plugs in a certain bronze bar kept at Westminster in England or the exact length of a metal bar kept at Washington, D.C. All *yard* measures are marked off from either of these, so that the *yard* as we use it today is always the same length. Our other measures of length are taken from the established, or standard, *yard*. $5\frac{1}{2}$ such lengths make one *rod*. $\frac{1}{3}$ of a *yard* is our *foot*, and a twelfth part of a *foot* is our *inch*. The word *inch* comes from a Latin word meaning *twelfth part*. An old English law declared that the length of the *inch* must be that of "three grains of barley dry and round" placed end to end. And so, in early times they used to say: "3 barleycorns make one inch; 12 inches make one foot," etc. It is interesting to notice that the old English law stated that grains of barley had to be placed end to end. It was speaking of *applying* a grain of barley as a measure to tell how long an inch should be.

It took the people of former days a long time to get together in their use of measures of length enough to determine upon **exact** measures, such as we use today. But that is what they had to do — work out, or decide upon, a *measure of length* before they could measure length exactly. When they had decided upon a measure, the next thing to do was *apply it*. Let us remember these two important things that must be done in order to measure *lengths*, or anything else, exactly:

1. Decide upon a *measure*.
2. *Apply* the measure.

Measuring Surfaces

Bob and Betty were interested in the sizes of the whole vegetable garden, the whole playground, and all the space in their rooms, not just the distances they were long and wide. How big is Betty's room? Of course Betty knew, when she had measured the room, just as we would know it, that the room was 12 feet long and 9 feet wide. And, of course, in measuring, she just measured along two sides of the floor. What she wanted to know was how big is the *whole surface* of the floor, not merely how big it is along two sides.

In measuring the garden, Bob measured first along one edge of it, then along another edge. But Bob wanted to know how big the *whole garden* is, not merely how big it is along its edges.

The garden, the playground, and the floors in the two children's rooms are *surfaces*, not lengths. A *surface* has length just as a piece of thread has length, but the *surface* of a garden is quite different from the *length* of a thread.

We must learn how to *measure surfaces*. In order to tell how big a *surface* is, we must do two things:

1. Decide upon a *measure of surfaces*.
2. *Apply* the measure.

Let us now do each of these in turn.

2. Method of Procedure in Square Measure

When the pupil has in mind the two steps of the procedure he is to undertake — namely, to decide upon a measure of surfaces, and to apply the measure — he may proceed to take the two steps in turn. The first task is to become acquainted with the *square foot*, the convenient unit of square measure. To do this, the pupil must be led to study the openings between lines, and the particular sized opening, which is called the right angle; next, he must give his attention to 'square-cornered' surfaces, including the particular kind, called 'squares'; he must study the characteristics of the square; and finally, he must give especial attention to the square foot, making for his use out of cardboard a square that approximates as closely as possible the square foot. Only by taking all these steps in succession can the pupil become familiar with the peculiar properties of the square and with the exact size of the square foot.

Now, when he has selected his measure of surfaces, he can proceed to apply it in the actual measuring of surfaces. Out of the actual measuring of surfaces, he may be led to derive the rule of the rectangle, which provides an indirect, but very convenient, means of measuring surfaces.

A Lesson on Applying the Square Foot

1. Draw on the blackboard a rectangle exactly 2 feet high and 4 feet long. (Perhaps your teacher will have it drawn for you.)

How large is this rectangle? The question asks: How many *square feet* are there in the rectangle? *Apply your measure*, the square foot, and find out.

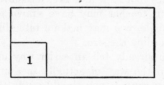

Lay your square foot in one of the corners, say at 1, so that it just covers the corner, and make marks on the rectangle to show how much space is covered. That is 1 square foot. Measure another square foot space, and mark it off. That will be another square foot. Continue in this way to measure the space in the rectangle, counting the square feet, until all the space is measured. (Do not miss any of the space in the rectangle, and do not measure any part of it twice.)

When you have finished measuring the rectangle that is 2 feet high and 4 feet long, you will have spaces, each a square foot in size, marked off upon it like this:

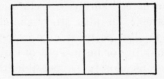

How large is this rectangle that is on the board? That is, how many *square feet* in size is it?

2. Draw a square (rectangle) on the board that is 3 feet high and 3 feet long. Measure it, and write down how large it is.

3. Draw a rectangle on the floor 3 feet wide and 4 feet long. Measure it, and make a record of its size (write down how many square feet are in it).

4. Draw another rectangle on the floor 4 feet wide and 5 feet long. Measure it, and record its size.

5. Draw a square with sides each 5 feet long. Measure it, and record its size.

6. Draw a rectangle 5 feet wide and 6 feet long. Measure it, and record its size.

7. Draw a rectangle 9 feet wide and 12 feet long. Measure it, and record its size.

Using your square foot as a measure, measure the size of other rectangles that your teacher may have drawn for you. As you measure each rectangle, you may make a table like the one shown below to use in recording the size.

Perhaps you can already tell an easier way of finding the size of a rectangle than the way of actually measuring it with your square foot. If you cannot, you should study the table. Let us study it together.

1. When you measured the first rectangle on the board, which was 2 feet high and 4 feet long, you found that the size was 8 square feet. You learned by actual measuring that 8 square feet is the exact size. Look at the two lengths, 2 feet and 4 feet. Can you tell what one should do with the numbers 2 and 4 to get 8? If you can tell, you do not need actually to measure the surface with your square foot.

I	II	III	IV
	Lengths of Sides		Size of Rectangle
Number	Feet Wide	Feet Long	Number of Square Feet in It
1	2 feet	4 feet	8 square feet
2	3 feet	3 feet	9 square feet
3	3 feet	4 feet	12 square feet
4	4 feet	5 feet	20 square feet
5	5 feet	5 feet	25 square feet
6	5 feet	6 feet	30 square feet
7	9 feet	12 feet	108 square feet
8			
9			
10			

Study the other figures, and compare the sizes of the sides with the sizes of the surfaces, as given in the table.

2. What should one do with 3 and 3 to give 9?

3. What should one do with 3 and 4 to give 12?

4. What should one do with 4 and 5 to give 20?

5. What should one do with 5 and 5 to give 25?

6. What should one do with 5 and 6 to give 30?

7. What should one do with 9 and 12 to give 108?

Perhaps you can now make your rule for finding the size of the surface of a rectangle, without actually having to use the square foot to measure it. The rule will be something like this:

To find the size of a rectangle in square feet, *multiply* the number of feet long by the number of feet wide.

Likewise:

To find the size of a rectangle in square yards, *multiply* the number of yards long by the number of yards wide.

To find the size of a rectangle in square inches, *multiply* the number of inches long by the number of inches wide.

To find the size of a rectangle in square rods, *multiply* the number of rods long by the number of rods wide.

3. Studying Other Measures of Surfaces

When the pupil has developed the square foot as a measuring instrument, has used it in the measuring of surfaces, and, from the two steps of procedure, has developed the rule of the rectangle, he should continue his studies of surfaces. The following materials suggest three methods: (1) comparing surfaces with perimeters; (2) determining the relations between the various divisions and multiples of the unit of square measure; and (3) studying through familiar comparisons the sizes of typical surfaces.

Teaching the Distinction between Distance Around and Size

You have learned how to find the size of any surface that is shaped like a rectangle. The *size* is *measured* in, and stated in, square feet, square yards, etc. The *size* of a surface is not the same as the *distance around* it, although some children confuse the two. Let us notice the difference.

1. Mr. Beetham was planning a little chicken yard at the end of his lot. He staked it off (drove little stakes at the four corners) and measured between the corners to see just how long it was. The chicken yard measured 20 feet wide and 30 feet long. He now built a fence around the chicken yard. How big is the chicken yard? How long is the fence that goes around it?

Let us draw a diagram of the chicken yard. It will be like this:

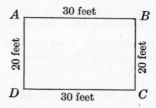

How big is the chicken yard; that is, how many square feet in it? $30 \times 20 = 600$ square feet. How long is the fence that goes around it; that is, how many feet around it?

The distance from A to B is 30 feet.

The distance from B to C is 20 feet.

The distance from C to D is 30 feet.
The distance from D to A is 20 feet.
The distance all the way around is 100 feet.
Thus we get our answers:
The *size* of the chicken yard is 600 *square feet.*
The *distance around* the chicken yard is 100 *feet.*
See whether you can tell another way of finding the *distance around.*

Teaching Square Inches, Square Feet, Square Yards

1. How many square inches are there in a square foot?

Draw on a piece of paper or on cardboard a square foot. Or use the *square foot* you used a while ago to measure the size of surfaces before you learned the rule.

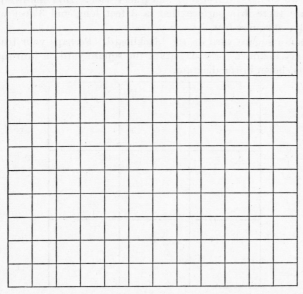

Using your rule, mark the edges off *exactly* in inches, as shown in the diagram, and connect with straight lines the opposite points that you have marked. When you get all the lines drawn you will have the square foot marked off into little squares. How large is each little square? The sides of each little square are exactly 1 inch long, so each is a *square inch* in size.

Count the square inches in the square foot. This is the way to do it: Count the square inches along the row at the bottom. How many square inches in 1 row? Next, count the number of rows. Now multiply the number of square inches in one of the rows by the number of rows. $12 \times 12 = 144$ square inches.

A shorter way to find the number of square inches in a square foot is to measure the length of the square foot in inches, and the width in inches. You will find that the square foot (perhaps you already know it) is exactly 12 inches long and 12 inches wide. How many square inches are there in a surface that is 12 inches long and 12 inches wide? $12 \times 12 = 144$.

2. How many square feet are there in a square yard? A square yard, we know, is 3 feet long and 3 feet wide. How many square feet are there in a surface that is 3 feet long and 3 feet wide? $3 \times 3 = 9$ square feet.

Draw a square yard on the blackboard. Perhaps your teacher will have it drawn for you. Mark the square yard off into square feet, as shown in the diagram.

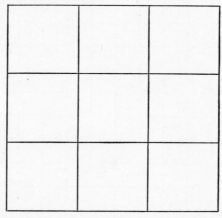

3. How many square yards are there in a square rod? You can think how to find the answer, like this: A square rod measures $5\frac{1}{2}$ yards long and $5\frac{1}{2}$ yards wide. There are then $5\frac{1}{2} \times 5\frac{1}{2}$ square yards in a square rod, or $30\frac{1}{4}$ square yards.

Compare the tables given below:

Table of Length	*Table of Square Measure*

Table of Length	Table of Square Measure
12 inches = 1 foot	144 square inches = 1 square foot
3 feet = 1 yard	9 square feet = 1 square yard
5½ yards = 1 rod	30¼ square yards = 1 square rod
320 rods = 1 mile	160 square rods = 1 acre
	640 acres = 1 square mile

A Lesson to Show How Large an Acre Is

Acre once meant merely an open field, or a piece of open land; later, *acre* was used as an inexact *measure* of land, meaning the amount of land a man could plow in a day with a team of oxen; still later, *acre* came to mean a strip of land 4 *poles* wide and 40 *poles* long (look up definitions of *acre* in the dictionary); finally, the *acre* has come to mean a piece of land exactly 160 square rods in size.

We use the *acre* today as a *measure* of pieces of land that are larger than the ordinary city lot. The size of farms, parks, etc., is measured in *acres*. We speak of a man owning a farm of 40 *acres*, or 115 *acres*, or 785 *acres*.

An *acre* is the size of a *square* the sides of which are slightly more than 208.7 feet in length. It is the size of a rectangle that is 200 feet wide and 217.8 feet long, or of one that is 175 feet wide

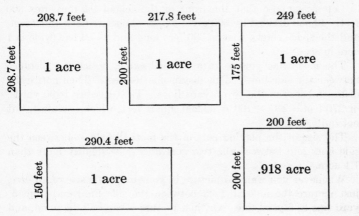

and about 249 feet long, or of one that is 150 feet wide and 290.4 feet long. A square with sides 200 feet in length is slightly more than .9 of an *acre*.

There are 43,560 square feet in 1 acre.

Measure the front of your school lot in feet. Divide 43,560 by the number of feet the lot measures in front. The number you get is the number of feet to measure back on your school lot to give a piece of ground the size of 1 acre.

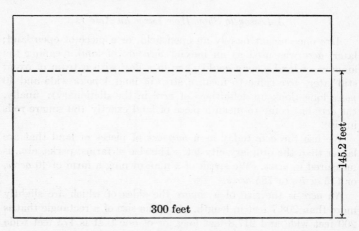

300 feet

145.2 feet

Let us suppose that the front of the school lot measures 300 feet. 43,560 divided by 300 gives 145.2. Measure back 145.2 feet, and the space shown that is 300 feet long and 145.2 feet wide is 1 acre in size.

The next time you go to a football game, notice the distance between the side lines. This distance is 160 feet. Then notice the distance between the two 5-yard lines. This distance is 90 yards, or 270 feet. 270 × 160 = 43,200 square feet, which is almost, but not quite, 1 acre.

The size of the playing part of the football field — between the side lines and between the two goal lines — is slightly more than 1.1 acre.

Whenever you want to picture in your mind the size of an *acre*, just picture the football field between the side lines and from 5-yard line to 5-yard line. Or, just picture a baseball diamond, and

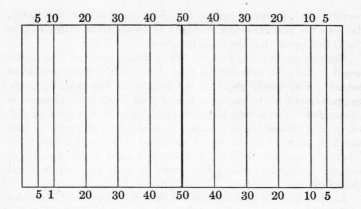

think that 1 acre is as large as 5 baseball diamonds. (Actually 1 acre is about the size of $5\frac{2}{5}$ baseball diamonds.)

Problems about the Acre

1. A field is 40 rods long and 20 rods wide. How many square rods are in the field? How many acres are in the field?

2. A certain farm is 240 rods long and 180 rods wide. In order to find how many acres there are in this farm, what should one do? Find the number of acres in the farm.

3. Mr. Wright purchased 4 lots in the new addition to the city. The lots were each 60 feet wide and 200 feet long. Did he purchase as much as an acre of ground?

4. James' father gave him a piece of ground for a garden that measured 66 feet long and 66 feet wide. How much ground did James have for his garden? What part of an acre did James have?

There are 43,560 square feet in an acre.

5. Measure the length and width of your school lot. How large is your school lot? Is it as large as 1 acre or is it larger than 1 acre?

Using the Different Square Measures

Sometimes a person wishes to know how large a certain space is in square feet, square yards, or (if it is large enough) in square rods and acres. In whatever terms (square feet, square yards, square rods, or square inches) he wishes to have the size stated, he uses the corresponding *measures of length* (foot, yard, rod, or inch) to measure the length of the sides.

Suppose you wish to find how many *square yards* of floor covering it would take to cover the floor of the library reading room at school. You would measure the lengths of the sides in *yards*. Suppose you wish to know the size of your living room at home in *square feet*. You would measure the lengths of the sides in *feet*. Suppose a farmer wishes to know how many *square rods*, or how many *acres*, there are in one of his fields. He would measure the lengths of the sides in *rods*. Suppose you want to find the size of a picture in *square inches*. You would measure the lengths of the sides in *inches*.

1. How large is your schoolroom floor in square feet? In order to find the answer to this question, what must you do? Find the number of square feet.

2. How large is your schoolroom floor in square yards? In order to find the answer to this question, what must you do? Find the number of square yards.

3. Can you suggest another way of finding the number of square yards in your schoolroom floor without actually having to measure the lengths of the sides a second time?

XI. Developing a Method of Attack

The material just presented illustrates what appears to be a very roundabout manner of developing the rule of the rectangle when it is remembered that the pupils can memorize the rule in a five-minute exercise. If it were merely the rule of the rectangle and its use in finding answers in which we are concerned, we could readily choose the memory exercise in preference to the long-drawn-out series of development lessons here illustrated. Our concern, however, is not in getting the pupils to acquire a rule-of-thumb procedure, but in helping them to understand square measure and to develop a method of attack upon the various problems of measuring surfaces. The method of attack upon the rectangle may not be so important if rectangles were the only kind of surfaces to be measured. There are other kinds of surfaces, however, to which the pupils must give their attention. When the pupils have developed a general method of attack, they may proceed to the study of surfaces other than the rectangle.

The material shortly to be presented illustrates how the pupil may proceed to the measurement of the parallelogram that is not a rectangle, the triangle, and the circle. It is supposed that the properties of each of these surfaces have already been studied. The problem confronting the pupils is how to apply the unit of square measure first to one, then another, of the surfaces indicated. When they study the first kind of surface, they meet the difficulty of applying the unit of square measure to it. They are confronted with the problem of changing the figure so that the unit can be applied. In each succeeding surface studied a similar difficulty arises, and the same problem is met. Whether the pupils solve the problem in each case or are assisted in solving the problem is not material. The matter of paramount importance is whether the pupils understand the problem that needs solution. Since the problem was first presented as a method of procedure in connection with the rectangle, and since the problem arises again and again in each of the surfaces to be studied, the problem takes on more and more definite shape in the minds of the pupils. The solution will be understood, however it may be secured, if the problem is clear. The following material will illustrate the procedure in bringing the problem again and again to the attention of the pupils.

Teaching Pupils to Apply the Unit of Square Measure

As you already know, one can find the size of a surface that has square corners, like the square or the rectangle, either by applying the unit of square measure — square inch, square foot, square yard, etc. — or by multiplying the length by the width. If the figure has square corners, one can apply the square foot (and the other square measures), because the square foot will fit exactly into the corners. But suppose the surface is one that does not have square corners, like the parallelogram, the triangle, or the circle. In such a case, one faces a problem. Let us see what the problem is.

Draw the following figures on the blackboard with the dimensions shown in the figures below:

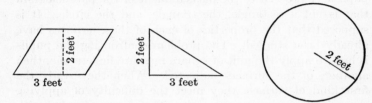

Now take a square foot — a piece of cardboard that is exactly 1 square foot in size — and try to apply it to each of the figures to see how many square feet there are in each of them.

One may try and try to apply the square foot to the figures, and he will find that the square foot cannot be applied exactly and entirely to any one of the figures, because in each case the square foot *will not fit exactly and entirely within the figure.* In each case, the square foot sticks out at some point or points. What can one do? How can he ever find the number of square feet in such figures as the parallelogram, the triangle, and the circle?

There is one way, and only one way, and that is, if it is at all possible, to change the figure in which the square foot does not fit into a figure into which the square foot will fit.

Into what kind of figure will the square foot fit? The square foot (square inch, or square yard, etc.) will fit into any figure that has square corners, such as the rectangle or the square.

Now, if one wishes to measure the size of the parallelogram, the triangle, or the circle, he can either give up the task in defeat, or he can try to find some way to change the figure into one with square corners, like the rectangle. The problem one faces in measuring such figures as the parallelogram, the triangle, or the circle, is first to change the figure to a rectangle *with square corners;* that is, into a figure to which the unit of square measure can be applied.

Let us try to solve the problem of each figure. To solve it, we must keep in mind at all times exactly what the problem is.

What is the problem?

Read over this topic again until you are sure that you know exactly what the problem is.

Measuring the Parallelogram

When one attempts to measure the size of the parallelogram by applying the unit of square measure, he finds that the unit of square measure will not apply exactly. He finds that he must first change the parallelogram to a figure, like the rectangle, to which the unit of square measure can be applied.

What can one do to change the parallelogram to a rectangle? Let us see.

Draw a parallelogram like ABDC on a piece of cardboard or paper. Cut it out along the lines AB, BD, CD, and AC.

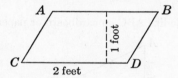

Draw a line from A to the base CD so as to make square corners with the line CD at the point E. Cut out the triangle ACE along the line AE, move the triangle over to the other side of the figure, and place it alongside the line BD, as shown in the figure below.

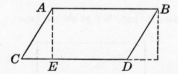

When you move the triangle over and place it by the side BD, what kind of figure do you have? How long is it? How wide is it?

Since you know how to find the size of a rectangle by multiplying the length by the width, you can find the size of the rectangle into which you have changed the parallelogram, and when you find the size of the rectangle, you will know the size of the parallelogram with which you started. Whenever one changes a parallelogram to a rectangle, he gets a rectangle that is as long as the *base* of the parallelogram and as wide as the *altitude* of the parallelogram. Since the size of the rectangle is

$$Area = length \times width,$$

the size of the parallelogram with which one starts is

$$Area = base \times altitude.$$

Measuring the Triangle

When one attempts to measure the size of the triangle by applying the unit of square measure, he finds that the unit of square measure will not apply exactly. He finds that he must first change the triangle to a figure, like the rectangle, to which the unit of square measure can be applied.

What can one do to change the triangle to a rectangle? Let us see.

Draw a triangle like ABC on cardboard or paper.

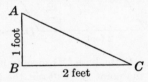

Cut it out along the lines AC, AB and BC.

Draw another triangle that is exactly the same size, and cut it out.

Put the two triangles together as shown here:

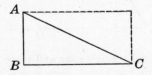

What kind of figure do you now have? How long is it? How wide is it? How do you find its size?

How does the size of the triangle with which you started compare with the size of the rectangle you now have? If you know, or can find, the size of the rectangle, you can find the size of the triangle with which you started, because you can see that the triangle is exactly one half the size of the rectangle.

Since the size of the rectangle is

$$\text{Area} = \text{length} \times \text{width},$$

and since the length of the rectangle is the same as the base of the triangle and the width of the rectangle is the same as the altitude of the triangle, the size of the triangle is

$$\text{Area} = \frac{\text{base} \times \text{altitude}}{2},$$

or

$$\text{Area} = \tfrac{1}{2} \text{ of the base times the altitude.}$$

Suppose one wishes to find the size of a triangle that does not have one square corner like the triangle you have just been studying. One can find the size in exactly the same way. Let us see how to find the area of a triangle like this one:

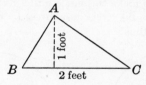

Draw a triangle like the one shown, and cut it out. Draw another triangle exactly the same size, and cut it out. Place the two triangles together, and see what kind of figure the two triangles make. The new figure will look like this one:

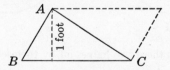

that is, like a parallelogram that has a base 2 feet long and an altitude 1 foot long.

Since you already know that the size of a parallelogram is

$$\text{Area} = \text{base} \times \text{altitude},$$

and since the size of the triangle with which you started is exactly one half the size of the parallelogram that you have made, the area of the triangle is

$$\text{Area} = \frac{\text{base} \times \text{altitude}}{2},$$

or

$$\text{Area} = \tfrac{1}{2} \text{ of the base times the altitude.}$$

Measuring the Circle

When one attempts to measure the size of the circle by applying the unit of square measure, he finds that the unit of square measure will not apply exactly. He finds that he must first change the circle to a figure, like the rectangle, to which the unit of square measure can be applied.

In order to change a circle to a rectangle, one must be able to use his imagination a bit. Let us see how well you are able to use your imagination.

Suppose we try to make this circle into a rectangle.

First, let us divide the circle into halves by drawing a diameter through the center, thus:

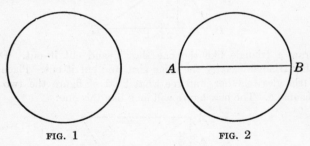

FIG. 1   FIG. 2

Next, let us set these two halves off by themselves, thus:

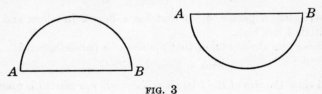

FIG. 3

Notice that the distance around from A to B in each of the half-circles is exactly half of the circumference. We must remember this.

Now, let us draw lines (radii) from the center of each half-circle, dividing each into smaller parts, thus:

FIG. 4

Let us imagine that many, many radii have been drawn in each half-circle, dividing each into many, many parts.

Now, let us imagine that we can take hold of the ends of the half-circumference, at A and at B, in the first half-circle, and pull it out into a straight line, thus:

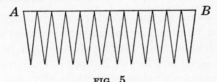

FIG. 5

The straight line AB is half of the circumference straightened out. Hanging down from the straightened out half-circumference AB are saw-tooth bits of the circle, each of which is equal to the radius in length.

Let us do the same straightening out with the second half-circle, and we shall have a figure like this

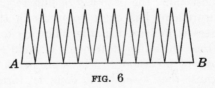

FIG. 6

which is exactly the same size as the first one. Now, let us imagine that we fit the two stretched out half-circles together. As we imagine putting them together, we can see how the 'saw teeth' of the one fit into the 'saw teeth' of the other. We now have a figure like Fig. 7,

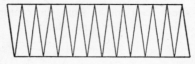

FIG. 7

which is one half of the circumference long and as wide as the radius.

How large is a circle? If you have used your imagination well, you can tell that the area of a circle is $\frac{1}{2}$ of the circumference times the radius.

XII. The Meaning of Measurement

Our discussions to this point carry the suggestion that measures and weights are not merely concrete instruments that the individual may pick up for certain practical uses and then lay aside and forget, but are in reality the concrete representations of a method of thinking that man has slowly and gradually developed and that he has used to transform the world in which he lives. The yardstick is such a common thing as to be found in every household; anyone can possess it and learn to put it to certain practical uses. But the yardstick is more than a piece of furniture; it carries within it the story of man's rise from savagery to civilization; it is a kind of milepost along the pathway of human progress.

What measurement has come to mean in the story of human progress is indicated in the following quoted paragraphs from the concluding statements of Judd's chapter on the psychology of precision.[12] The statements are quoted at length because they assemble in compact form a number of points that have been merely implied in our discussions,

[12] From C. H. Judd. *The Psychology of Social Institutions.* (By permission of The Macmillan Company, publishers, New York, 1926.)

give emphasis to them in a very striking way, and carry our thinking in the direction of the real meaning of measurement.

Our review has given us ample ground for several generalizations. The first is that measurement is a form of comparison which begins with the most concrete objects easily accessible to the observer. Parts of the body, grains of wheat, stones, and natural vessels for holding liquids are the first standards.

The second generalization is that the motives for different kinds of measurement are so various that weights and measures tend at the outset to show great diversity, with the result that different kinds of units are not thought of as belonging together. Thus weight is not determined in terms of cubical dimensions. Furthermore, the various peoples of the earth, indeed, the different localities within the same country, have different units. A late and very striking example of this is the fact that in the United States today the number of pounds which the statutes of the various states require for a bushel of such commodities as buckwheat and sweet potatoes vary by as much as twenty percent.

The third generalization is that as the demands of civilization progress in the direction of precision, the standards of measurement are themselves subjected to more searching scrutiny. Put in terms of our general discussion, this can be stated as follows: When the importance of the institution of weights and measures becomes a matter of explicit recognition, attention is diverted from the uses of the institution and is bestowed upon the perfection of the institution itself. The perfection of the system is regarded by individuals and nations as justified by the superior serviceableness of the precise weights and measures thus evolved. In the economy of society as a whole, it becomes an advantage to set aside energy for the indirect and apparently abstract good of perfecting weights and measures.

The fourth generalization is that in successive stages of an evolutionary series, the purposes which prompt men to give attention to the system gradually change. In the first stages of the evolution of weights and measures the purposes were wholly practical. In later stages the desire for uniformity brought it to pass that the authority of organized society was called in to regulate and systematize the institution, because men had arrived at the level where they desired consistency as much as practical utility. In a still later stage the more abstract virtue of exact scientific comparability between all standards is demanded in order that thought may be made general in the full sense of the word. So long as commerce was the only incentive for securing uniformity of weights and measures, men got on very well with rough approximations; but when they came to think about the dimensions of the earth and the wave-length of light, they saw that the measurements of different countries must be made comparable, and they saw also that all the units must be made sufficiently precise to make critical judgments possible. Measurement becomes in these last stages the highest form of controlled thinking. Systems of measurement take on a kind of sanction and a kind of fixity which civil authority, unsupported by scientific authority, could never give them.

In the evolution of weights and measures we have another striking illustration of the fact that man has introduced into his environment an institution which essentially changes his relation to nature. He has created by the exercise of his genius an instrument for the guidance of his behavior which insures economy of material and effectiveness of conduct in the highest degree. At the same time he has set up a guide for individuals and a means of compelling the individual to conform to the practices of society, which are among the most potent factors of civilization.

It may not be amiss to emphasize once more the fact that there is absolutely no instinct in the animal world or in human nature which responds to weights and measures. It is utterly futile to attempt to bring these creations into the class of biological facts which are dealt with in the ordinary applications of the principle of biological variations and natural selection. Weights and measures constitute one of the institutions of civilization. The history which has been sketched in the foregoing pages shows what a vast amount of energy has been bestowed on the erection of this institution. The history of men's thinking which parallels the facts regarding weights and measures is a history of the transfer of attention from superficial qualities to fundamental values and exact determinations. Modern man thinks in terms of units of measurement, whereas his remote ancestors thought only in the roughest approximations. Modern man thinks in terms of social equity as determined by standards which he and his fellow men are prepared to protect and enforce. Primitive man had no such ethical notions about quantities and no such devotion to exact descriptions. Primitive man had no remotest notion of the possibilities of exact measurements of the forces and substances of nature, which even the common man of every civilized nation understands. We live in a world where the luxuries of life are delivered to us through meters, reported in Arabic numerals, and paid for in coin. Truly, civilization has left nature and primitive modes of life far behind.[13]

XIII. WHAT MEASUREMENT MAY MEAN TO THE PUPIL

It is not to be expected that the pupil of the elementary school will be able to grasp the meaning of measurement which the foregoing quoted paragraphs suggest as belonging to it, or even the meaning which the casual reader may be able to get from them. The paragraphs are included to suggest the kind of story of measurement which may be told the pupil, and the kind of picture of man's efforts to move ahead in the direction of precision in thought which may be held up before the pupil for him to look upon. The paragraphs suggest a possibility in learning — the possibility that the pupil may catch a glimpse here and there of the pathway of human progress, noting a few at least of the mileposts along the way, and thus make a beginning in appreciating a phase or two of the world in which he lives.

The teacher may be satisfied with the presentation of measures and weights as useful devices in the daily work of the world and with training the pupil in the few computa-

[13] Judd. *Op. cit.*, pp. 149–151.

tions that from time to time are necessary in connection with the uses of measures and weights. In such case, the content of the course will be exceedingly meager. There will not be a great deal for the pupil to learn, because the teacher will have difficulty in justifying the inclusion of a good many topics merely on the grounds of usefulness. The content will in many cases be reduced to those commonly used measures and weights with which the pupil, when he chances to come into contact with their uses, can familiarize himself just about as well without the benefit of school instruction. In such case, the study of measures and weights might just as well be excluded from the curriculum in arithmetic. It is worth considering whether the school is ever justified in including a topic in its curriculum unless it is prepared to carry the development of the topic to greater lengths than is possible in the daily affairs of life.

On the other hand, the teacher may be interested in teaching the uses of common measures and weights and the computations their uses require only as a prelude, or an introduction, to the meaning of measurement as a human invention that has helped to shape the course of human progress. In such case, uses of measures and useful computations will not be neglected; indeed, they will receive an emphasis that a narrowly conceived course cannot give. The pupil will not merely acquire some devices that are useful to other people; he will also develop the knowledge and skill that will make them useful to him. Moreover, whether the pupil may forget the devices before he has a chance to use them will cease to be a source of worry. His gaining of meanings will supply the pattern into which the useful devices may be set and that may enable the problem of memory to solve itself. What is more to the point, however, is the fact that the topic on measures and weights may become for the pupil a chapter on the progress of civilization. The chapter admittedly will not be a completed one in the case of the elementary pupil. It will, however, present some things that he can see and appreciate, and it will provide a glimpse of others that may be sufficient to invite later exploration. The extent of his view may not be so great as his teacher's; it certainly will not exceed the view his teacher has been able to gain.

CHAPTER XXI

HELPING THE RETARDED PUPIL

ARGUMENT

1. Many pupils fail in arithmetic. Failures in arithmetic are cumulative.

2. Failure is often permitted to become extreme before it is realized that a well-planned attempt to deal with failure should be made.

3. Illustrations of extreme failures are quoted from the report of Buswell and John.

4. The failure of a pupil is as much a positive condition as it is a negative one. It frequently is the result of learning inadequate, rule-of-thumb, and confusing methods of work.

5. A test will reveal where the pupil stands; it may fail to trace the course by which he has arrived. Brownell is quoted to indicate that understanding does not always accompany accuracy and speed of performance, but frequently appears independently of accuracy and speed.

6. The results of tests may be very misleading. It is as important for the teacher to discover how the pupil performs as to discover what his results are.

7. Remedial instruction is frequently an immediate necessity; it generally does not strike at the roots of failure.

8. Remedial instruction ought not to be mistaken for curative instruction. To be curative, instruction must strike back of evident difficulties to their causes.

9. Frequently the cause of failure is removed when the review of poorly understood processes is so devised as to provide a new, and an enlarged view. New views and enlarged views serve the needs of the pupils who are succeeding as well as of those who are failing.

10. Lesson materials are offered to illustrate what is meant by new and enlarged views and how they may be provided.

I. The Distribution of Arithmetically Retarded Pupils

More pupils fail in arithmetic than in any other elementary subject. Pupils with sufficient mentality to develop facility in the use of their mother tongue and to master the relations between meanings and their printed signs in reading often show a surprising lack of mastery of number. Pupils who have taken the first step in number development, represented by a mastery of counting, appear to be confronted by insurmountable difficulties in their attempts to take some of the succeeding steps. In spite of the fact that the understanding and use of number seem so easy to the child and adult who have succeeded, the learning of arithmetic seems an almost impossible task to others.

There appears to be little middle ground in this matter of learning arithmetic. Pupils either learn arithmetic or they do not. They either succeed or fail. In other subjects, one may find pupils distributed all along the road from failure to mastery — a few at the point of failure, more at the points approaching 'average' attainment, a large number at the middle points of 'average' attainment, not so many who may be called 'superior,' and about the same number of 'excellent' attainment as of failures. In arithmetic, however, pupils seem to be grouped either on one side or the other of a dividing line between success and failure. To be sure, there are partial failures and extreme failures as well as somewhat varying degrees of success; but, in the main, the pupils either understand division or percentage, for example, or they fail to understand.

Failures in arithmetic are cumulative. Each succeeding grade witnesses a larger number of failures than the grade preceding. The partial failure of a pupil in the primary grades usually turns out to be a complete failure in the intermediate grades. In other subjects, the partial failure at a given point may be turned into success at a later point. If, for instance, a pupil does poor work in his study of the geography of Africa, he is not prevented thereby from doing much better work in his study of South America. In arithmetic, however, the various topics are so intimately related that departure from the main road at any point results in extraordinary difficulty in getting back on the road at a later point. So much depends upon continuous travel over the main road that the pupil must usually be taken back to the point of original departure before he can be set moving again in the right direction.

II. Illustrations of Failures

Teachers are aware of the presence of retarded pupils in their classes in arithmetic. They often are at a loss about the way to deal with them. The following extreme cases of failure have been reported by Buswell and John,[1] not as illustrations of typical performance in elementary-school classes, but as illustrations of the extremity to which failure is permitted to proceed without any well-planned attempt on the part of the school to deal with it. We quote at length from Buswell and John's report.

Tula, a pupil in the third grade, was rated by her teacher as poor in arithmetic. Her work in subtraction illustrates some of her difficulties. In the case of the example, 58 minus 4, she first tried to get the answer by counting. Beginning at 51, she counted, "51, 52, 53, 54," but she was not able to decide what the answer should be. She said that she wished she had a little paper. When a piece of paper was given to her, she made fifty-eight marks on it and then crossed out three. She counted the remaining marks and gave her answer as 55. When she was asked why she had crossed out three marks instead of four, she replied that she had forgotten one. After crossing out another mark, she counted the marks a second time, again giving the answer 55. When her work was

[1] G. T. Buswell and Lenore John. *Diagnostic Studies in Arithmetic.* (Department of Education, The University of Chicago, Chicago, 1926)

checked, it was found that she had made one mark too many and had counted wrong the first time. She habitually used this method of making marks and counting, even to the extent of making eighty-six marks for the example, 86 minus 4. When the examples given her to solve contained somewhat smaller numbers, she tried to count on her fingers. In the case of the example, 17 minus 9, she tried to get the answer by imagining an extra hand and using two fingers on this third hand twice to represent the number 17. She then counted off all the fingers on one hand and four fingers on the other to equal the number 9, which was to be subtracted. She gave her answer as 1, only one finger remaining in sight. She seemed confused, decided that this was wrong, and finally asked for a piece of paper, on which she made tally marks, as in the case of the examples previously described. Evidently, Tula could not be expected to show any great efficiency in arithmetic so long as she used such methods as these.

Jane, who also had considerable difficulty with arithmetic, was in the fifth grade. In subtracting, she generally counted backward to get her answers; as a result, she made frequent errors. A typical illustration of her work appears in the example, 9546 minus 8687. A verbatim report of the way in which she obtained her answer is as follows: "7 from 16 leaves 16, 15, 14, 13, 12, 11, put down 1 and carry 1; 8 from 13 leaves 13, 12, 11, 10, 9, 8, 7, 6, and 1 is 7; 6 from 14 leaves 15, 14, 13, 12, 11, 10, put down 0 and carry 1; 8 from 8 is 0 and 1 is 1." Jane was far from perfect in manipulating even the clumsy technique which she had adopted, as evidenced by the errors made in this example.

Kurt was a bright boy in the third grade who had received his previous instruction at home and who entered school for the first time in this grade. He experienced many difficulties with both addition and subtraction. Some of his difficulties were of a peculiar type, especially those relating to his reading of numbers. In the example, 58 minus 4, he read the 58 as 85, then counted back to 81, and wrote the answer 18. He was very frequently confused by 6's and 9's, not being sure which was 6 and which was 9. In the example, 79 minus 3, he said, "67," both inverting and reversing numbers. He counted back "67, 58, 47," stopped, and wrote the answer 74. In the next example, 98 minus 5, he read the 98 as 86 and then began to count back as follows: "86, 76, 66." When he reached 66, he said, "Oh, no," and counted as follows: "86, 85, 84, 83, 82." He reversed the 82 and wrote his answer as 28. In the case of the example, 89 plus 7, he said, "89, 99, 100, 102, 103, 104, 105" and wrote 105 as the answer. In adding 53 and 8, he said, "53 and 8 is 43, no, 53, 63, 73, 83, 93. Well, I don't know which number this is [pointing back to the 53]. Is it 50 or 30?" He then counted, "54, 55, 56, 57, 58, 59, 60." In writing the final answer, he reversed the digits and wrote 06. The methods and processes which Kurt used were rich in variety. His work showed an interesting mixture of erratic procedure and erroneous logic. Nothing but a detailed analysis of his mental processes could indicate to a teacher the kind of help that he needed.

Thomas was a fifth-grade boy who was rated by his teacher as poor in arithmetic. In the case of division he showed a number of curious methods. He repeatedly added the remainder resulting from one stage of the process to the next figure of the quotient. For example, in dividing 17385 by 3, he said, "3 into 17 goes 5 times and 2 over; 3 into 3 goes once and 2 [the previous remainder] is 5; 3 into 8 goes 2 and 2 over; 3 into 5 goes once and 2 [the second remainder] is 3 and 2 over." His answer was $5523\frac{2}{3}$. He used this method in all examples in short division in which there were remainders. He frequently counted in order to get the quotient. In the case of the example, 46 divided by 2, he followed this complicated process: "2 into 24, 12; 12 more 2's make 48; go back 2 to 46; makes 23." He continually used the short-division method for examples which should have been worked by long division. In the case of the example, 16354 divided by 34, his answer was $428\frac{20}{34}$, which he obtained as follows: After trying 7 and 5, he finally decided that 34 would go into 163 four times. He wrote the 4 in his answer, multiplied 34 by 4 correctly, and, subtracting the result from 163, secured the correct remainder, 27. He divided 54, the last two digits in the dividend by 34, getting an answer of 1 with a remainder of 20. He then added the first remainder of 27 to the second quotient of 1, giving 28, which he wrote in the answer, and used the remainder from the last division as a fractional remainder, writing $\frac{20}{34}$. The important fact about Thomas' work is not that he was getting wrong answers, but that he could never get correct answers by the methods which he was pursuing. His work could not show improvement until his methods were changed.

Pauline, another pupil in the fifth grade, had considerable difficulty with both addition and multiplication. A diagnosis of her work showed that practically all her trouble was due to one fact; namely, that she did not know how to carry. For example, in multiplying 43 by 8, she said, "8 times 3 is 24," and wrote the 4 but ignored the 2, arriving at the wrong answer, 324. She followed the same procedure when zeros appeared in the numbers. In the case of the example, 705 times 7, her answer was 4905. In two- and three-place multiplication she showed the same type of error in adding her partial products. She habitually discarded all numbers which were to be carried, writing down only the units' digit. In a test in multiplication containing forty-eight examples, she failed on twenty-eight. In twenty-four of the cases failure was due to mistakes in carrying. Analysis and specific teaching in her case would doubtless have yielded large returns.[2]

III. FAILURE IS A POSITIVE CONDITION

The cases of failure in arithmetic that have been described in the foregoing quotation stand out in sharp contrast with cases of successful accomplishment with which every teacher is familiar. The teacher cannot help drawing a contrast between the pupil who is failing and the pupil who is succeeding. Such contrast brings to the forefront of attention the fact that what the latter has succeeded in learning the former has not succeeded in learning. The one pupil can divide, for example, and the other cannot divide; and the contrast between the two is so impressive that the teacher is compelled toward the view that the failing pupil is just

[2] Buswell and John. *Op. cit.*, 1–3.

the opposite of the succeeding pupil. Moreover, since both pupils are to be found in the same classroom, the conclusion is easily reached that the failing pupil merely stands in need of a repetition of the same kind of instruction under which the succeeding pupil has learned to thrive.

It is true that failure on the part of a pupil is evidence of trial and lack of success. Failure means much more, however; though in many respects it is a negative condition, it is also a very positive condition. The pupil who has failed to learn his arithmetic at any point not merely exhibits the lack of accomplishment; he also exhibits in a very positive way the accomplishment of something that is misleading and that prevents success. He has, to be sure, failed to learn what he should, but he has succeeded in learning something. Instead of putting forth the right kind of effort, he has put forth the wrong kind; instead of making real progress in his learning, he has made progress in the wrong direction. Stimulation to renewed effort or to an increase of effort may succeed only in driving him into more confusions than those already experienced. To return to our figure of the 'road of learning,' the failing pupil has moved off the main road and needs to be led to retrace his steps to the point where he left it and there to take a new start.

For example, the pupil who has failed to learn division has not failed because he has had no instruction in division or no contacts with division. He has failed because he has had the wrong kind of instruction, or because he has been misled by the instruction he has had, or because he took the wrong view of division from the beginning. He has, to be sure, learned to give some correct answers to division questions when they are put to him, but he is never certain, because his memory fails him at times, or because the mere remembering of so many correct answers to division questions brings them into confusion. He has learned, let us say, that "two goes into ten five times," but since "goes into" has no meaning for him — or for anyone else for that matter — he must depend entirely upon memory for the answer "five," when the question is put, "How many times does two go into ten?" Sooner or later, he confuses this answer with other 'goes into' answers, and the teacher concludes that he needs more drill on the particular 'goes into' exercise in question. As a result of drill, or more time spent, and of increased effort, the pupil may learn the 'goes into' answers, but he never thereby learns division. What the pupil needs, when he has failed to learn what division means, is not more instruction in the same kind of meaningless division that he succeeded in learning at the outset, but instruction in the real meaning of division. He will have to forget about his 'goes intos,' if he can, and learn what the exercise in division really asks him to do.

IV. TESTING TO DISCOVER FAILURES

The discovery of failures by the teacher necessarily precedes any constructive aid the teacher may be able to give to failing pupils. It is generally recommended that the teacher should resort to the use of frequent tests as means of discovering failures.

A test at the beginning of the year is very helpful in acquainting the teacher with the outstanding abilities and disabilities of the members of the class. If the test is planned to cover certain specific points of possible progress, the test will give some indication whether the pupils have succeeded in reaching the points covered. An examination of the results attained by a given pupil will indicate whether he has had marked success in his previous work or has been an outstanding failure. What has been the course of the pupil's progress or what is the cause of his failure will, of course, not be revealed. What is secured is a 'quantitative' measure; what is needed is, as it were, a 'qualitative analysis.'

The results of a test are, however, nothing more than indications. All the teacher has at the conclusion are the pupil's scores, which give no indication of the pupil's methods of thinking. The scores show either correct results or incorrect results and the speed with which the results were attained. Because they have to be made to apply so specifically to the points covered in the test, they exclude from consideration other important items that may be very valuable. The following extended quotation from Brownell's discussion of the limitations of testing as a means of measuring progress makes it clear that the results of a test may be very misleading. Discussing popular theories regarding the nature of the process of teaching and the process of learning arithmetic, he writes as follows:

A third questionable theory is that progress in the development of ability in arithmetic may be adequately measured by measuring either the rate or the accuracy, or both the rate and the accuracy of performance. This theory is a natural corollary of that conception of the learning process in arithmetic which views learning as the mere establishment of direct connections, or bonds, between a host of items, such as $7 + 5$, $9 \div 3$, and $6 - 5$, and their corresponding answers, 12, 3, and 1. When learning in arithmetic is thought of in the way described by those who support the theory of bonds, there are but two dimensions to the process; namely, rate and accuracy of performance. Method of performance, being invariably the recall of rote memory associations and therefore a constant factor, may be safely disregarded. Measurement of degrees of development only in terms of rate and of accuracy is also in perfect accord with the conception of teaching in arithmetic as drill, for drill is designed to set up the rote memory associations which make uniform all the processes and all the methods employed by children in dealing with numbers. Since, according to this view, there is no variation in methods of dealing with numbers, degrees of development in arithmetic are adequately measured when the two functions, rate and accuracy, are measured.

The individual analyses of the mental processes employed by pupils in dealing with visual concrete numbers, the additive combinations, and three-digit addition should go far toward convincing the reader that the views set forth in the foregoing paragraph are fundamentally erroneous. Children do not use a single method of dealing with numbers. Neither do they learn number facts in a single way, even though the type of instruction is drill and even though every effort is directed toward securing uniformity of mental processes. Children differ markedly in the ways in which they think of numbers and in the ways in which they learn number facts. No adequate measurement of degrees of development can be made, therefore, unless the measures of speed and accuracy are supplemented by a measure of the maturity of the processes employed in dealing with numbers.

Two cases may be cited as a means of emphasizing once more the truth of these last statements. The first shows the importance of method or manner of performance in the matter of the meaning and understanding of numbers; the second, the importance of method in the matter of the mechanics of the fundamental operations. Both these aspects of number ability, namely, meaning and the mechanics of the processes, manifestly condition success in learning arithmetic.

The first case is Subject 305. Previous to the scoring of the test in addition, the teacher of Grade III A was asked to name the three pupils in her class whom she regarded as the best in arithmetic. Subject 305 was designated as one of the three. He was the tenth pupil in the grade to complete the speed test in addition and the sixth pupil to complete the accuracy test. He made four errors and five errors, respectively, in the two tests. In the individual tests he counted to perform eight of the thirteen second additions; he counted in five cases where the additions were within the limits of the simple additive combinations. His frequent use of counting is clear evidence of the fact that, while, from the standpoint of speed and accuracy in the group tests in addition, he appears to be above the average for the grade in the degree of his development in arithmetic ability, he is, as a matter of fact, very much retarded in his understanding of numbers and their relations. His speed and accuracy in addition are deceptive as an index of the true degree of his ability; he is simply rapid and accurate at a low stage of development. His teacher has incorrectly come to regard him as representing an unusually apt pupil in arithmetic because, as most teachers do, she accepts surface indications of efficiency as evidence of real ability.

The second case to be cited illustrates the importance of method in the matter of mechanics of addition — a phase of ability in arithmetic which is not considered, except very indirectly, when degrees of development are measured in terms of rate and accuracy of performance.

In learning the additive combinations, pupils are likely to prefer some combinations to others and to prefer one statement of a number fact to the statement in the reverse order. For example, pupils may prefer $8 + 2$ to $5 + 2$, $2 + 5$, $8 + 5$, $5 + 8$, etc., and may prefer the statement $8 + 2$ to the reverse form $2 + 8$, with the result that, when the combination is given in the latter form, they may reverse it to $8 + 2$ in order to recall the required sum more readily. In the example

2
$\underline{8}$, it may seem unimportant to the teacher whether a pupil in the second grade begins at the top or at the bottom, so long as he secures the correct answer. She may therefore permit him to add the digits in the preferred order rather than in the order as given from top to bottom. Consequently, in this example he adds upward in order to have the combination in the preferred arrangement and thus secures further practice on the known fact and no practice on the unknown. Later,

2
5
in the third grade, the pupil is given the example $\underline{8}$ and promptly announces the correct answer 15. The promptness and the accuracy of the computation convince the teacher that the pupil has met all possible requirements in the situation. Inquiry might reveal the fact that the pupil first combined $2 + 8$, because he preferred first to combine these digits, rather than $2 + 5$, $5 + 2$, $5 + 8$, or $8 + 5$ and, further, that he added the digits 2 and 8 in the order $8 + 2$, beginning at the bottom, skipping the 5 in the middle, and then coming back to the 5 to add it to the sum 10. The teacher's failure to determine the pupil's methods of procedure within the column results in the pupil's continuing to get practice (1) on

preferred combinations, (2) on the preferred statements of these combinations, and (3) in the rearrangement of columns of digits to suit these preferences. Drill in addition provides for the pupil an opportunity for practice on undesirable habits, on faulty mechanics. Later, when the pupil is in the fourth grade, he is given the following example (left-hand column):

8 (1) The methods which the pupil used in short examples
5 (7) in addition in the earlier grades are now decidedly
6 (5) ineffective, and the slowness and the inaccuracy of
2 (2) the pupil's work may finally acquaint the teacher
8 (9) with his faulty procedures. She may question him
7 (8) and learn that he has added the digits in the order
4 (3) indicated by the numbers in parentheses at the
9 (4) right of the example. The order of addition shown
5 (6) was actually found in the case of a boy in Grade
       IV A. To make certain that he had correctly re-
ported his procedure, the same example was given to him a second time, after an interval of a few minutes. The order of addition reported for the second trial differed from that reported for the first trial only by the fact that in the second trial he added the 6 after the two 5's instead of before.

There is little wonder that this boy is one of the problems of the teacher in the arithmetic class. His difficulties are not properly described, nor his level of development indicated, when measurement is made only in terms of rate and accuracy in adding pairs of digits. His slowness and his inaccuracy in dealing with long columns are only indexes of a difficulty of a deeper and more fundamental sort. Furthermore, it is incorrect to speak of this boy as an arithmetic problem in the fourth grade; he was as truly a problem in the second grade and in the third grade, but his teachers, measuring his earlier degrees of development in terms of rate and accuracy, did not know it. His difficulty only came to the surface in the fourth grade, but it is of long growth and undoubtedly can be traced to his failure to develop efficient procedures and mechanics in earlier stages of arithmetic.[3]

[3] W. A. Brownell. *The Development of Children's Number Ideas in the Primary Grades* (Department of Education, The University of Chicago, Chicago, 1928), pp. 201–204.

V. The Deceptiveness of Test Scores

The quotation from Brownell illustrates in a very striking way the manner in which both the teacher and the educational statistician are frequently misled by testing procedures. One sets out to measure certain specifics in a subject, secures the results of measurement, and becomes so impressed (or blinded) by the definiteness and tangibility of the results that he considers them as measures of the entire subject, of which they are evidently measuring only a part. One may go so far even in his regard for the results of tests as to work modifications in the course of study in terms of them. Reference has been made in a previous chapter to the fact that 'zero combinations' came into the curriculum as a result of the discovery that pupils made mistakes in dealing with integers when zeros were present. Let us turn to other illustrations of the deceptiveness of tests.

In the early stages of his training in the development of a given idea — percentage, let us say — the pupil frequently exhibits a type of response that indicates an amount of progress far in excess of any that has actually been made. Not being able to grasp the idea as rapidly as it has been unfolded to him, he turns his attention to the computational demonstration of the idea. If it is that phase of the idea employed in the 'first kind of problem,' for example, that is being demonstrated, the pupil finds it very easy to avoid thinking about the possible meaning of percentage and to devote his efforts toward remembering the rule: "multiply by the percent." The words of the rule can be remembered more easily than the idea to which the rule applies can be gained; so the pupil attends to the rule, and 'applies' it in the exercises that follow. His score on a test involving the first case in percentage will be high, and it will, accordingly, hide the fact that the pupil really does not understand percentage.

Let us suppose that the pupil finally begins to grasp what

the idea of percentage really means, to understand the significance of the demonstrations that have been called to his attention. In other words, he diverts some of his energy away from computational procedure to the processes of thought. At first, these thought processes proceed somewhat slowly and uncertainly. Let the pupil now take a test in percentage, and his score will be lower than it was a few days or few weeks earlier. His performance score indicates retrogression instead of progression, when in reality the pupil is forging ahead and making real progress for the first time. His lowered score, appearing as the opposite of progress, is really, in the particular instance mentioned, a necessary concomitant of progress.

Let us carry the illustration further. Sometime after the pupil has had instruction in percentage, he is given a test that includes exercises in both the first and the third cases of percentage. Let us suppose that he responds, as a good many pupils do, by multiplying in each exercise by the percent. His score will indicate a mastery of the first case and a lack of mastery of the third case; it will indicate perfection in the one case and a lack of understanding in the other; in reality the pupil's total performance should be interpreted as demonstrating the absence of any mastery of percentage. Unless the teacher goes back of the test score to the pupil's manner of performance, he will miss the real significance of the pupil's confusion of the third case of percentage with the first.

The writer has viewed the scores of a number of pupils in the fifth grade on a twenty-problem test involving the four fundamental processes. One of the papers showed that the pupil had added the numbers given in every one of the twenty problems. The score on the paper was 5. The score, taken at its face value, indicated that the pupil was able to deal correctly with exercises involving addition, but not with those involving subtraction, multiplication, and division. The pupil's method of performance, however, indicated that, though he could add, he was deficient with regard to the real meaning of addition.

Again, pupils quickly learn to compute the areas of rectangles by following the simple rule of the rectangle. Their frequent inability to understand the meaning of area is not revealed by the scores they are able to produce on a test, even in those instances when they confuse perimeter with area and find the distance around a rectangular figure by multiplying the length by the width.

Test scores, then, are merely indications of success or failure. A high score often accompanies lack of understanding, and a low score often parallels progress. Test scores are misleading and deceptive. One must go back of the test scores to the way they were produced if he wishes to gain an idea of the standing of pupils.

VI. Methods of Diagnosis

With their diagnostic tests in the four fundamental processes, Buswell and John propose a specific plan of diagnosis. Their plan places such emphasis upon a study of the pupil's methods of work and draws such a sharp distinction between diagnosing and testing that we quote it at length:

Individual work. — It is recommended that the diagnostic chart be used in the case of all pupils who are doing unsatisfactory work in arithmetic. The most economical method is to make a list of the names of the pupils whose work is to be analyzed and then to proceed systematically with the diagnoses, giving the other children in the group practice exercises or seat work until the diagnoses are completed. The diagnoses should be made individually and should cover only one of the four fundamental operations at a time. After assigning practice exercises or seat work to the class, the teacher should select a child whose work is to be diagnosed and sit down with him at her desk or at a table in the corner of the room. She should make the child feel as much at home as possible, since the success of the diagnosis depends on the extent to which the teacher becomes acquainted with the details of the pupil's method of work. Since the causes of failure in arithmetic are generally poor methods of work, successful teaching depends, first of all, on finding out what methods are used.

Work with one process at a time. — The diagnostic chart covers the four processes of addition, subtraction, multiplication, and division. Ordinarily, only one process should be diagnosed at a given time, and in no case should the diagnosis be continued until the pupil becomes fatigued. After the teacher becomes skilled in the use of the materials, a period of fifteen or twenty minutes will be sufficient to reveal the characteristic habits of work of most pupils. The diagnostic chart should be preserved for future use, and subsequent diagnoses should be made to determine whether the pupil is abandoning the habits which are not conducive to good work.

Procedure. — After the teacher and the pupil are seated at the table where the work is to be done, the pupil should be provided with a work sheet, the teacher having a diagnostic chart before her. The blank spaces at the top of the chart for the pupil's name, age, grade, etc., should be filled in before proceeding with the diagnosis. The teacher should then direct the child to work the examples in the operation to be observed, as for instance, addition. The child should be told to work the examples in the way that he ordinarily does and to write his answers in the usual manner. He should be told that the teacher wishes to know just *how* he gets his answers and that, for this reason, he is to do as much of his work as he can aloud. A careful explanation by the teacher, together with an illustration by her, is ordinarily sufficient to indicate to the child exactly what is wanted; after the first example or two, the child usually proceeds in a natural fashion. If a pause in the child's work indicates that he is not expressing all of his thinking, he should be asked, immediately following the pause, to tell 'how he thought that out.' This should be done at the end of each pause rather than at the end of the example, because the child will probably not remember his mental processes. It is very important that the teacher find out just what the child is doing as he works, since the explanation of poor work generally lies in the method which the child pursues. The technique of diagnosis therefore comes to be the technique of skillful questioning on the part of the teacher as the child does his work.

Since the success of this type of diagnosis depends on discovering how the child works under *normal* conditions, the teacher should make no attempt in the diagnostic process to suggest methods of working or to correct the pupil's bad habits of working. This should be done later. In the diagnosis the aim is to find out just how the pupil works when he is working independently. The child should be made to feel as natural as possible, and a cordial relationship between the teacher and the child during this period is very necessary. The teacher should guard against expressing dissatisfaction with the pupil's work and against indicating in any way that the child's methods of work are wrong. Her attitude should be one of genuine interest in the pupil's methods of work, and she should make the child understand clearly that what she is interested in at the time is not the answer but the method of obtaining the answer.

As the child works, the teacher should check on the diagnostic chart the habits which are observed, at the same time recording the child's procedure in the space opposite the examples. The most satisfactory way to do this, at least for the first few times, is to record, in the exact words of the pupil, the habit observed. If the habit appears later in other examples, it is sufficient to refer back to the earlier procedure. As a result of the diagnosis, the teacher should have a clear knowledge of the specific habits which are responsible for the pupil's poor work.

Distinction between diagnosing and testing. — One particular distinction between the method of diagnosis and the method of testing should be pointed out. After a test is given, the final score is computed, which indicates the grade of work which the pupil is doing. Ordinarily, attention centers simply on the score, which is used for purposes of classification. In the method of diagnosis there is no final score. The procedure is used not for purposes of classification but rather for purposes of teaching. Consequently, the desired result is a clear understanding on the part of the teacher of *just how the pupil does his work*, in order that more effective teaching may follow. Since this is the case, the teacher should not be satisfied simply with making the diagnosis and checking the items. She should study carefully the characteristics of the pupil's work and formulate in her own mind the most appropriate plan of remedial teaching.

It should be repeated here that not every habit listed in the chart may be regarded as a bad habit. The habit of using scratch paper is an illustration in point. In the judgment of the writer, this is not an economical method of procedure in dealing with the fundamental operations, since ultimately these operations should be so well mastered that no scratch paper is needed. However, in a number of schools it was found that pupils were directed to use scratch paper; in such a case, the use of scratch paper simply indicates that the pupil is following directions. Some of the habits are poor simply because they are time-consuming and uneconomical. Habits of work should be thought of in relation to the ultimate goal, which may be stated as the ability to use the fundamental operations accurately, rapidly, and with understanding.[4]

VII. REMEDIAL INSTRUCTION

The third step in the commonly recommended technique of helping the retarded pupil, following the steps of testing and diagnosing, is that of providing remedial instruction at the points of failure. Testing is the means proposed of discovering failure, and diagnosis is the means proposed of discovering the causes of failure. Low scores in the one step are treated as symptoms, and improper methods of work in the next are treated as the defects to be remedied. The third step is recommended with the idea that remedial instruction will be applied at the points where improper methods of work are discovered. The purpose of the remedial instruction is to substitute proper methods of work for improper methods.

[4] Buswell and John. *Op. cit.*, pp. 155–158.

Remedial instruction at the points of failure is excellent in theory. It undertakes to provide aid at the specific points where aid is needed. It distinguishes one kind of difficulty from another, and is planned to help the pupil over first one difficulty after another. It has the peculiar virtue of calling the pupil's attention to specific and definite things to be overcome, and to specific and definite things to be undertaken. Moreover, as Brueckner remarks:

> The use of such clinical methods in teaching and diagnosis brings to classroom instruction the same refinement of techniques that is found in other professions, such as medicine. No one would think of submitting to treatment by a physician who used such random methods of diagnosis as were employed by medical science a few generations ago. Modern clinical medicine uses diagnostic devices which determine with precision what the cause of the difficulty is and in the light of such information prescribes the remedial treatment. The profession of teaching may be raised to higher levels if increased use is made of diagnostic techniques such as have been described and if teachers consciously try to avert the development of faulty habits and systematically seek to determine the causes of difficulty apparent of pupils making little progress.[5]

The peculiar virtue of remedial instruction applied at the points of difficulty is also its peculiar shortcoming. It tends to emphasize faults, and it is remedial rather than curative.

Remedial instruction is for the remedying of faults. The nature of the fault suggests the remedy. The remedy is devised and applied according to the fault. It is the fault that is to be overcome; so the fault tends to become the center of attention. To be sure, the correct procedure, which is to be substituted for the incorrect one, receives a large share of the emphasis, perhaps the major share; but the fault, as something to be abandoned or overcome, must needs

[5] L. J. Brueckner. "Diagnosing pupil difficulties." *Journal of the National Education Association*, 21: April, 1932, p. 125.

receive its share of emphasis, and it may continue to distract attention from the real goal.

It is not suggested that faults should never be emphasized. Sometimes an effective way to start to overcome a fault is to be made very conscious of it. The danger lies in being too conscious of the fault and conscious of it for too long a time. Real progress cannot be made so long as one is influenced by the distractions of previous blunders and mistakes. Real progress requires a direction to follow, not one to be avoided. It may be repeated that the purpose of remedial instruction is to substitute proper for improper methods of work.

VIII. REMEDIAL AND CURATIVE INSTRUCTION

Faults need to be remedied, and the remedies should be specific and immediate. Remedies are highly important because they make possible the taking of curative measures. Remedies touch the points of outward and obvious failings, but they do not strike deep at the real causes of failure. They give temporary relief; but, when depended upon as the only means of relief, they must be repeated at new outbreaks of difficulty. They provide new and better methods of procedure for older and misleading methods, but they provide no attack upon the original cause of failure and no guard against the adoption of incorrect procedures in the later stages of the pupil's work. When the remedy is applied, the fault may disappear; but it takes something more than a remedy to strike at the cause.

We may draw an illustration from the work of the modern dentist. He examines the child's teeth. The examination reveals faults. The first and immediate task of the dentist is to correct the faults. He cuts away the decayed spots, and fills the cavities. His work at remedying faults requires skill and patience, and it is of great and practical importance; but his remedial work is not the end of his responsibility. He now gives attention to the original causes of the faulty teeth. Perhaps the teeth have not been cleaned properly. Perhaps the child's diet has not been such as to build strong teeth. Recommendations are made looking toward the prevention of future possible faults in the teeth, and toward the avoidance of the necessity for future remedies.

With regard to faults in arithmetic, remedies are needed; but something more than remedies may be needed. Thus, if the pupil makes mistakes in addition, and it is discovered that his mistakes are due to carelessness, or inattention, or distractions, or insufficient practice upon certain processes, remedies are perhaps all that are needed. If the pupil understands addition and knows what he is about when he needs to add, a certain amount of drill may be the obvious remedy. If, however, the pupil does not understand addition, to show him the proper methods of adding and to drill him upon these methods will do no more than remove the outward and obvious manifestations of his lack of understanding. The remedies in the latter case will never develop insight into addition. It is insight that the pupil needs in order to move ahead in his work using proper methods of procedure; and it was lack of insight that produced the original difficulties.

When the pupil fails to understand the significance of different methods of grouping, the importance of position, the peculiar usefulness of the group of ten, the methods of representing size and number, and the like, he may use proper methods of work at some points mechanically, but improper methods at other points. In such case, remedial instruction is a discouraging and almost hopeless task. First one proper method after another may be substituted for an improper one; but as the pupil proceeds to new stages of his work, he develops more faults that demand correction. Moreover, in the very multiplicity of the many new procedures to be learned and substituted, the pupil may become confused; whereupon he is often likely to fall back upon his older improper methods, for the simple reason that he has used them longer than he has used the new and proper ones that the teacher is trying to show him. The teacher needs to inquire why it is that some pupils, perhaps only a few, use proper methods in all of their work. Is it because of drill, or because the pupils have good memories for dozens of proper procedures; or is it because the pupils understand the number relations with which they have to deal? The good pupil does not need to try to recall this proper method or that one. He is in possession of ideas of combination and of number relations that throw light upon everything he has learned and upon the new things he is called upon to learn. The failing pupil is failing because he does not possess such ideas. He will remain a failure until he is brought into possession of the ideas by methods other than those of remedial instruction.

IX. Reviews and New Views, with Some Illustrations

We may summarize the discussions of the foregoing exposition in the statements (1) that remedial instruction has only an immediate usefulness and a temporary value; (2) that remedial instruction is useful for minor defects, but does not strike deep at the roots of the defects; and (3) that the failing pupil is generally in need of curative instruction of the kind that will give him some insight into the number system. In short, *the failing pupil stands more in need of ideas of procedure than of methods of procedure.*

It should be clear that the review of the work of preceding grades that usually features the first work of a school year does not provide the kind of curative instruction needed by the failing pupil. Since this review is a repetition, the failing pupil may be hindered rather than helped by it, as the review may serve to implant still more deeply the wrong methods of work and the wrong attitude toward what is required in the subject. The failing pupil will not be helped by a repetition of the same kind of instruction and of the same kind of work that originally were responsible for his difficulties. He already has an incorrect view of his work; he must be provided with a view that is different — a *new* view.

The customary review naturally may be definitely helpful to the pupil who is succeeding. He may have given insufficient attention at some point in his instruction, or he may have partially forgotten during vacation the importance of certain aspects of the work he has had. A review then is helpful. Moreover, the review is frequently very helpful, in the case of the pupil who is succeeding, as a means of suggesting the connection between the things already learned and a new step in the work he is ready to undertake. Even so the mere review is not a maximal benefit; an *enlarged* view is better for him than the review.

The following illustrative lesson material is included to indicate what is meant by a *new* view or an *enlarged* view of work already done. It is assumed that the pupils have studied fractions, decimals, and the beginnings of percentage. The material as it is given may provide the needed *enlarged* view which the succeeding pupil needs before he proceeds to the work which follows. The material may need a good deal of elaboration in order to provide the needed *new* view for the pupil who is failing or who is on the verge of failure. The amount of the elaboration is in proportion to the amount of the pupil's defects and failings. The failing pupil has learned a few things, at least; he needs the kind of help which will enable him to collect into a single scheme of thought the few things he has learned. He may need a good deal of repetitive drill also; but such drill as is given should be delayed until the pupil gains a little vision and a little insight into the processes upon which he must drill.

Illustrative Lesson on Size and Number

Whenever a person thinks about the amount or quantity of anything — that is, about *how much* or *how many* — he has to pay attention to two things. He has to pay attention to the *size* and to the *number*.

1. Mother sent Robert to the store to get some canned pineapple. How much canned pineapple did Robert bring home?

Of course, there is no way of telling from the way the problem is stated just how much canned pineapple Robert brought. Suppose we are told that Robert brought home 2 cans of pineapple. Now, can you tell just how *much* Robert brought home? What other thing must you know? Does the *size* of the cans have anything to do with the amount of pineapple? Suppose we are told that Robert brought home 2 cans, and that in each there were 10 ounces of pineapple. (The number of ounces in a can tells the *size* of the can.) Now do you have an idea of how much pineapple he brought home with him?

2. Mother ordered some canned peaches and some canned tomatoes from the grocery. The grocer brought 3 cans of peaches and 2 cans of tomatoes. Did he bring more peaches than tomatoes, or more tomatoes than peaches? Do you have to know anything else in order to decide? Suppose that you know that each can of peaches was 1 pound, 4 ounces, in *size*, and each can of tomatoes was 1 pound, 14 ounces, in *size*. Now can you decide?

3. Mabel went to the store to buy some cans of tomatoes for her mother. She noticed the *size* of the cans. (Do you think that she was wise? Why?) She noticed three *sizes* of cans, as follows:

> Large size — 1 lb. 14 oz., or 30 ounces
> Medium size — 1 lb. 4 oz., or 20 ounces
> Small size — 10 oz., or 10 ounces

She bought 6 cans of tomatoes. How many tomatoes did she buy? Can you tell the answer? Why?

State the problem so that it will be possible to tell *exactly* how many tomatoes Mabel bought.

4. Which is the most, 6 small-size cans, 3 medium-size cans, or 2 large-size cans?

A Lesson on Size and Number of Parts

When one thinks about and makes use of *fractions*, he must constantly give his attention to both *size* and *number*. The *size* of the parts is quite as important as the *number* of parts. Usually a pupil will pay attention to *number* of parts in working with fractions, but sometimes he forgets to pay attention also to the *size*.

Whenever he is forgetful about *size*, he makes some curious blunder. For example, this is the way such a pupil has been known to add $\frac{1}{2}$ and $\frac{1}{3}$:

$$\frac{1}{2} + \frac{1}{3} = \frac{2}{5}$$

This pupil's trouble was that he failed to remember that the figures, 2 and 3, below the lines, showed *sizes* of the parts he was to add.

The figure above the line is the *numerator* of the fraction. It is used to show the *number* of the parts. The larger the numerator, the larger is the fraction; the smaller the numerator, the smaller is the fraction.

Rewrite these fractions, arranging them in order of size, the largest first, then the next largest, and so on:

$$\frac{2}{17}, \ \frac{8}{17}, \ \frac{14}{17}, \ \frac{1}{17}, \ \frac{15}{17}, \ \frac{6}{17}, \ \frac{13}{17}, \ \frac{10}{17}, \ \frac{3}{17}$$

The figure below the line is the *denominator* of the fraction. It is used to show the *size* of the parts. The larger the denominator, the smaller is the fraction; the smaller the denominator, the larger is the fraction.

Rewrite these fractions, arranging them in order of size, the largest first, then the next largest, and so on:

$$\frac{3}{7}, \ \frac{3}{8}, \ \frac{3}{5}, \ \frac{3}{14}, \ \frac{3}{16}, \ \frac{3}{20}, \ \frac{3}{10}, \ \frac{3}{4}, \ \frac{3}{25}$$

It is very easy to become confused about a fraction; but if you will remember about *number* of parts and *size* of parts, you need never be confused. Let us study why one is often confused and learn how to avoid being confused.

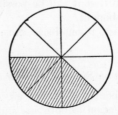

Let us divide a circle into 8 equal parts, and let us shade 3 of the parts. The shaded portion is $\frac{3}{8}$ of the circle.

Sometimes in thinking about what the fraction, $\frac{3}{8}$, tells us, we think that the 8 stands for the *number of parts* into which the circle has been divided. The 3, of course, stands for the *number of parts* in the fraction, or the *number of parts* in the shaded portion of the circle. Thinking in this way is how we become confused: we think that 8 means *number of parts* and that 3 also means *number of parts.*

Now it is true that the circle has been divided into 8 equal parts, but the 8 in the denominator *does not stand for these 8 parts.* (If we had 8 in the numerator, thus, $\frac{8}{8}$, then the 8 above the line would stand for these 8 parts.) The 8 in the denominator, whether the fraction is $\frac{3}{8}$, $\frac{8}{8}$, or $\frac{1}{8}$, is written there just to *show the size* of the parts, or the *size* of each part. The 8 in the denominator is not really 8; it is *eighth*, or *eighths;* and anyone should know that an *eighth* and the number *eight* are different. We just write 8 in the denominator, instead of 8th, or eighth, for convenience.

Although the denominators of the following fractions

$$\frac{1}{2},\ \frac{2}{3},\ \frac{3}{4},\ \frac{2}{5},\ \frac{5}{6},\ \frac{4}{7},\ \text{and}\ \frac{3}{8}$$

are written as 2, 3, 4, 5, 6, 7, and 8, they really are not the *numbers* two, three, four, five, six, seven, and eight, but the *sizes* half, third, fourth, fifth, sixth, seventh, and eighth. So let us remember that while the denominator of a fraction is *written* the same as a number, it is written that way just for convenience, and *is never called a number*, because it *stands for size.*

In the fraction, $\frac{8}{8}$, the 8 in the numerator shows a number, and the 8 in the denominator does not show a number, but a *size* — an *eighth*, not eight.

$$\frac{\text{Numerator}}{\text{Denominator}} \qquad \frac{\text{Number of parts}}{\text{Size of parts}}$$

1. On one of mother's pantry shelves there are 3 cans of tomatoes, and on another shelf there are 5 cans. How much (what amount of) canned tomatoes are on both shelves?

To what else must one pay attention besides the numbers of cans?

2. Add $\frac{3}{4}$ and $\frac{5}{6}$. Is it correct to add 3 and 5? Why? To what else must one pay attention besides the numbers of parts? What must be done before the parts in the two fractions can be added? Why?

A Lesson on Size and Number of Groups

In the writing of all quantities, we use just nine symbols, or figures: 1, 2, 3, 4, 5, 6, 7, 8, and 9. For each of the quantities to nine, we use one of the figures. For every quantity above nine, we use one or more of the same figures, and we show the larger quantity by the *position* in which we place the figures. In writing a quantity that requires us to use two or more figures, we find that each figure helps to keep the others *in their proper positions*. Thus, the figures, 2, 3, and 4, when written as 234, show 2 *hundreds*, 3 *tens* (thirty), 4 *units*. Sometimes, however, in writing a quantity larger than nine, we have more positions to show than we have figures, and we make use of the *zero* to help hold the figures *in their proper positions*. Thus, the figures, 6 and 5, when written with the zero as 6050, show 6 *thousands*, 5 *tens* (fifty). 6 5 would not show 6 *thousands*, *fifty*, because no one would be sure of the *positions* of 6 and 5. We use the zero to *hold a place*, and to help keep the figures *in their proper positions*. In every case when we write a quantity, the figure we write shows *number* and the place where we write it shows *size*. Let us see.

When you were in the primary grades you learned that addition and multiplication meant, among other things, to find out 'how many *tens?*' For example, in order to find the sum of 5 and 8, you learned to take 5 objects and 8 objects, and to arrange them into a group of *ten* and three:

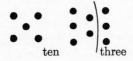

ten   three

When you had so arranged the objects and noted that 5 and 8 are the same as *ten* and three, you wrote the answer as 1 *ten* and 3, or 13. The 3 in 13 shows *number*, and the place where 3 is written shows that the *size* of each is a *unit*, or *one*. The 1 in 13 shows *number*, and the *place* where 1 is written shows that the *size* of the group is *ten*.

Similarly, in order to find the product of 4 and 9, or four nines, you learned to take four groups of nine objects each, and to arrange them into groups of *ten:*

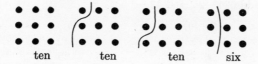

ten   ten   ten   six

When you had so arranged the objects and noted that four nines are the same as 3 *tens* and six, you wrote the answer as 3 *tens* and 6, or 36. The 6 in 36 shows *number*, and the *place* where 6 is written shows that the *size* of each is a *unit*, or *one*. The 3 in 36 shows *number*, and the *place* where 3 is written shows that the *size* of each of the 3 groups is *ten*.

Likewise, when any quantity is written, the figure in each place shows *number*, and the *place* where it is written shows *size*. In the numbers, 8500, 8503, 8590, the 8 shows *number*, and its *position* shows that the *size* of the group is a *thousand;* the 5 shows *number*, and its *position* shows that the *size* of the group is a *hundred;* and so on.

The figure shows *number;* its *position* shows *size.*

A Lesson Stressing the Importance of Position

All through your work in arithmetic you have learned how important it is to write numbers in their proper positions. You have learned that, if a person is careful to write each number *in its proper place*, position will take care of everything else for him. Perhaps you remember that whenever you had something new to learn, like multiplying and dividing by tens, adding and subtracting decimals, and so on, you were told to write each number *in its proper place* and each part of the answer *in its proper place*. Why was there so much said about *position*, or *place?* Because position shows *size*, and it is necessary in one's work in arithmetic not to mix *sizes*, but to *keep the same sizes together.*

Have you ever noticed how the grocer keeps the various *sizes* of his canned goods all sorted out and arranged on his shelves? For instance, he has all of his small-size cans of tomatoes together, all of his medium-size cans of tomatoes together, and all of his large-size cans together. Why do you suppose it is so important for the grocer to keep the various sizes of canned tomatoes sorted out so they will not be all mixed up on his shelves?

Let us add 6342, 25, and 43.

(a)	(b)
6342	6342
25	25
43	43
10892	6410

Why is (a) incorrect, and (b) correct?

$$\begin{array}{c} 3 \\ 2 \\ \hline \end{array}$$

In (a) we have the sizes all mixed. In the column, $\frac{3}{2}$, we have mixed 3 *hundreds*, 2 *tens*, and 3 *units*, and added. We get 8, but nobody knows what *size* the 8 stands for. In adding, we must keep numbers *of the same size* together — *units* with *units*, *tens* with *tens*, *hundreds* with *hundreds*, and so on, as in (b). Then when we add a column, we know exactly what size the number is that we get for an answer.

Let us subtract 25 from 462.

(a)	(b)
462	462
25	25
212	437

In (a) we have mixed the sizes. In (b) we have kept the numbers *of the same size* together.

A Lesson on the Size and Number of Decimal Parts

In a common fraction it is easy to tell the numerator (number of parts) and the denominator (size of parts). In a decimal fraction it is just as easy to tell the numerator and denominator. In a common fraction we write both the numerator and the denominator. In a decimal fraction we write only the numerator, and we show the denominator *by position.*

In the decimal, .5, the 5 shows the *number* of parts, and its *position* in *tenth's* place shows the *size* of the parts.

In the decimal, .05, the 5 shows the *number* of parts, and its *position* in *hundredth's* place shows the size of the parts.

In the decimal, .005, the 5 shows the *number* of parts, and its *position* in *thousandth's* place shows the *size* of the parts.

In order to tell the *size* of the parts in a decimal fraction, we look at the *position* of the last figure on the right.

.25 shows 2 in *tenth's* place and 5 in *hundredth's* place. .25 shows 2 *tenths* and 5 *hundredths*. But since 2 *tenths* is the same as 20 *hundredths*, 2 *tenths* and 5 *hundredths* are 25 *hundredths*. So we read .25 as 25 *hundredths*. 25 is the *number* of parts, and the *position* of the 5 tells us the *size*.

.20 shows 2 in *tenth's* place. We read .20 as 20 *hundredths*. 20 shows the *number* of parts, and the *position* of the zero tells us the *size*.

.625 shows 6 *tenths*, 2 *hundredths*, and 5 *thousandths*. But since 6 *tenths* is the same as 600 *thousandths*, and 2 *hundredths* is the same as 20 *thousandths*, .625 is read as 625 *thousandths*. 625 shows the *number* of parts, and the *position* of the 5 shows the *size*.

.620 is read 620 *thousandths*. 620 shows the *number* of parts, and the *position* of the zero shows *size*.

Just as in the adding and subtracting of whole numbers, we must keep *numbers of the same size together;* so in the adding and subtracting of decimals, we must keep *parts of the same size together*.

Let us add .5, .42, and .625.

(a)	(b)	
.5	.5	.500
.42	.42 or	.420
.625	.625	.625
.672	1.545	1.545

Why is (a) incorrect? Why is (b) correct?

Let us subtract .024 from .36.

(a)	(b)	
.36	.36	.360
.024	.024 or	.024
.12	.336	.336

Why is (a) incorrect? Why is (b) correct? Remember: *Keep parts of the same size together*. Why?

A Lesson on Size and Number in Percents

The sign % means *percent*, and percent means *hundredth*, or *hundredths*.

6% is read 6 *percent*. It means 6 *hundredths*.

25% is read 25 *percent*. It means 25 *hundredths*.

When we write 6%, or 25%, we write the 6, or the 25, to show *number* of parts, and the sign % to show the *size* of the parts.

When we want to use 6%, or 25%, in figuring, we write them as .06, or as .25.

How does one change a *percent* to a *decimal?* Change these to decimals: 50%; 62.5%; 6.25%; 15.75%; 12.5%; 42%.

How does one change a *decimal* to a *percent?* Change these to percents: .50; .875; .065; .1675; .83; .075.

CHAPTER XXII

OUTLINE OF THE COURSE IN ARITHMETIC

Argument

1. The grade-placement and sequence of the topics in arithmetic that preceding chapters have described are suggested in outline.

2. The development of number ideas by the pupil is briefly described.

3. A pupil's progress may be stated in terms of the general ideas he has developed. Ability to engage in computation is never an adequate measure of progress.

4. A pupil's progress may be stated in terms of his understanding of the number system.

5. The number system is universal in the possibilities of its use by one who understands it.

6. The arithmetic of the school has the single function of introducing the pupil to the meaning and use of the number system.

The present chapter will undertake (1) to present a brief outline of the main topics in the course in arithmetic, indicating the grade in which each probably belongs, and (2) to bring together into a summary statement the themes, purposes, and points of view of our discussions to this point.

I. The Course in Outline

The outline that follows shows grade-placement and sequence of topics. Of sequence one can be reasonably certain; of grade-placement there must, of course, be considerable doubt. The placement of topics follows closely the placement to be found in courses of study and textbooks in common use. If at any time it should appear that the placement of a topic needs to be changed, the change cannot properly be abrupt, but will have to be made on the basis of prevailing practice.

Attention is called especially to the postponement of the introduction of measures and weights until the fourth grade is reached and to the close union of three frequently separated topics; namely, fractions, decimals, and percentage. The placement of minor topics is not clearly indicated in the outline. The reader is referred to the preceding discussions for suggestions about the relations of minor topics to major topics.

Grades I and II

1. Counting
2. The Study of Groups to Ten
3. The Idea of Ten — Grouping by Tens
4. Enlarging the Number Ideas
   a. Adding and Subtracting Tens
   b. Higher-Decade Combinations
   c. Column Addition

5. Grouping into Tens (This is to comprise additions to $\frac{9}{9}$, and the corresponding subtractions, also the corresponding activities listed above in Topic 4.)

No sharp line can be drawn setting off the work of Grade I distinctly from the work of Grade II. It is suggested that Topics 1 to 3, as they relate to the groups to ten, be considered first-grade work; and that Topics 4 and 5, including relations to and repetitions of the preceding topics, be considered second-grade work. If, however, the work of the first grade includes no more than Topics 1 and 2, the work of the second grade must start, after the necessary reviews, with Topic 3.

Grade III

1. Review (an enlarged view of things already learned)
2. Tens in Addition and Multiplication (including carrying)

3. Using Tens in Subtraction
4. Grouping into Tens (in multiplication, with corresponding divisions)
5. Dividing Tens and Hundreds
6. Partition

Grade IV

1. Review (an enlarged view of things already learned, to include a comparison and a contrast of the processes of addition, subtraction, multiplication, and division)
2. Multiplying by Tens
3. Measures and Weights (introducing the common measures of length, capacity, and weight)
4. Dividing by Tens
5. Two-Step Problems
6. Measures and Weights (introducing the common measures of time and the uses of common measures in 'two-step' problems)
7. Comparing Parts (including the addition and subtraction of fractions in common use)

Grade V

1. Review (an enlarged view of things already learned, to include assembling into a single topic for study the various uses of ten and position already learned)
2. Fractions (including the 'three kinds of problems')
3. Decimals (including the 'three kinds of problems')
4. Percentage (including the 'three kinds of problems')
5. The Relations between Numbers
6. Measuring Surfaces (the rule of the rectangle)

Grade VI

1. Review (an enlarged view of things already learned; this includes a bringing together of the ideas and uses of ten, position, size, and number under the general topics of size and number of groups and of parts)

2. Everyday Problems (introducing the uses in daily
   affairs of number operations already learned: averages,
   buying, selling, accounts, etc.)
3. Applying Percents (interest, investment, discount, com-
   mission, etc.)
4. Gain and Loss
5. Measuring Surfaces and Volumes

II. The Pupil's Progress in Arithmetic

The foregoing chapters deal with the development of the
pupil's number ideas in the elementary-school grades. They
point out how the development begins in the systematic
study of groups, and how the development continues through
the orderly comparison of one number idea with another.
They indicate the growth of ideas of relation between numbers that comes about through the procedures of building
large groups out of smaller ones and of dividing large groups
into smaller ones, and through the use of meaningful terms
to express one number idea in its relation to another. They
describe and recommend a large number of activities that at
first glance seem to be very different and widely unrelated
activities, but that are in reality intimately interrelated in
that they all are useful in helping the pupil to develop and
clarify his ideas of number.

III. The Development of Ideas

At the outset the pupil studies groups that he can see in
detail, handle, and comprehend. He thus develops clear and
usable ideas of such groups; and he thus learns to deal with
them in a systematic way, and to think of each and to express
each in its relation to the others. And he learns something
else. He learns, in the dealing with the groups that are
easy to handle, methods of dealing with groups that are not
easy to handle. He can thus proceed in the later stages of his
work to develop ideas of large groups through the extension

of the methods of procedure he learned in handling small groups. Such methods are methods of combination, or methods of arrangement, or methods of making, thinking, and expressing relations. They are just as important as the ideas of number that develop with them through the study of groups.

The methods of procedure to which reference has been made are not merely methods; they are also ideas of procedure. In other words, the study of groups and of their methods of arrangement not merely impresses methods through repetition; it also makes the methods understandable. The pupil not only learns to do what he is told, but also, because he first deals with groups that are easily manageable, understands and sees the significance of what he does.

IV. The Service of 'Problems'

Special method is used to impress the methods and ideas of procedure, to clarify and enlarge them, and to make them familiar. Whether the ideas are those of addition, subtraction, multiplication, and division, or those of the fraction, percentage, the average, etc., the method is much the same. It is the method first, of presenting the idea, which already has been introduced, in a variety of familiar situations, each of which serves to make the idea stand out, and second, of giving the pupil practice in recognizing the idea. Such situations go by the name of 'problems,' and such activity is 'problem-solving,' so-called, at the earlier levels. The purpose is, as indicated, to make the ideas or methods familiar, so that they may be used in developing new number ideas and new relations and applications of number. At the later levels, after the ideas have become sufficiently familiar, the pupil can use them in his study of new personal, practical, business, and social situations, like buying and selling, budgeting, saving, investing, measuring, interest, insurance, and the like. These, likewise, are frequently presented in illustrative exercises, which also go by the name of 'problems,' and demand an activity in dealing with them that is called 'problem-solving' at the later levels.

V. LEARNING THE NUMBER SYSTEM

To state the matter in another way, the pupil develops ideas of the numbers to ten, learns to give special attention to ten, and finally, proceeds to deal with tens as he dealt in the beginning with the numbers that precede ten. The pupil first learns to arrange the numbers to ten in various ways, and next learns to arrange tens 'just like units,' until he arrives at the combination of ten tens, or one hundred, and then proceeds to deal with hundreds, also, 'just like units,' and so on up the scale. As the pupil proceeds, he learns to express his ideas of ten, hundred, etc., by the use of the familiar symbols for units placed in different positions. The system of notation serves both to express the relations of units to tens, tens to hundreds, and so on, and to impress upon the user the fact that tens, hundreds, thousands, etc., may be dealt with in all respects just as units are dealt with.

Supplementing the impressions about relations between tens and powers of ten that are conveyed by the system of notation are the ideas of the part, or percent, which the pupil develops as ideas and expressions of relation. Such ideas the pupil learns to use as a means of gaining and of expressing a clear and usable idea of any given number as it relates to another number that may be relatively more familiar. Thus, the number that is relatively unfamiliar or about which a clearer idea is needed is expressed, in connection with one that may be known, in terms of a part, or a percent. The relatively unfamiliar number thus takes to itself the qualities of familiarity that attach to the known number. Thus, the idea of the part, or percent, becomes the device by which one balances one number against another, or conceives one number in terms of another.

VI. COMPUTATIONS

In the process to which reference has been made the pupil learns a large number of computations, some of which are useful in life's affairs, and many more of which are not useful. Whether or not the computations that are learned, both the useful and those which may be useless in the affairs of life, have a value for the pupil depends upon the manner in which they are learned. If learned in close relationship to the number system, both kinds of computations are of service in enlarging the pupil's ideas of numbers, large and small, and of establishing important relations between them. The computations of dividing by hundreds and thousands, for example, may never be useful to certain pupils in their later activities; but learning to divide by hundreds and thousands may serve to fix in mind the relations between the results so secured and the results secured when one divides by tens and units. Similarly, the computations in the second and third cases of percentage may never be brought into use by certain pupils in dealing with the situations they will meet in later life, but the thinking that may be involved in connection with the computations mentioned may help to establish and to perfect the idea of percent as a meaningful and revealing expression of relations between numbers, and may, in addition, lead to a better insight into the meanings of the numbers themselves. The computations mentioned may prove to be very useless, but the training they may give may be very useful. Computations may be learned as ends in themselves, or they may be learned as means to more important ends. When learned as ends, and without relation to the number system they may serve to illustrate, even the useful combinations may prove to be useless to the pupil, for he may not gain the insight sufficient to make them useful to him.

Let us turn to the physical education of children for an illustration of the relative importance of means and ends.

In classes in physical education, the pupil is taught to play a game — volleyball, let us say. Volleyball may be useful to him at the present moment; it may help to fill his life with a wholesome and pleasurable activity; but it will not be useful to him in his later years. Why take the time to teach the pupil a game that he may not play when he is thirty, forty, or fifty? The reason is that the pupil will receive through the playing of volleyball some training in muscular coördination, in coöperation, in teamwork, in respect for rules, and so forth, that he can carry into the life of his later years. By means of volleyball, which may or may not be useful in later life, the pupil receives training that will be useful.

VII. The Functions of Arithmetic

Brueckner [1] has described four functions of arithmetic; namely, the computational, the informational, the sociological, and the psychological. Under the first, he places skill in computation; under the second, information about money, trade, stocks, measurement, how various businesses use arithmetic, etc.; under the third, applications to "various aspects of business, consumption, production, government, and social relationships which lend themselves to quantitative study and analysis"; and under the fourth, information and intelligence about number as a system of precise thinking.

Brueckner's analysis of arithmetic into the four functions is an adult's analysis which may be useful to the adult as a reminder that arithmetic may be viewed from various angles and that thorough-going training in arithmetic may be broadening in its results, instead of narrowing. It may help the teacher to remember a number of items of content that otherwise may be forgotten or neglected. On the other

[1] L. J. Brueckner. "A critique of the Yearbook." *Report of the Society's Committee on Arithmetic* (The Twenty-Ninth Yearbook of The National Society for the Study of Education. Public School Publishing Company: Bloomington, Ill., 1930), pp. 686–692.

hand, the analysis may be very misleading if it is considered as a description of the arithmetic the pupil should learn. The discussions of our foregoing chapters carry the suggestion that a leading difficulty in the arithmetic the pupil is frequently called upon to learn arises from the fact that 'computation' is separated from 'information,' that 'application' follows as something new and different, and that the number system is incidental and is left to fit in where it can.

The teacher must, of course, make analyses, since the pupil cannot learn everything at once; but the teacher must be concerned with syntheses and with helping the pupil to be so concerned. As the pupil learns one thing, then another, he must be assisted in relating each to its proper place in the number system. It is the number system that is the end to be served.

Instead of there being four functions of arithmetic, there is only one, which, copying Brueckner's term, we may call the "psychological." This is the function that has to do with orderly methods of arranging things or experiences into a common system that has come to be understandable. In other words, everything the pupil is required to learn in arithmetic may be thought of in terms of its relation to the number system. Computations must be learned; they may contribute to the development of the number system in the mind of the pupil, and what he has already learned of the system may make the computations clear. Information must be acquired; much information about numbers and number relations is acquired through computations; moreover, an understanding of number relations is very useful in gaining information about society and social situations. The transactions of business must be studied; a variety of business situations, not otherwise related, may be brought into relation as illustrations of a given way of thinking and expressing the relations between numbers. It is the number system that must develop in the mind of the pupil as a result of various methods of illustration, and it is the number system upon which the pupil must learn to rely to bring order into various personal, business, social, and measurement situations that the school leads him to study. The arithmetic of the school does not have a four-fold function; it has a single function; namely, that of introducing the pupil to the meaning and use of the number system.

VIII. The Universality of Number

Number, when it is learned, is used with everything. It marks off the events of history into convenient and manageable periods. It makes possible the division of time and space into understandable units, and distinguishes one unit from another. It assembles huge masses of information into a single statement and enables comparison of one item with another. It brings order into a complex business or governmental enterprise and brings into balance resources and liabilities. The number system, to quote Judd:

is a universal scheme which man has learned to transfer to almost everything. If man wants to make the location of houses on the streets of his city quite definite, he numbers them. If man wants to designate the members of the police force so he can readily refer to them, he numbers them. He numbers the convicts in his prisons and the customers waiting for their turns in the barber shop. If there is anything which cannot be numbered from unhatched chickens to one's debts, it would be interesting to know what it is. Transfer of the number system from one situation in which it was learned to other situations which need to be put in order is so common that the psychologists who deny transfer have overlooked it, just as most people overlook the obvious laws of nature in the most familiar experiences.

Nor can the psychologists who tell us that transfer of ideas is uncommon escape from their impossible position by saying that transfer takes place only when there are present identical elements. Of course there are identical elements present after the transfer has taken place. Number is present where number is present. The identical element is exactly the subject under discussion. To say that the identical element was there from the beginning is to overlook the fact that the mechanics of the transfer took place in a world which had no number in itself but was invaded by a mind which was informed and equipped with number. Number is a device for arranging experiences; it is one of the most general of all generalizations [2] . . .

The universality of number may be illustrated by the use that children make of counting when they first learn to count. They count everything that comes within the range of attention — the buttons on their shoes, the plates on the table, the chairs in the room, the pictures on the wall, the people on the street. They do this, however, only after they have learned to count. The objects mentioned do not make themselves countable, and they do not impress their possibilities of orderly arrangement upon the child. He brings his counting ability, once he has gained it, to them and applies it to them.

Similarly, the complex world does not impress the number system upon the individual. The individual brings the system, if and when he has learned it, to the complex world and uses it as a means of bringing order out of complexity. When the system is learned, it attaches to anything and everything. No difficulty is experienced. The application of the number system, once it is learned, seems so easy and so natural that one is inclined to assume the system to be a part of one's natural endowments. Or the number system appears to be so much a matter of 'second nature' that the teacher is inclined, when he gives any thought to it, to assume that children will naturally grow into it. Perhaps this is the reason why reference to the number system is so conspicuously absent from the arithmetic of the schools.

Counting is easy, and its application is easy, once it is

[2] C. H. Judd. "Informational mathematics versus computational mathematics." P. 192. *The Mathematics Teacher*, 22: April, 1929, 187–196.

learned. Counting is not a natural endowment, however; it has to be taught. The number system is simple, and its application is simplicity itself, once it is learned. The number system is not a gift of nature, however; the number system must be taught. Both counting and the number system are not discoverable in the natural world; both are brought into the world as means of setting it in order by the mind that has been trained. The discussions of this book have aimed to describe the number system and to suggest means of making children intelligent about it.

APPENDIX

A BIBLIOGRAPHY ON THE PSYCHOLOGY
AND TEACHING OF ARITHMETIC

In the preparation of a bibliography two courses are open to the author. He may choose a list of 'selected references' to accompany each chapter, or he may group all his references at the end of his volume. The former course is especially appropriate when each chapter stands by itself more or less as a distinct entity, or when the materials of each are drawn more or less directly from definite portions of the available literature. The latter course is to be preferred when all the chapters unite in the development of a central theme.

The point of view developed in this book may be regarded as a composite of the author's personal reactions, unfavorable as well as favorable, to the available literature on arithmetic and its teaching. The point of view has also been shaped by his experiences over a period of years, and it falls into an organized form that is somewhat at variance with the customary classification of the literature under such headings as 'history,' 'psychology,' 'methods,' 'drill,' 'problem-solving,' and the like. The exposition in each chapter is more an expression of personal opinion than an expression of a combination of views set forth in given references and is derived more directly from the central theme of the whole book than from the volumes, chapters, and articles of other writers. As a consequence, the writer has found it exceptionally difficult to name specific references that are directly responsible for his own views and difficult to assign a given reference to any given chapter.

In listing references, accordingly, it has seemed expedient to provide a separate section on 'Bibliography' that affords a medium for the listing both of those references that have contributed directly to the writer's own point of view and of those references whose contributions have been primarily to provoke unfavorable reactions to the position advocated.

This separate section should likewise suit the taste of the reader. He can find such references as he cares to read cited as wholes rather than alluded to in parts; and he is not exposed to the suggestion that a selected paragraph, page, or chapter should be read apart from its context. The writer's influence ought not to extend beyond his own textual material.

The references that follow are grouped simply in three main divisions: I. Books; II. Monographs; and III. Periodical Literature. Because of the distinct character of the idea of measurement, a separate division — IV. Measures and Weights — is provided for the references which fall under that heading.

I. BOOKS

ANDREWS, F. E. *New Numbers* (Harcourt, Brace and Company: New York, 1935)

BALL, W. W. R. *A Short Account of the History of Mathematics.* (The Macmillan Company: New York, 1908)

BROOKS, EDWARD. *The Philosophy of Arithmetic as Developed from the Three Fundamental Processes of Synthesis, Analysis, and Comparison.* (Sower, Potts and Company: Philadelphia, 1876)

BROWN, J. C. and COFFMAN, L. D. *The Teaching of Arithmetic.* (Row, Peterson and Company: Chicago, 1925)

BRUECKNER, L. J. *Diagnostic and Remedial Teaching in Arithmetic.* (John C. Winston Company: Philadelphia, 1930)

CAJORI, FLORIAN. *A History of Elementary Mathematics.* (The Macmillan Company: New York, 1917)

CONANT, L. L. *The Number Concept.* (The Macmillan Company: New York, 1896)

DANTZIG, TOBIAS. *Number: The Language of Science.* (The Macmillan Company: New York, 1930)

DRUMMOND, MARGARET. *The Psychology and Teaching of Number.* (World Book Company: Yonkers-on-Hudson, 1922)

FREEMAN, F. N. *The Psychology of the Common Branches.* Chap. IX. (Houghton Mifflin Company: Boston, 1916)

GARRISON, S. C. and GARRISON, K. C. *The Psychology of Elementary School Subjects.* Chaps. XIX–XXI. (Johnson Publishing Company: Richmond, 1929)

GOW, JAMES. *A Short History of Greek Mathematics.* (Cambridge University Press: Cambridge, England, 1884)

GUILER, W. S. *Objectives and Activities in Arithmetic.* (Rand, McNally and Company: Chicago, 1926)

HOWELL, H. B. *A Foundational Study in the Pedagogy of Arithmetic.* (The Macmillan Company: New York, 1914)

JESSUP, W. A. and COFFMAN, L. D. *The Supervision of Arithmetic.* (The Macmillan Company: New York, 1916)

JUDD, C. H. *The Psychology of Social Institutions.* Chap. V. (The Macmillan Company: New York, 1926)

KARPINSKI, L. C. *The History of Arithmetic.* (Rand, McNally and Company: Chicago, 1925)

KLAPPER, PAUL. *The Teaching of Arithmetic.* (D. Appleton-Century Company: New York, 1916)

KNIGHT, F. B. and BEHRENS, M. S. *The Learning of the One Hundred Addition Combinations and the One Hundred Subtraction Combinations.* (Longmans, Green and Company: New York, 1928)

LAMBORN, E. A. G. *Reason in Arithmetic.* (Oxford University Press: Oxford, England, 1930)

LENNES, N. J. *The Teaching of Arithmetic.* (The Macmillan Company: New York, 1923)

LINDQUIST, THEODORE. *Modern Arithmetic Methods and Problems.* (Scott, Foresman and Company: Chicago, 1917)

McLELLAN, J. A. and DEWEY, JOHN. *The Psychology of Number.* (D. Appleton-Century Company: New York, 1895)

MORTON, R. L. *Teaching Arithmetic in the Primary Grades.* (Silver Burdett Company: Newark, 1927)

MORTON, R. L. *Teaching Arithmetic in the Intermediate Grades.* (Silver Burdett Company: Newark, 1927)

NEWCOMB, R. S. *Modern Methods of Teaching Arithmetic.* (Houghton Mifflin Company: Boston, 1926)

OSBURN, W. J. *Corrective Arithmetic.* (Houghton Mifflin Company: Boston, 1925)

OVERMAN, J. R. *A Course in Arithmetic for Teachers and Teacher-Training Classes.* (Lyons and Carnahan: New York, 1923)

ROANTREE, W. F. and TAYLOR, M. S. *An Arithmetic for Teachers.* (The Macmillan Company: New York, 1925)

SMITH, D. E. *History of Mathematics, I and II.* (Ginn and Company: Boston, 1923, 1925)

SMITH, D. E. *Rara Arithmetica, I and II.* (Ginn and Company: Boston, 1908)

SMITH, D. E. *The Progress of Arithmetic.* (Ginn and Company: Boston, 1923)

SMITH, D. E. and KARPINSKI, L. C. *The Hindu-Arabic Numerals.* (Ginn and Company: Boston, 1911)

SMITH, D. E. and MIKAMI, Y. *A History of Japanese Mathematics.* (The Open Court Publishing Company: Chicago, 1914)

SUZZALLO, HENRY. *The Teaching of Primary Arithmetic.* (Houghton Mifflin Company: Boston, 1911)

THORNDIKE, E. L. *The New Methods in Arithmetic.* (Rand, McNally and Company: Chicago, 1921)

THORNDIKE, E. L. *The Psychology of Arithmetic.* (The Macmillan Company: New York, 1922)

WHEAT, H. G. *The Psychology of the Elementary School.* Chap. IV. (Silver Burdett Company: Newark, 1931)

WILSON, G. M. *What Arithmetic Shall We Teach?* (Houghton Mifflin Company: Boston, 1926)

YOUNG, J. W. A. *The Teaching of Mathematics in the Elementary and Secondary School.* (Longmans, Green and Company: New York, 1924)

II. MONOGRAPHS

ADAMS, R. E. *A Study of the Comparative Value of Two Methods of Improving Problem-Solving Ability in Arithmetic.* (University of Pennsylvania Press: Philadelphia, 1930)

BOND, E. A. *The Professional Treatment of Arithmetic for Teacher Training Institutions* (Teachers College, Columbia University: New York, 1934)

BONSER, F. G. *The Reasoning Ability of Children of the Fourth, Fifth, and Sixth School Grades.* (Teachers College, Columbia University: New York, 1910)

BOWDEN, A. O. *Consumers Uses of Arithmetic.* (Teachers College, Columbia University: New York, 1929)

BROWN, J. C. *Curricula in Mathematics.* (Bureau of Education Bulletin No. 45. Government Printing Office: Washington, 1914)

BROWNELL, W. A. *The Development of Children's Number Ideas in the Primary Grades.* (Department of Education, The University of Chicago: Chicago, 1928)

BROWNELL, W. A. and others. *The Teaching of Arithmetic.* (Tenth Yearbook of the National Council of Teachers of Mathematics, Teachers College, Columbia University: New York, 1935)

BROWNELL, W. A. and STRETCH, L. B. *The Effect of Unfamiliar Settings on Problem-Solving.* (Duke University Press: Durham, North Carolina, 1931)

BURNETT, C. J. *The Estimation of Number.* (Harvard Psychological Studies, II, 349–404. Houghton Mifflin Company: Boston, 1906)

BUSWELL, G. T. and JOHN, LENORE. *Diagnostic Studies in Arithmetic.* (Department of Education, The University of Chicago: Chicago, 1926)

BUSWELL, G. T. and JOHN, LENORE. *The Vocabulary of Arithmetic.* (Department of Education, The University of Chicago: Chicago, 1931)

BUSWELL, G. T. and JUDD, C. H. *Summary of Educational Investigations Relating to Arithmetic.* (Department of Education, The University of Chicago: Chicago, 1925)

CLAPP, F. L. *The Number Combinations.* (Bureau of Educational Research Bulletin No. 2. University of Wisconsin: Madison, 1924)

COUNTS, G. S. *Arithmetic Tests and Studies in the Psychology of Arithmetic.* (Department of Education, The University of Chicago: Chicago, 1917)

HALL, G. S. *Educational Problems,* II, 341–396. (D. Appleton-Century Company: New York, 1911)

HANNA, P. R. *Arithmetic Problem-Solving.* (Teachers College, Columbia University: New York, 1929)

HYDLE, L. L. and CLAPP, F. L. *Elements of Difficulty in the Interpretation of Concrete Problems in Arithmetic.* (Bureau of Educational Research Bulletin No. 9. University of Wisconsin: Madison, 1927)

JACKSON, L. L. *The Educational Significance of Sixteenth-Century*

Arithmetic from the Point of View of the Present Time. (Teachers College, Columbia University: New York, 1906)

JUDD, C. H. *Psychological Analysis of the Fundamentals of Arithmetic.* (Department of Education, The University of Chicago: Chicago, 1927)

KIRBY, T. J. *Practice in the Case of School Children.* (Teachers College, Columbia University: New York, 1913)

KNIGHT, F. B. and others. *Report of the Society's Committee on Arithmetic.* (Twenty-Ninth Yearbook of the National Society for the Study of Education. Public School Publishing Company: Bloomington, Illinois, 1930)

KRAMER, GRACE A. *The Effect of Certain Factors in the Verbal Arithmetic Problems upon Children's Success in the Solution.* (Johns Hopkins University Press: Baltimore, 1933)

LAZAR, MAY. *Diagnostic and Remedial Work in Arithmetic Fundamentals for the Intermediate Grades.* (Board of Education: New York, 1928)

LAZERTE, M. E. *The Development of Problem-Solving Ability in Arithmetic.* (Clark, Irwin and Company, Ltd.: Toronto, 1933)

MESSENGER, J. F. *The Perception of Number.* (Psychological Review Monograph Supplement, Vol. V, No. 5. The Macmillan Company: New York, 1903)

MONROE, W. S. *Development of Arithmetic as a School Subject.* (Bureau of Education Bulletin No. 10. Government Printing Office: Washington, 1917)

MONROE, W. S. *How Pupils Solve Problems in Arithmetic.* (Educational Research Bulletin No. 44. University of Illinois: Urbana, 1929)

MONROE, W. S. and ENGLEHART, M. D. *A Critical Summary of Research Relating to the Teaching of Arithmetic.* (Educational Research Bulletin No. 58. University of Illinois: Urbana, 1931)

NEULEN, L. N. *Problem-Solving in Arithmetic.* (Teachers College, Columbia University: New York, 1931)

OVERMAN, J. R. *An Experimental Study of Certain Factors Affecting Transfer of Training in Arithmetic.* (Warwick and York, Inc.: Baltimore, 1931)

REBARKER, HERBERT. *A Study of the Simple Integral Processes of Arithmetic.* (George Peabody College for Teachers: Nashville, 1926)

STONE, C. W. *Arithmetical Abilities and Some Factors Determining Them.* (Teachers College, Columbia University: New York, 1908)

TERRY, P. W. *How Numerals Are Read.* (Department of Education, The University of Chicago: Chicago, 1922)

WELLS, F. L. *A Study of the Instructional Material of Textbooks of Arithmetic.* (State University of Iowa: Iowa City, 1928)

WHEAT, H. G. *The Relative Merits of Conventional and Imaginative Types of Problems in Arithmetic.* (Teachers College, Columbia University: New York, 1929)

WILSON, G. M. *Motivation of Arithmetic* (Bureau of Education Bulletin No. 43. Government Printing Office: Washington, 1926)

WILSON, G. M. and others. *Connersville Course of Study in Mathematics for the Elementary Grades.* (Warwick and York, Inc.: Baltimore, 1922)

WOODY, CLIFFORD. *Nature and Amount of Arithmetic in Types of Reading Material for Elementary Schools.* (Bureau of Educational Reference and Research. University of Michigan: Ann Arbor, 1932)

III. PERIODICAL LITERATURE

ANDREWS, F. E. "The dark ages of arithmetic." *Atlantic Monthly,* 156: July, 1935, 64–68.

ARNETT, L. D. "Counting and adding." *American Journal of Psychology,* 16: July, 1905, 327–336.

BAILEY, M. A. "The Thorndike philosophy of teaching the processes and principles of arithmetic." *Mathematics Teacher,* 16: March, 1923, 129–140.

BENZ, H. E. "Diagnosis in arithmetic." *Journal of Educational Research,* 15: February, 1927, 140–141.

BOBBITT, FRANKLIN. "Technique of curriculum-making in arithmetic." *Elementary School Journal,* 25: October, 1924, 127–143.

BRADFORD, E. J. G. "Suggestion, reasoning, and arithmetic." *Forum of Education,* 3: February, 1925, 3–12.

BRESLICH, E. R. "Arithmetic one hundred years ago." *Elementary School Journal,* 25: May, 1925, 664–674.

BROWN, J. C. "An investigation on the value of drill work in the fundamental operations of arithmetic." *Journal of Educational*

Psychology, 2: February, 1911, 81–88; 3: November and December, 1912, 485–492, 561–570.

BROWN, J. C. "A summary of some significant conclusions reached by investigators relative to arithmetic." *Elementary School Journal,* 25: January, 1925, 346–357.

BROWNELL, W. A. "Remedial cases in arithmetic." *Peabody Journal of Education,* 7: September, 1929, 100–107.

BROWNELL, W. A. "The place of 'crutches' in instruction." *Elementary School Journal,* 34: April, 1934, 607–619.

BROWNELL, W. A. and CHAZEL, C. B. "The effects of premature drill in third-grade arithmetic." *Journal of Educational Research,* 29: September, 1935, 17–28.

BROWNELL, W. A. and WATSON, B. "The comparative worth of two diagnostic techniques in arithmetic." *Journal of Educational Research,* 29: May, 1936, 664–676.

BRUECKNER, L. J. "Analysis of difficulties in decimals." *Elementary School Journal,* 29: September, 1928, 32–41.

BRUECKNER, L. J. "Analysis of errors in fractions." *Elementary School Journal,* 28: June, 1928, 760–770.

BRUECKNER, L. J. "Certain arithmetic abilities of second-grade pupils." *Elementary School Journal,* 27: February, 1927, 433–443.

BRUECKNER, L. J. "Diagnosis in arithmetic." *Thirty-Fourth Yearbook of the National Society for the Study of Education,* Chap. XIV. (Public School Publishing Company, 1935)

BRUECKNER, L. J. "Social problems as a basis for a vitalized arithmetic curriculum." *Journal of Experimental Education,* 1: June, 1933, 320–322.

BRUECKNER, L. J. "The nature of problem-solving." *The Journal of the National Education Association,* 21: January, 1932, 13–15.

BUCKINGHAM, B. R. "How much number do children know?" *Educational Research Bulletin* (Ohio State University), 8: September, 1929, 279–284.

BUCKINGHAM, B. R. "Teaching addition and subtraction facts together or separately." *Educational Research Bulletin* (Ohio State University), 6: May, 1927, 228–229, 240–242.

BUCKINGHAM, B. R. "The additive versus the take-away method of teaching the subtraction facts." *Educational Research Bulletin* (Ohio State University), 6: September, 1927, 265–269.

BUCKINGHAM, B. R. "When to begin the teaching of arithmetic." *Childhood Education*, 11: May, 1935, 339–343.

BUSWELL, G. T. "Curriculum problems in arithmetic." *Second Yearbook of the National Council of Teachers of Mathematics*, 79–93. (Teachers College, Columbia University: New York, 1927)

CAJORI, FLORIAN. "A review of three famous attacks upon the study of mathematics as a training of the mind." *Popular Science Monthly*, 80: April, 1921, 360–372.

CALKINS, M. W. "A study of the mathematical consciousness." *Educational Review*, 8: October, 1894, 269–286.

CARMICHAEL, R. D. "Number and clear thinking." *Scientific Monthly*, 41: December, 1935, 490–500.

CHASE, V. E. "The diagnosis and treatment of some common difficulties in solving arithmetic problems." *Journal of Educational Research*, 20: December, 1929, 335–342.

CLARK, J. R. and VINCENT, E. L. "A comparison of two methods of arithmetic problem analysis." *Mathematics Teacher*, 18: April, 1925, 226–233.

COIT, W. A. "The demons of elementary mathematics." *School Science and Mathematics*, 29: January, 1929, 50–58.

COLE, L. W. "Adding upward and downward." *Journal of Educational Psychology*, 3: February, 1912, 83–94.

COLLAR, D. J. "A statistical survey of arithmetical ability." *British Journal of Psychology*, 11: Part I, October, 1920, 135–158.

COLLIER, MYRTIE. "Learning to multiply fractions." *School Science and Mathematics*, 22: April, 1922, 324–329.

CONANT, L. L. "The beginnings of counting." *School Science and Mathematics*, 5: June, 1905, 385–394.

CONANT, L. L. "The historical development of arithmetical notation." *Pedagogical Seminary*, 2: June, 1892, 149–152.

CONDELL, C. H. "A plea for arithmetic." *Education*, 46: November, 1925, 170–178.

COURT, S. R. A. "Numbers, time, and space in the first five years of the child's life." *Pedagogical Seminary*, 27: March, 1920, 71–89.

COURT, S. R. A. "Self-taught arithmetic from the age of five to the age of eight." *Pedagogical Seminary*, 30: March, 1923, 51–68.

COURTIS, S. A. "Measurement of growth and efficiency in arithmetic." *Elementary School Teacher*, 10: October and December, 1909, 58–74, 177–199; 11: December, 1910; March and June, 1911, 171–185, 360–370, 528–539.

DEFABREGA, H. P. "Numeral systems of the Costa Rican Indians." *American Anthropologist*, 6: July–September, 1904, 447–458.

DEGRANGE, MCQUILKIN. "Statisticians, dull children, and psychologists." *Educational Administration and Supervision*, 27: November, 1931, 561–573.

DEMAY, A. J. "Arithmetic meanings." *Childhood Education*, 11: June, 1935, 408–412.

DEANS, EDWINA. "Materials and methods." *Childhood Education*, 11: May, 1935, 359–366.

DEWEY, JOHN. "Some remarks on the psychology of number." *Pedagogical Seminary*, 5: January, 1898, 426–434.

DICKEY, J. W. "Much ado about zero." *Elementary School Journal*, 32: November, 1931, 214–222.

DIXON, R. B. and KROEBER, A. L. "Numeral systems of the languages of California." *American Anthropologist*, 9: October–December, 1907, 663–690.

DOUGHERTY, M. L. "An experiment in teaching arithmetic in the third grade." *Elementary School Journal*, 22: May, 1922, 665–676.

DOUGLASS, H. R. "Development of number conception in children of preschool and kindergarten ages." *Journal of Experimental Psychology*, 8: December, 1925, 443–470.

DURELL, FLETCHER. "Solving problems in arithmetic." *School Science and Mathematics*, 28: December, 1928, 925–935.

EVANS, ROY. "Remedial cases in arithmetic: Case 2." *Peabody Journal of Education*, 7: January, 1930, 208–217.

FISHER, S. C. "Arithmetic and reasoning in children." *Pedagogical Seminary*, 19: March, 1912, 48–77.

FREEMAN, F. N. "Grouped objects as concrete basis for the number idea." *Elementary School Teacher*, 12: March, 1912, 306–314.

GARBERT, M. L. "Remedial cases in arithmetic: Case I." *Peabody Journal of Education*, 7: November, 1929, 147–155.

GODDARD, H. H. "A side light on the development of the number concept." *Supplement to the Training School*, 1: December, 1907, 20–25.

GOOD, H. G. "An eloquent arithmetic." *Educational Research Bulletin* (Ohio State University), 6: September, 1927, 243–247.

GORDON, G. B. "On the use of zero and twenty in the Maya time system." *American Anthropologist*, 4: April–June, 1902, 237–275.

GRAY, OLIVE. "Teaching pupils to read arithmetic and other subject matter." *Elementary School Journal*, 26: April, 1926, 607–618.

GREENE, H. A. "Directed drill in the comprehension of verbal problems in arithmetic." *Journal of Educational Research*, 11: January, 1925, 33–40.

GREENWOOD, J. M. "The evolution of arithmetic in the United States." *Education*, 20: December, 1899, 193–201.

GROSSNICKLE, F. E. "An experiment with a one-figure divisor in short and long division." *Elementary School Journal*, 34: March and April, 1934, 496–506; 590–599.

GROSSNICKLE, F. E. "Classification of the estimations in two methods of finding the quotient in long division." *Elementary School Journal*, 32: April, 1932, 595–604.

GROSSNICKLE, F. E. "Errors and questionable habits of work in long division with a one-figure divisor." *Journal of Educational Research*, 29: January, 1936, 355–368.

GROSSNICKLE, F. E. "How to estimate the quotient figure in long division." *Elementary School Journal*, 32: December, 1931, 299–306.

GROSSNICKLE, F. E. "How to test the accuracy of the estimated quotient figure." *Elementary School Journal*, 32: February, 1932, 442–446.

GROSSNICKLE, F. E. "Reliability of diagnosis of certain types of errors in long division with a one-figure divisor." *Journal of Experimental Education*, 4: September, 1935, 7–16.

GROSSNICKLE, F. E. "To check or not to check." *Elementary School Journal*, 36: September, 1935, 35–39.

GROSSNICKLE, F. E. "The incidence of error in division with a one-figure divisor when short and long forms of division are used." *Journal of Educational Research*, 29: March, 1936, 509–511.

GUILER, W. S. "Current tendencies in course of study-making in arithmetic." *Educational Administration and Supervision*, 14: January, 1928, 46–51.

GUNDERSON, A. G. "Nature and amount of arithmetic in readers for Grades I and II." *Elementary School Journal*, 36: March, 1936, 527–540.

HALL, F. H. "Imagination in arithmetic." *Proceedings and Addresses of the National Education Association*, 35: 1897, 621–628.

HALL, G. S. "Contents of children's minds on entering school." *Pedagogical Seminary*, 1: 1891, 139–173.

HALL, G. S. and JASTROW, JOSEPH. "Studies in rhythm." *Mind*, 11: January, 1886, 55–62.

HANNA, P. R. "Methods of arithmetic problem-solving." *Mathematics Teacher*, 23: November, 1930, 442–450.

HARAP, H. L. and MAPES, C. "The learning of fundamentals in an arithmetic activity curriculum." *Elementary School Journal*, 34: March, 1934, 515–526.

HORNBROOK, A. R. "The pedagogical value of number forms — A study." *Educational Review*, 5: May, 1893, 467–480.

HUNKINS, R. V. and BREED, F. S. "The validity of arithmetical reasoning tests." *Elementary School Journal*, 23: February, 1923, 453–466.

JOHN, LENORE. "Difficulties in solving problems in arithmetic." *Elementary School Journal*, 31: November, 1930, 202–215.

JOHN, LENORE. "The effect of using the long-division form in teaching division by one-digit numbers." *Elementary School Journal*, 30: May, 1930, 675–692.

JONES, H. I. and JONES, B. P. "A little-understood principle in multiplication." *School Science and Mathematics*, 25: January, 1925, 36–43.

JUDD, C. H. "Needed research in elementary education." *Studies in Education*, 56–65. (Yearbook Number XV of the National Society of College Teachers of Education, University of Chicago Press: Chicago, 1926)

JUDD, C. H. "The fallacy of teaching school subjects as tool subjects." *National Education Association: Addresses and Proceedings*, 1927, 249–252.

JUDD, C. H. "Informational mathematics versus computational

mathematics." *Mathematics Teacher*, 22: April, 1929, 187–196.

KALLOM, A. W. "Analysis of and testing in common fractions." *Journal of Educational Research*, 1: March, 1920, 177–192.

KALLOM, A. W. "The importance of diagnosis in educational measurement." *Journal of Educational Psychology*, 10: January, 1919, 1–12.

KARPINSKI, L. C. "A unique collection of arithmetics." *Popular Science Monthly*, 77: September, 1910, 226–235.

KARPINSKI, L. C. "The first arithmetic in the United States." *School and Society*, 19: March 22, 1924, 349–351.

KELLER, J. W. "Warren Colburn's Mental Arithmetic." *Pedagogical Seminary*, 39: June, 1923, 162–171.

KIRKPATRICK, E. A. "An experiment in memorizing versus incidental learning." *Journal of Educational Psychology*, 5: September, 1914, 405–412.

KNIGHT, F. B. "The superiority of distributed practice in drill in arithmetic." *Journal of Educational Research*, 15: March, 1927, 157–165.

KNIGHT, F. B., RUCH, G. M. and LUTES, O. S. "How shall subtraction be taught?" *Journal of Educational Research*, 11: March, 1925, 157–168.

KNIGHT, F. B. and SETZAFANDT, A. O. H. "Transfer within a narrow mental function." *Elementary School Journal*, 24: June, 1924, 780–787.

KULP, C. L. "A method of securing real-life problems in the fundamentals of arithmetic." *Elementary School Journal*, 29: February, 1929, 428–430.

LEWIS, E. O. "Popular and unpopular school subjects." *Journal of Experimental Pedagogy*, 2: June, 1913, 89–98.

LINDLEY, E. H. and PARTRIDGE, G. E. "Some mental automatisms." *Pedagogical Seminary*, 5: July, 1897, 41–60.

McCLELLAND, W. W. "An experimental study of the different methods of subtraction." *Journal of Experimental Pedagogy*, 4: December, 1918, 293–299.

McCLURE, WORTH. "Learning to read arithmetic problems." *Teachers Journal and Abstract*, 1: March, 1926, 183–188.

MACDOUGALL, ROBERT. "Rhythm, time, and number." *American Journal of Psychology*, 13: January, 1902, 88–97.

MacDougall, Robert. "The influence of eye-movements in judgments of number." *American Journal of Physiology*, 37: May, 1915, 300–315.

McFarland, B. B. "A plea for arithmetic in the first grade." *Kindergarten and First Grade*, 7: January, 1922, 1–7.

McGee, W. J. "The beginning of mathematics." *American Anthropologist*, 1: October, 1899, 646–674.

MacLatchy, Josephine. "Addition in the first grade." *Educational Research Bulletin* (Ohio State University), 9: October, 1930, 391–393, 406.

MacLatchy, Josephine. "Number abilities of first-grade children." *Childhood Education*, 11: May, 1935, 344–347.

McLaughlin, K. L. "Number ability of preschool children." *Childhood Education*, 11: May, 1935, 348–353.

McLaughlin, K. L. "Summary of current tendencies in elementary-school mathematics as shown by recent textbooks." *Elementary School Journal*, 18: March, 1918, 543–551.

MacLear, Martha. "Mathematics in current literature." *Pedagogical Seminary*, 30: March, 1923, 48–50.

McMurry, F. M. "The question that arithmetic is facing and its answer." *Teachers College Record*, 27: June, 1926, 873–881.

McMurry, F. M. "What is the matter with arithmetic?" *Education*, 54: April, 1934, 449–451.

Manuel, H. T. "Adding up or down: Another consideration." *Journal of Educational Research*, 17: April, 1928, 297–298.

Meserve, H. G. "Mathematics one hundred years ago." *Mathematics Teacher*, 21: October, 1928, 336–343.

Metter, H. L. "Trends in the emphasis on various topics of arithmetic since 1860." *Elementary School Journal*, 34: June, 1934, 767–775.

Miller, G. A. "On the history of common fractions." *School Science and Mathematics*, 31: February, 1931, 138–145.

Mitchell, Claude. "The specific type of problem in arithmetic versus the general type." *Elementary School Journal*, 29: April, 1929, 594–596.

Mitchell, F. D. "Mathematical prodigies." *American Journal of Psychology*, 18: January, 1907, 61–143.

Monroe, W. S. "A series of diagnostic tests in arithmetic." *Elementary School Journal*, 19: April, 1919, 585–607.

MONROE, W. S. "The ability to place the decimal point in division." *Elementary School Journal*, 18: December, 1917, 287–293.

MONROE, W. S. "Warren Colburn on the teaching of arithmetic, together with an analysis of his arithmetic texts." *Elementary School Teacher*, 12: May and June, 1912, 421–426, 463–480; 13: September, 1912; January and February, 1913, 17–24, 239–246, 294–302.

MOORE, R. C. "The psychology of number: A study of numerical ability." *Journal of Experimental Pedagogy*, 4: June, 1918, 221–236.

NEWCOMB, R. S. "Teaching pupils how to solve problems in arithmetic." *Elementary School Journal*, 23: November, 1922, 183–189.

NOON, P. G. "The child's use of numbers." *Journal of Educational Psychology*, 10: November, 1919, 462–467.

OLANDER, H. T. "Transfer of learning in simple addition and subtraction." *Elementary School Journal*, 31: January and February, 1931, 358–369, 427–437.

OSBURN, W. J. "How shall we subtract?" *Journal of Educational Research*, 16: November, 1927, 237–246.

OTIS, A. S. "The visual method of solving arithmetic problems." *Mathematics Teacher*, 21: December, 1928, 483–489.

OTTO, H. J. "Remedial instruction in arithmetic." *Elementary School Journal*, 28: October, 1927, 124–133.

OVERMAN, J. R. "An experimental study of the effect of the method of instruction on transfer of training in arithmetic." *Elementary School Journal*, 31: November, 1930, 183–190.

PARTRIDGE, C. M. "Number needs in children's reading activities." *Elementary School Journal*, 26: January, 1926, 357–366.

PATRICK, G. T. W. "Number forms." *Popular Science Monthly*, 42: February, 1893, 504–514.

PHILLIPS, D. E. "Genesis of number-forms." *American Journal of Psychology*, 8: July, 1897, 506–527.

PHILLIPS, D. E. "Number and its application psychologically considered." *Pedagogical Seminary*, 5: October, 1897, 221–281.

PHILLIPS, D. E. "Some remarks on number and its application." *Pedagogical Seminary*, 5: April, 1898, 590–598.

POFFENBERGER, A. T. "The influence of improvement in one

simple mental process upon other related processes." *Journal of Educational Psychology*, 6: October, 1915, 459–474.

POLKINGHORNE, ADA L. "Young children and fractions." *Childhood Education*, 11: May, 1935, 354–358.

SANFORD, VERA. "Extraneous details." *Mathematics Teacher*, 21: February, 1928, 83–91.

SANFORD, VERA. "Roman numerals." *Mathematics Teacher*, 24: January, 1931, 22–27.

SCHMITT, CLARA. "Extreme retardation in arithmetic." *Elementary School Journal*, 21: March, 1921, 529–547.

SLAUGHT, H. E. "Romance of mathematics." *Mathematics Teacher*, 20: October, 1927, 303–309.

SMITH, D. E. "Suggestions on the arithmetic question." *Mathematics Teacher*, 18: October, 1925, 333–340.

SMITH, E. W. "Mental confusion in arithmetic." *Forum of Education*, 7: November, 1929, 211–226.

SMITH, J. H. "Individual variations in arithmetic." *Elementary School Journal*, 17: November, 1916, 195–200.

SMITH, N. B. "An investigation of the uses of arithmetic in the out-of-school life of first-grade children." *Elementary School Journal*, 24: May, 1924, 621–626.

SPRINGER, ISIDORE. "Ideational types in arithmetic." *Journal of Educational Psychology*, 5: September, 1914, 418–422.

TAYLOR, J. S. "Omitting arithmetic in the first year." *Educational Administration and Supervision*, 2: October, 1916, 87–93.

TAYLOR, J. S. "Subtraction by the addition process." *Elementary School Journal*, 20: November, 1919, 203–207.

TERRY, P. W. "The reading problem in arithmetic." *Journal of Educational Psychology*, 12: October, 1921, 365–377.

THORNDIKE, E. L. "The psychology of drill in arithmetic." *Journal of Educational Psychology*, 12: April, 1921, 183–194.

TROUSDALE, M. S. "Remedial cases in arithmetic: Case 3." *Peabody Journal of Education*, 7: March, 1930, 290–298.

UHL, W. L. "The use of standardized materials in arithmetic for diagnosing pupils' methods of work." *Elementary School Journal*, 18: November, 1917, 215–218.

UPTON, C. B. "The influence of standardized tests on the curriculum in arithmetic." *Mathematics Teacher*, 26: April, 1925, 193–208.

VOORHEES, MARGARETTA. "New methods in arithmetic." *Progressive Education,* 5: April–May–June, 1928, 125–130.

WASHBURNE, C. W. "Comparison of two methods of teaching pupils to apply the mechanics of arithmetic to the solution of problems." *Elementary School Journal,* 27: June, 1927, 758–767.

WASHBURNE, C. W. "One reason children fail in arithmetic." *Progressive Education,* 9: March, 1932, 215–233.

WASHBURNE, C. W. and MORPHETT, M. V. "Unfamiliar situations as a difficulty in solving arithmetic problems." *Journal of Educational Research,* 18: October, 1928, 220–224.

WASHBURNE, C. W. and OSBORNE, RAYMOND. "Solving arithmetic problems." *Elementary School Journal,* 27: November and December, 1926, 219–226, 296–304.

WASHBURNE, C. W. and VOGEL, MABEL. "Are any number combinations inherently difficult?" *Journal of Educational Research,* 17: April, 1928, 235–255.

WESLEY, M. J. "Social arithmetic in the early grades." *Childhood Education,* 11: May, 1935, 367–370.

WHEAT, H. G. "More ado about zero." *Elementary School Journal,* 32: April, 1932, 623–627.

WHITE, H. M. "Does experience in the situation involved affect the solving of a problem?" *Education,* 54: April, 1934, 451–455.

WHITING, M. C. "The individuality of numerals." *Pedagogical Seminary,* 2: June, 1892, 107–110.

WHITSON, W. E. "Remedial cases in arithmetic: Case 4." *Peabody Journal of Education,* 7: May, 1930, 362–372.

WILSON, ESTALINE. "Improving the ability to read arithmetic problems." *Elementary School Journal,* 22: January, 1922, 380–386.

WILSON, G. M. "For 100 percent subtraction, what method? A new approach." *Journal of Educational Research,* 27: March, 1934, 503–508.

WILSON, G. M. "The present impasse in arithmetic." *Educational Method,* 11: November, 1931, 65–72.

WINCH, W. H. "'Equal additions' versus 'decomposition' in teaching subtraction: An experimental research." *Journal of Experimental Pedagogy,* 5: June and December, 1920, 207–220, 261–270.

Woody, Clifford. "Diagnosis of difficulties in the solution of verbal problems in arithmetic." *Education*, 54: April, 1934, 464–473.

Woody, Clifford. "Types of arithmetic needed in certain types of salesmanship." *Elementary School Journal*, 22: March, 1922, 505–520.

IV. MEASURES AND WEIGHTS

Achievements of Civilization: Number 3, "The Story of Weights and Measures"; Number 4, "The Story of Our Calendar"; Number 5, "Telling Time Throughout the Centuries." (American Council on Education: Chicago, 1932, 1933)

Adams, J. Q. *Report of the Secretary of State upon Weights and Measures.* State Papers, Sixteenth Congress of the United States, Second Session, VIII, 1–246. (Gales and Seaton: Washington, 1821)

Brearley, H. C. *Time Telling Through the Ages.* (Doubleday, Page and Company: New York, 1919)

Fischer, L. A. *History of the Standard Weights and Measures of the United States.* (Miscellaneous Publications, Bureau of Standards, No. 64. Government Printing Office: Washington, 1925)

Harkness, William. "The progress of science as exemplified in the art of weighing and measuring." *Annual Report of the Board of Regents of the Smithsonian Institution*, 597–633. (Government Printing Office: Washington, 1888)

Hubbard, H. D. "The romance of measurement." *Scientific Monthly*, 33: October, 1931, 356–358.

Hubbard, H. D. "Unmeasured goals." *Baltimore Bulletin of Education*, 10: March–April, 1932, 161–167.

Judd, C. H. *The Psychology of Social Institutions*, Chaps. VI and VII. (The Macmillan Company: New York, 1926)

Measurements for the Household. (Circular of the Bureau of Standards, No. 55, Government Printing Office: Washington, 1915)

National Bureau of Standards: Its Functions and Activities. (Circular of the Bureau of Standards, No. 1, Government Printing Office: Washington, 1925)

Nicholson, Edward. *Men and Measures.* (Smith, Elder and Company: London, England, 1912)

NILSSON, M. P. *Primitive Time-Reckoning*. (Oxford University Press: Oxford, England, 1920)

SEELY, F. A. "The development of time-keeping in Greece and Rome." *American Anthropologist*, 1: 1888, 25–50.

WILSON, G. M. "Why non-metric measures in metric Europe?" *Education*, 52: February, 1932, 319–324.

INDEX

Abacus: discussion of, 40 ff.; Chinese, 44; counting on, 42; Japanese, 44; medieval, 44 f.; operations on, 42 ff.; Roman, 41; Russian, 41; use of numerals on, 70 f.; variations of, 44 f.

Acre, lesson on size of, 505 ff.

Adams, J. Q., 477, 478, 480, 484.

Addition: and multiplication, 201 ff., 359 f.; and subtraction, 360 f.; as general idea, 148; carrying in, 317, 318 f.; column, 278 ff., 298 f.; combinations, 197 f., 291; downward, 285 f.; meaning of, 131; of decimals, 407 ff.; of fractions, 390 ff., 394; of tens, 261 f., 297; in higher decades, 266 ff.; the learning of, 189 ff.; use of term of, 198.

Ancient numerals, 48 ff.

Arithmetic: analysis of, 121 ff., 156 f.; course of study in, 553 ff.; development of, 55 ff., 102 ff.; functions of, 560 ff.; present tendencies in, 118 ff.; purpose of, 140.

Arithmetic of Pellos, 93.

Attention: to arrangement, 184 ff., 212, 228 ff., 349 f.; directing, 198 f.; steps of, 194, 212 f., 228 f.; to groups, 2 ff.; to objects, 5 ff.

Babylonian numerals, 50, 53 f.

Ballard, P. B., 322.

Base, number, 26 ff.

Bibliography, 565 ff.

Brooks, Edward, 117.

Brown, J. C., and Coffman, L. D., 419, 480.

Brownell, W. A., 165, 175, 530, 533.

Brownell, W. A., and Stretch, L. B., 354, 355.

Brueckner, L. J., 221, 222, 540, 560.

Buswell, G. T., 165.

Buswell, G. T., and John, Lenore, 353, 524, 527, 536, 539.

Buswell, G. T., and Judd, C. H., 116, 117, 358.

Cancellation, 383 f.

Carrying tens, illustrative lessons in, 317 ff., 320 ff.; in addition, 317, 318 f.; in division, 326 f.; in multiplication, 317 ff.; in subtraction, 319 ff.

Chinese numerals, 50.

Coffman, L. D., and Brown, J. C., 419, 480.

Colburn, Warren, 113, 116, 117.

Collier, Myrtie, 396.

Column addition: discussion of, 278 ff., 298 f.; illustrative lesson in, 282 f.; practice in, 279 f.; purpose of, 279; relation of, to simple addition, 280 f.

Combinations: addition, 179 f., 291; division, 301, 307, 310; learning of, 184 ff.; multiplication, 302 f., 307, 310; number facts and, 121 ff.; practice in, 228 ff.; subtraction, 197 f.

585